Biology
on the
Cutting Edge

Concepts, Issues, and Canadian Research
around the Globe

EDITED BY

Sharon L. Gillies, University of the Fraser Valley
Sarah Hewitt, Mount Royal University

Pearson Canada
Toronto

Library and Archives Canada Cataloguing in Publication

Biology on the cutting edge: concepts, issues, and Canadian research around the globe / [compiled by] Sharon L. Gillies, Sarah Hewitt.—Canadian ed.

Includes bibliographical references and index.
ISBN 978-0-13-213502-3

1. Biology—Textbooks. I. Gillies, Sharon L. (Sharon Louise), 1953– II. Hewitt, Sarah

QH308.2.B576 2010   570   C2010-902910-0

ISBN: 978-0-13-213502-3

Vice-President, Editorial Director: Gary Bennett
Acquisitions Editor: Michelle Sartor
Marketing Manager: Kim Ukrainec
Developmental Editor: Maurice Esses
Production Editor: Melissa Churchill
Copy Editors: Dawn Hunter, Deborah Cooper-Bullock
Proofreaders: Dawn Hunter, Deborah Cooper-Bullock, Melissa Churchill
Lead Project Manager: Patricia Ciardullo
Compositor: Aptara®, Inc.
Photo Researcher: Terri Rothmann
Permissions Researcher: Terri Rothmann
Art Director: Julia Hall
Cover Designer: Quinn Banting
Interior Designer: Quinn Banting
Cover Image: Getty Images/Rawlins

1 2 3 4 5   14 13 12 11 10

Printed and bound in the United States of America.

Contents

List of Contributors

Nathan Ackroyd (Mount Royal University)
Gail S. Anderson (Simon Fraser University)
Marica Bakovic (University of Guelph)
Logan Banadyga (University of Alberta)
Michele Barry (University of Alberta)
Samantha A. Beck (University of British Columbia)
Mark Belmonte (University of Manitoba)
David Bird (Mount Royal University)
Julia C. Boughner (University of Saskatchewan)
Trevor A. Day (Mount Royal University)
Graham Dellaire (Dalhousie University)
Evelyn F. Field (Mount Royal University)
Lyanne Foster (Alberta Prion Research Institute)
Brenda Frick (University of Saskatchewan)
Patrick Gagnon (Memorial University of Newfoundland)
Sharon L. Gillies (University of the Fraser Valley)
T. Ryan Gregory (University of Guelph)
Sandra Haney (PrioNet Canada)
George Haughn (University of British Columbia)
Sarah Hewitt (Mount Royal University)
Jay Ingram (Discovery Channel)
Heather Jamniczky (University of Calgary)
Barbara Johnston (Parks Canada)
Alyson L. Kenward
Ljerka Kunst (University of British Columbia)

Ebba U. Kurz (University of Calgary)
Oliver P. Love (University of Windsor)
Vera Michel (University of Guelph)
Martin G. Scanlon (University of Manitoba)
Rick J. Scavetta (The Max Planck Institute for Evolutionary Biology)
Joan Sharp (Simon Fraser University)
Ron Wilen (University of the Fraser Valley)
Niki Wilson (Parks Canada)
Michelle Wong (PrioNet Canada)

List of Reviewers

Edith Camm (University of the Fraser Valley)
Ian Dawe (Selkirk College)
Barbara Dowding (University of New Brunswick - Saint John)
Peter Freeman (Northwest Community College)
James Todd Harper (Douglas College)
Alida Janmaat (University of the Fraser Valley)
Christian Levesque (John Abbott College)
Colin Montpetit (University of Ottawa)
Barbara Moon (University of the Fraser Valley)
Cynthia Paszkowski (University of Alberta)
Gregory Schmaltz (University of the Fraser Valley)
Anthony Stea (University of the Fraser Valley)
Jayne Yack (Carleton University)

Preface to the Student

If you are reading this preface, then you are probably enrolled in an introductory biology course. A huge textbook, packed full of diagrams and information can be a little overwhelming, but don't despair, an inquisitive mind is all you need to succeed in science. With just a few of the biology basics under your belt, the latest research becomes accessible and comprehensible. Sometimes, however, as you're learning the details of photosynthesis or gene regulation, it's easy to get fooled into thinking that if we already know all this, is there anything else to discover? We hope this collection of essays shows you that endless discoveries are waiting to be made, perhaps by someone like you.

We, the authors, have always had a passion for science, for the way the answers to its mysteries are slowly revealed with each new experiment. Our purpose in preparing this collection is to open your eyes to the breadth of research taking place not only in Canada, but also around the world. We selected topics that demonstrate the diversity of the field of biology. In this collection, you will find subjects ranging from the genome to contemporary evolution, viruses to biofuels, fossils to conservation, and many more. With the help of some of our collaborators, we initially drafted an extensive list of topics. It was a difficult job to pare it down; however, if we had included everything, you might not have been able to pick up this book! We hope that you will find these topics interesting and that each essay helps answer a commonly heard question in first-year science classes: "*How* did they ever figure that out?"

The essays are divided into three categories: research, issues, and concepts. **Research essays** highlight specific findings from individual or collaborating research groups. These essays are presented in a layout similar to a research paper. In particular, each research essay includes concise statements of the research question and the working hypothesis. Actual data are presented and the reasons for performing a particular experiment are discussed. **Issues essays** present either contentious issues or topics that are especially important in today's world. **Concept essays** cover a range of findings in a particular field and will bring you up to date about the current state of research in that area. Together, the three types of essay show research from different angles. After you have learned the relevant basic concepts from the textbook, you should be able to follow the arguments presented.

Each essay begins with a list of **Key Concepts** to show you how the material relates to important basic ideas in the field of biology. And, each essay concludes with the following items:

- Three **Critical Thinking Questions** that will encourage you to analyze the material presented and to consider its implications.
- One **Further Research Question** that will guide you in conducting further research, either on your own or with some of your fellow students.
- A list of **References**. Many of these references are primary research papers. The key references are marked with an asterisk (*).

Whether or not you continue with science, we hope that you take something valuable from your introductory biology course: not just the details, but an understanding of the *process of science*. We encourage you to read these essays with a critical and questioning eye, as you should read everything. As our world gets increasingly complex, scientific literacy is more important than ever. You are the next generation of decision makers. It is up to you to think scientifically, to critically evaluate ideas, and to communicate them clearly, not just in biology but in all domains.

We sincerely hope that you enjoy the stories that each essay tells and that you come to appreciate the decades of hard work from thousands of scientists that has brought us to where we are today.

Acknowledgements

This book would not have been possible without the determined effort of all our contributors who worked on multiple drafts and met our tight deadlines. Thank you! Our reviewers also did a great job, helping us with the editing process and pointing out areas that needed clarifying. Finally, a big thank you to the editors at Pearson Canada for their support with this project.

This collection of essays is dedicated to the following people:

To my husband, Larry. Thanks for your help and invaluable support. —S.L.G.

To my parents, Christopher, and Josip—Thank you for being wonderful. And to Banff Science Communications 2009—I couldn't have done this without all of you for many reasons. —S.H.

Sharon L. Gillies
Sarah Hewitt

Adult Neurogenesis:
Hormones and Sex Are Good for Your Brain

Sarah Hewitt
Mount Royal University

Introduction

When you hear the words *sex* and *hormones*, what do they bring to mind? For anyone who has gone through puberty, those words probably conjure many thoughts! From failed, to current, to imagined future relationships, to Hollywood movies and television shows, these words are everywhere. But have you ever thought about them in relation to your brain?

One hundred billion is a hard number to imagine, but that is about how many neurons you have in your brain. Some neurons die as you get older, leading to the memory loss that we associate with the aging process. Until recently, neuroscientists assumed that after the nervous system initially formed, no new neurons were born; the neurons you were born with were the ones you were stuck with forever, until they died as you aged. This assumption was challenged around 20 years ago, when it was discovered that adult songbirds develop new neurons to help them learn and remember new songs. Was this simply an anomaly in songbirds, or could this same process occur in other species? Scientists have now confirmed that new neurons can develop in adult mammals, such as humans, non-human primates, and rodents.

Neurogenesis is the process of forming new neurons and incorporating the new cells into the brain. Neurogenesis comprises four steps: (1) proliferation of progenitor cells, (2) cell differentiation, (3) migration to the appropriate location, and (4) cell survival. Each step is required for new neurons to form and take on a functional role.

Only two regions of the brain appear to demonstrate neurogenesis in adult mammals: the hippocampus and the olfactory bulb. The hippocampus is responsible for learning and memory of specific facts (such as your phone number), for events (such as what you did on your last vacation), and for spatial tasks (such as finding an alternative way home around a traffic jam on your usual route). The olfactory bulb detects odours and pheromones.

In adults, only these two brain regions retain neural stem cells that are capable of proliferating, differentiating, migrating to the appropriate location, and then making the proper functional connections to other neurons. What triggers neurogenesis in each brain region? What effects do these new neurons have on behaviour?

Although there are many triggers for neurogenesis, including learning, physical exercise, social interaction, cognitive stimuli, and antidepressants, here we will focus on the role of sex hormones and mating behaviours as potent triggers for the birth of new neurons. A team from the University of British Columbia (UBC) lead by Liisa Galea has

KEY CONCEPTS

- Neurogenesis in adult mammals involves the birth and incorporation of new neurons.
- Neurogenesis influences mating behaviours and reproduction.

studied how sex hormones affect neurogenesis in the hippocampus of males and females and the behavioural impact of neurogenesis in adults.

Sex Hormones and Neurogenesis

The gonads produce different types of sex hormones, including androgens (such as testosterone) and estrogens (such as estradiol). They are present in both genders but at significantly different levels. Galea's lab, by using rodents as a model, has investigated the correlation between the level of circulating sex hormones and neurogenesis in both males and females.

In human men, androgen levels tend to drop with age, and low blood levels of androgens are associated with memory loss in older men. This implies that androgens may be involved in maintaining hippocampal neurons. The UBC researchers investigated the effects of androgens on hippocampal neurons by comparing neurogenesis in male meadow voles (a type of rodent) that were either reproductively active or reproductively inactive. Reproductively active animals had higher levels of androgens, and this was correlated with a higher rate of survival of newly formed neurons. Surgically removing the gonads caused blood levels of androgens to drop and new neurons were less likely to survive. Giving testosterone to the animal after this procedure, however, meant that new neurons were again more likely to survive. Recall that neurogenesis relies on the birth, differentiation, migration, and survival of new cells, and it appears that androgens specifically enhance the *survival* of new neurons.

Estrogens (such as estrone and estradiol) play a crucial role in reproduction. Estrogens influence neurogenesis in females more potently than in males, and an acute injection of estrogens has a protective effect on neurons. When estrogens are given over a longer period (chronic administration), the effects on cell proliferation, cell survival, and cell death in the hippocampus are more difficult to interpret. However, a natural event provides the ideal time during which to look at responses to long-term changes in estrogen levels: during pregnancy. In pregnancy, estrogen levels increase progressively until birth and then drop off in the postpartum period. Importantly, the pregnancy and postpartum period are associated with striking fluctuations of a number of hormones. It is likely that the following findings are not due to estrogens alone but instead result from the interplay among many different hormones, including estrogens. During the late stages of pregnancy and the early postpartum period, 75 percent of women report forgetfulness and disorientation (known popularly as "baby brain"), and during this time, women perform more poorly on spatial memory tests (Buckwalter et al., 1999). In a series of studies, the UBC team investigated hippocampal function (by using behavioural tests) and neurogenesis during pregnancy and following birth. They showed that female rats also perform poorly on spatial learning and memory tasks and that neurogenesis decreases during the early postpartum period (see

PHOTO A.
Female rat with pups.
Source: ©iStockphoto.

Photo A). However, after the rat has weaned her pups, the mother's spatial and working memory improves. The researchers propose that the initial transition to motherhood requires that the mother learn a host of new maternal behaviours to be able to take care of new offspring and that the rebound neurogenesis that occurs after weaning may help with this process. Interestingly, mother rats that have previously given birth do not show the same level of neurogenesis after weaning, possibly because these mothers have already learned their maternal behaviours and therefore do not have to learn them again.

Pheromones and Neurogenesis

So far, we have discussed evidence for adult neurogenesis in the hippocampus, but what about the olfactory bulb? New neurons in the olfactory bulb are born from progenitor cells in a forebrain region called the subventricular zone. Once formed, the neurons migrate and integrate into the olfactory bulb. Neurogenesis in the olfactory bulb is also strongly linked to mating and offspring. In fact, the mere presence of an infant is enough to encourage maternal behaviour in female rats and in humans that have never had a baby. This maternal behaviour in rats is associated with neurogenesis of neurons that migrate to the olfactory bulb, suggesting that females might learn to recognize their babies by their odour. The olfactory epithelium also contains receptors for **pheromones**. Pheromones are chemical signals that are released outside the body and elicit physiological and behavioural responses in other members of the same species. Pheromones relay information about reproductive states, fitness, gender, social status, health, genetic advantage, and species identification. A number of different kinds of pheromones exist, including sex pheromones. A research team in Calgary, headed by Samuel Weiss, described a role for sex pheromones in stimulating neurogenesis (Mak et al., 2007).

Sex pheromones are important in mating behaviour, from choosing a mate to inducing mating behaviour. Mate selection is a complex process, but generally animals choose a mate based on producing offspring with the greatest likelihood of surviving and producing offspring of their own. This scenario may not be the most romantic way to think about choosing a mate, but a lot of evidence suggests that humans are greatly influenced by pheromones, even if they are not conscious of it. The influence of sex pheromones on mating behaviour is best understood in rodents. Female mice use male pheromone signatures to discriminate among prospective mates. Recognition and memory of the signatures from individual males may involve neural activity in both the olfactory bulb and the hippocampus. Given that male pheromones can induce mating behaviours in females and that these behaviours likely involve the olfactory bulb and the hippocampus, Weiss's team investigated a link between pheromones and neurogenesis in these two brain areas in female mice.

The researchers found that pheromones from dominant male mice, with which the females preferred to mate, stimulated neurogenesis in both regions. Pheromones from subordinate males did not stimulate neurogenesis (see Figure 1).

This research was the first demonstration of a single stimulus eliciting neurogenesis in both brain regions at the same time and suggests that the development of new neurons may play a role in our choice of mates. Just think—the person that you are attracted to might not just make your heart beat faster when they're around; they might actually be triggering new neurons to develop in your brain.

Conclusions

Research in the field is currently focusing on how neurogenesis might be able to alleviate symptoms of stress disorders, depression, and Alzheimer's disease, all of which are characterized by impaired hippocampal function. For a process that had eluded scientists

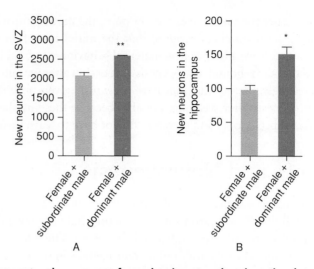

FIGURE 1. Exposure to pheromones from dominant male mice stimulates neurogenesis in the hippocampus and the olfactory bulb of female mice.

A. Pheromones from dominant male mice stimulated the birth of more new neurons in the subventricular zone (SVZ) in female mice than did pheromones from subordinate males. New neurons in the SVZ eventually migrate to the olfactory bulb.

B. Females exposed to pheromones from dominant males also showed significantly more neurogenesis in the hippocampus compared with females exposed to pheromones from subordinate males.

Note: Asterisks (*) denote that the results are statistically significantly different from control values: *$p < .05$; **$p < .01$.

Source: Reprinted by permission by Macmillan Publishers Ltd: Adapted from: Figure 1, panels e, f. Mak GK, Enwere EK, Gregg C, Pakarainen T, Poutanen M, Huhtaniemi I, Weiss S. 2007. Male pheromone-stimulated neurogenesis in the adult female brain: possible role in mating behaviour. Nature Neuroscience 10(8): 1003–1011. © 2007 Nature Publishing Group.

for so many years, neurogenesis has turned out to underlie some major life processes, from mating behaviours, to reproduction, to learning and memory, and it may soon provide hope for people with a number of neurological disorders. As it turns out, sex and hormones aren't just good for you for obvious reasons; they are even good for your neurons.

Critical Thinking Questions

1. Why does neurogenesis occur in the hippocampus and the olfactory bulb and not in other brain regions?
2. Shortly after a female gives birth, neurogenesis in the hippocampus is suppressed. What behavioural effects might you expect to find in women during this period?
3. What are pheromones?

Further Research Question

How might neurogenesis play a role in the treatment of mood disorders, such as depression?

References

Boehm U, Zou Z, Buck LB. 2005. Feedback loops link odor and pheromone signaling with reproduction. Cell. 123:683–695. Buckwalter JG, Stanczyk FZ, McCleary CA, Bluestein BW, Buckwalter DK, Rankin KP, Chang L, Goodwin TM. 1999. Pregnancy, the postpartum, and steroid hormones: effects on cognition and mood. *Psychoneuroendocrinology*. 24:69–84.

*Elder GA, De Gasperi R, Gama Sosa MA. 2006. Neurogenesis in adult brain and neuropsychiatric disorders. *Mt Sinai J. Med.* 73(7):931–940.

Furuta M, Bridges RS. 2009. Effects of maternal behavior induction and pup exposure on neurogenesis in adult, virgin female rats. *Brain Res. Bull.* 80(6):408–413.

*Galea LAM, Uban KA, Epp JR, Brummelte S, Barha CK, Wilson WL, Lieblich SE, Pawluski JL. 2008. Endocrine regulation of cognition and neuroplastcity: our pursuit to unveil the complex interaction between hormones, the brain, and behaviour. *Can. J. Exp. Psychol.* 62:247–260.

*Mak GK, Enwere EK, Gregg C, Pakarainen T, Poutanen M, Huhtaniemi I, Weiss S. 2007. Male pheromone-stimulated neurogenesis in the adult female brain: possible role in mating behaviour. *Nat. Neurosci.* 10(8):1003–1011.

Ormerod BK, Lee TT, Galea LAM. 2003. Estradiol initially enhances but subsequently suppresses (via adrenal steroids) granule cell proliferation in the dentate gyrus of adult female rats. *J. Neurobiol.* 55:247–260.

Pawluski JL, Galea LAM. 2006. Hippocampal morphology is differentially affected by reproductive experience in the mother. *J. Neurobiol.* 66:71–81.

Pawluski JL, Galea LAM. 2007. Reproductive experience alters hippocampal neurogenesis during the postpartum period in the dam. *Neurosci.* 149:53–67.

Arabidopsis thaliana, a Model Organism for Molecular Genetic Studies in Plants:
How and Why Was *Arabidopsis* Chosen Over Other Plants?

George Haughn and Ljerka Kunst
University of British Columbia

Introduction

Although millions of species inhabit Earth, only a select few are the subjects of intensive biological research. Have you ever wondered why a small number of species receive most of this scientific attention and how they were selected? Because of the similarities between related organisms, scientists commonly choose a single species to study as a representative for a broader group. This species is called a **model system**. Information obtained from studying the model system can be applied to related organisms as needed. The choice of a representative species is typically driven by how easy it is to obtain, grow, and manipulate, and how well it has been studied. Scientists who use different approaches or techniques normally choose a model that is best suited for the type of experiment. For example, in the past, plant biochemists frequently used spinach as a model because spinach was easy and inexpensive to obtain, and the thin walls of spinach leaf cells could be easily broken open by using a kitchen blender.

A model system for molecular genetic analysis must satisfy different needs. The isolation and characterization of mutants is an integral part of genetic research. A **mutation** in a gene normally results in a loss of function of the product (protein) and often has a negative consequence (defect) to the biology of that organism. The observed defect in the mutant (**phenotype**) provides information concerning the function of the protein in vivo and the process in which the protein is involved. For example, mutations in the gene encoding the globin protein can result in anemia, an outcome that connects hemoglobin to its role in carrying oxygen in the blood. Because the genetic analysis of mutants requires dealing with large populations and examining multiple generations of offspring, small organisms with fast life cycles and large numbers of progeny are favoured as models. Most biology students are familiar with the fruit fly (*Drosophila melanogaster*), adopted as a model system for genetic analysis by Nobel laureate Thomas Hunt Morgan. The plant species most commonly used for molecular genetics at present is the small member of the mustard family (Brassicaceae) *Arabidopsis thaliana* (arabidopsis; see Photo A). Unlike the fruit fly, which was adopted as a model at the beginning of the twentieth century, arabidopsis was not widely accepted as a model until relatively recently.

KEY CONCEPTS

- Model organisms are used for biological research.
- Arabidopsis is a model plant for molecular genetic research.
- Genetic analysis requires the study of progeny in multiple generations.

PHOTO A. An arabidopsis plant.
An approximately four-week-old arabidopsis plant with a rosette of leaves close to the soil and an inflorescence bearing flowers and seedpods (siliques; see arrows) is shown.
Source: Photo by Ljerka Kunst.

The Selection of Arabidopsis as a Model System

Before the 1980s, the most popular models for plant genetics were crop or horticultural plants, such as maize (*Zea mays*), tomato (*Solanum lycopersicum*), barley (*Hordeum vulgare*), and petunia (*Petunia x hybrida*). Genetic research on these species not only improved our understanding of plant biology but also yielded new traits that could be directly used for breeding better agricultural varieties. Maize played an instrumental role in genetic research during much of the twentieth century. In addition to its status as a major crop, its chromosomes were easily observed using microscopy, allowing researchers to draw correlations between changes in chromosome structure and genetic inheritance (**cytogenetics**). Barbara McClintock won a Nobel Prize (1983) for her discovery of transposable elements in maize using this approach. One problem with most of these early model plant genetic systems, including maize, was that their relatively large size required planting outdoors using farm machinery, unavailable to the large number of researchers in urban areas. In addition, the long generation times of such species (three to four months) limited the number of successive generations that could be planted in a year, slowing the pace of research in plant genetics.

Arabidopsis was first promoted as a model organism by Friedrich Laibach in 1943. Despite the fact that it had many of the attributes needed for genetic analysis, including a small size and short generation time, arabidopsis did not immediately become popular. Consequently, it lacked the critical number of researchers to develop it as an effective model system (see "Attributes of Arabidopsis as a Model Genetic System"). Some of its drawbacks included small chromosomes that were not well suited for cytological analysis, difficulties in regenerating whole plants from cells grown on defined medium, and its lack of commercial value. In the early 1980s, three major advances in arabidopsis research caught the attention of others. First, Maarten Koornneef and co-workers at Wageningen Agricultural University identified a large number of genes by mutation and mapped them to chromosomes, establishing the first comprehensive genetic map of the arabidopsis genome. Second, Christopher Somerville, working at the University of Illinois and Michigan State University, demonstrated the power of genetic analysis in plants by using mutants to characterize important biochemical processes (photorespiration, lipid biosynthesis). Finally, Elliot Meyerowitz (California Institute of Technology) and co-workers determined that the amount of DNA in the arabidopsis genome was smaller than any other seed plant described at that time. These discoveries prompted a large number of other well-established scientists to begin research on arabidopsis, resulting in a rapid increase in information on the species over the next three decades.

Attributes of Arabidopsis as a Model Genetic System

Arabidopsis has a number of natural attributes that collectively make it well suited for molecular genetic studies of flowering plants. First, the arabidopsis plant is very small. Following germination, the arabidopsis seedling produces a series of leaves on a short stem, resulting in a compact rosette close to the soil. On flowering, the stem elongates dramatically and a series of flowers are produced (**inflorescence**), each of which self-fertilizes to produce a seedpod (see Photo A). When grown alone in uncrowded conditions, the maximum diameter of the rosette is 4 to 6 cm, and the inflorescence reaches 30 to 40 cm in height. However, plants grown at high density will be considerably smaller. The small size allows large numbers of arabidopsis plants to be grown indoors in growth chambers and greenhouses, avoiding the need for researchers to have access to field plots. In addition, the small arabidopsis plants are easy to manipulate. For example, thousands of seeds can be sown, and plants grown until flowering, on defined agar medium in containers as small as bacteriological Petri plates (8 cm diameter), which allows for the evaluation of specific nutritional requirements or selection of mutants resistant to specific chemicals (see Photo B).

Second, relative to other seed plants, the generation time of arabidopsis is short. Under standard conditions of light and temperature ($100 \ \mu E/m^2/s$; 20°C), it will flower

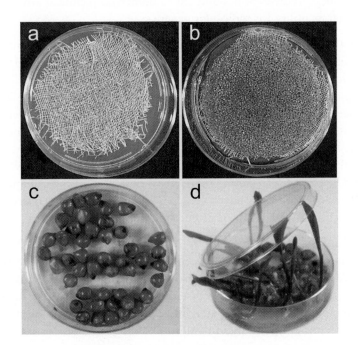

PHOTO B. Arabidopsis seeds and seedlings are very small compared with many other plant species. Because of their small size, thousands of arabidopsis seeds can be sown in an 8 cm Petri dish, with cheesecloth used to maintain a more even distribution (panel a). These seeds can be grown within the Petri dish until flowering (panel b). Species such as maize that have much larger seeds cannot be grown at high densities (panel c), and even very young seedlings are too big to be grown in the Petri dish (panel d).
Source: Photo by George Haughn.

PHOTO C. **Arabidopsis has a shorter generation time than many other seed plants.**
A three-week old arabidopsis plant (foreground) that is flowering stands in front of a tobacco (*Nicotiana tabacum*) seedling of the same age that will not flower for many more weeks.
Source: Photo by George Haughn.

within a month (see Photo C) and produce mature seeds within two months. The time from seed to seed can be shortened by two weeks if plants are grown under continuous light.

Third, the self-fertility and large numbers of progeny (>1000 seeds/plant) simplify the analyses of inheritance and the maintenance of genetic stocks. Fourth, the small diploid genome (125 megabase pairs) reduces the amount of labour and time needed to clone and manipulate genes. Last, the small number of chromosomes ($n = 5$) simplifies genetic mapping.

The exponential growth in arabidopsis research over the last three decades has made arabidopsis the best-studied species and led to numerous technical advances that have further increased its utility for molecular genetics:

1. In the 1990s, a fast, easy method for introducing engineered genes into the genome (**transformation**) was developed for arabidopsis (Clough and Bent, 1998). To date, this technique does not work efficiently in any other species.
2. The complete sequence of the arabidopsis genome was published in 2000 and was the first seed plant genome to be completed. This information ushered in the era of genomics for arabidopsis and began the drive to determine the function of every one of the approximately 28 000 genes in the genome.
3. **Insertional mutations** (mutations in which a foreign segment of DNA has inserted in the middle of a gene, resulting in the loss of function of the gene product) in virtually all arabidopsis genes have been created and identified. This resource allows for the functional analysis of any gene, providing the material for future generations of molecular geneticists.

The growing knowledge base has been organized and presented in the form of a website: The Arabidopsis Information Resource (TAIR; http://www.arabidopsis.org), and seed stocks and DNA clones are distributed by two separate stock centres: the Arabidopsis Biological Resource Center (http://abrc.osu.edu) and the European Arabidopsis Stock Centre (http://arabidopsis.info).

Conclusions

The small size, short generation time, large number of progeny per plant, and small genome of arabidopsis make it attractive for molecular genetic analysis. These attributes influenced a large number of scientists to adopt arabidopsis as a model plant for molecular genetic studies. Thirty years of research have made arabidopsis arguably the best-studied plant species and have resulted in the development of knowledge and resources that further increase its value as an experimental organism. Arabidopsis has much in common with other plant species, including the number, type, and arrangement of genes in the genome. Consequently, the information obtained relatively quickly in arabidopsis can be applied to other plants, including crops. However, it is important to note that the utility of arabidopsis as a model for studying another species depends on the degree of similarity they share. Arabidopsis is an excellent model for the closely related oilseed rape (*Brassica napus*, Canola) but not always as good a one for more distantly related crops. Legumes, such as beans, can fix nitrogen from the air by interacting with nitrogen-fixing bacteria, while arabidopsis cannot. So to understand the process of nitrogen fixation, a model legume species, *Medicago truncatula*, was developed. Similarly, rice was developed as a model for research questions specific to cereals. Even though arabidopsis is smaller and has a faster life cycle than most seed plants, it cannot serve as a model for biological processes that it does not share with other plants. Thus, the best model organism is determined by the nature of the question being asked and the scientific approach being employed. For most questions about seed plants that require molecular genetics, arabidopsis is the model of choice.

Critical Thinking Questions

1. What is important to consider when choosing a model organism for a particular type of research?
2. If a plant were discovered that had a smaller size, smaller genome, or a shorter life cycle than arabidopsis, could it replace arabidopsis as a model system for plant molecular genetics?
3. Explain why small size and short generation time are important features of a model system for molecular genetic research.

Further Research Question

The small roundworm *Caenorhabditis elegans* was developed as a model for genetic analysis in the 1960s despite the fact that several other model species, such as the fruit fly, were already available. For what specialized purpose was it developed and what were the characteristics of *C. elegans* that led to its development as a model?

References

Clough SJ, Bent AF. 1998. Floral dip: a simplified method for *Agrobacterium*-mediated transformation of *Arabidopsis thaliana*. *Plant J.* 16:735–743.

Estelle MA, Somerville CR. 1986. The mutants of *Arabidopsis*. *Trends Genet.* 2:89–93.

Somerville C, Somerville S. 1999. Plant functional genomics. *Science.* 285(5426):380–383.

Barcoding Biodiversity:
The Use of DNA Sequences to Identify Species

T. Ryan Gregory
University of Guelph

Introduction

You have carefully selected your desired items from among the thousands available and have loaded them onto the conveyor belt at the grocery store checkout. Some of the items are products you purchase every time you go to the store, that you grab without a second thought. Others products are new, but you have decided to try them based on their appealing packaging. For a few of the goods, you have read the labels carefully, perhaps to check for an ingredient to which someone in your household is allergic, to find out more about the nutritional content, or to determine when or where the product was manufactured. Now that your shopping is complete, you watch as the cashier passes each item over a laser scanner that registers the barcode printed on the packaging. You glance over at the computer screen on which a list of product names and prices scrolls. Unbeknownst to you, the process of scanning these product barcodes is also identifying any items that are on sale, updating the store's inventory, and generating data on sales patterns. This process is repeated for about 5 billion products every day around the world (Brown, 2001).

Because it is so routine, you probably don't give any thought to the significance of being able to access all this information about each product automatically and without any specialized knowledge of the food industry. To put this in perspective, imagine a very different scenario. The products in the store are not labelled. They are not even ordered in any way on the shelves. To you, the entire store seems like a chaotic jumble of unidentifiable boxes, cans, bottles, and packages of different colours and shapes. You may be able to distinguish pop from popcorn, but how much information could you really access about these products? Which of them pose a risk to your peanut-allergic roommate? Were they produced locally or imported from another country? Are they of nutritional value, or are they junk food? Suddenly your lack of grocery expertise becomes frustratingly apparent.

A Wall of Green

For all but the most highly trained specialists, a hike through an average forest is very much like a visit to the hypothetical grocery store full of unlabelled products. A few trees and other plants, birds, mammals, and insects will be familiar, but for the most part the forest alongside the hiking trail will be little more than an unidentifiable wall of green. Even professional biologists may be unable to identify the majority of species in the forest; in fact, in many forests in the world the majority of species probably do not

KEY CONCEPTS

- Only a small percentage of the biodiversity that is thought to exist has been described to date.
- Accessing information about species is very difficult, and this has consequences for how we interact with Earth's biodiversity.
- DNA-based identification methods can greatly facilitate species identification and discovery, and have a wide range of implications and applications.

yet have formal names. The same limitations apply in nearly every habitat on Earth, from forests to lakes to oceans to deserts. For the most part, we remain ignorant of the **biodiversity** that surrounds us. Even if most of us spent years training to become specialists in the **classification** of a particular group of organisms, we still would have access to knowledge about only a tiny fraction of the world's diversity.

It is remarkable that, to date, biologists have formally described nearly 2 million species of animals, plants, fungi, and single-celled organisms. It is an even more remarkable fact that this represents only a minority of the actual diversity that is thought to exist on our planet. After 250 years of dedicated effort, we still do not even know to within an order of magnitude how many species there are: current estimates range from about 10 million to 100 million species.

Linnaeus's Legacy

To be considered formally classified, a species must be given a **scientific name** and be adequately described in terms of its identifying features and other relevant biological characteristics. You may not be an expert in **taxonomy**, the science of naming and classifying species, but you are almost certainly familiar with such scientific names as *Homo sapiens* (humans), *Canis lupus familiaris* (domestic dogs), and *Felis catus* (domestic cats). All three of these names, and the system of taxonomy that is still in use today, were introduced by the eighteenth-century Swedish naturalist Carolus Linnaeus (1707–1778). Linnaeus himself described thousands of species of animals and plants—an incredible contribution, but truly just a scratching of the surface of Earth's biodiversity.

The year 2007 marked the three-hundredth anniversary of Linnaeus's birth, an event that was commemorated in the scientific community around the world. For its part, the prestigious British journal *Nature* published a series of articles discussing and celebrating Linnaeus's enduring legacy (www.nature.com/nature/focus/linnaeus300/). The cover of the March 15, 2007, issue of *Nature* depicted the famous naturalist kneeling confidently among some plants, as he surely had done many times during his career. Such an image would not in itself be surprising were it not for the fact that, in this case, Linnaeus is clad in the garb of a modern field biologist and is holding up a barcode of the kind that you find on nearly every consumer product today (see Photo A). What possible connection could there be between the eighteenth-century grandfather of taxonomy and modern product barcodes?

PHOTO A. A modern day Linnaeus?
Source: Reprinted by permission of Macmillan Publishers Ltd: Nature Vol. 446. Issue no. 7133. 15 March 2007. © 2007 Nature Publishing Group.

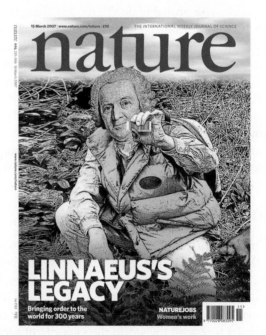

DNA Barcoding: A Brief Overview

Modern commercial barcodes, or Universal Product Codes (UPC), use a series of bars and spaces to encode 12-digit numbers, each of which is unique to a given product. Each digit, in turn, is specified by a sequence of 7 bars or spaces that spell out a 7-bit binary code; for example, a sequence of space-bar-bar-space-space-space-bar translates into the binary sequence 0110001, which specifies the number 5 at that position in the 12-digit barcode. A code consisting of 12 positions, each of which can be occupied by any of 10 digits (0 through 9), provides 10^{12}—that's 1 000 000 000 000—possible sequences.

Several key features make commercial barcodes very effective for rapidly identifying products. First, they are digital, meaning that each position in the sequence is occupied by one and only one digit. Second, there are enough combinations of digits to provide unique labels for every imaginable product. Third, reading the barcodes can be done automatically and requires only minimal training for store employees. Finally, each barcode links to a unique product record stored in an accessible database. You can probably imagine why Linnaeus might have wished for a "barcode" system with these same features that could be used to identify animals and plants. If such a thing were available, simply reading the barcode of a species would provide access to all the information known about it—such as whether it is poisonous, or endangered, or invasive—without requiring years of specialized training.

Unfortunately, living animals and plants do not sport series of black and white lines that spell out unique and easily readable sequences of numbers; however, they do carry a digital code within their cells in the form of DNA. Each DNA molecule is made up of a series of **nucleotides**, each of which includes one of four possible **bases**: adenine (A), guanine (G), thymine (G), or cytosine (C). Each position in a DNA sequence is occupied by one and only one base. Although there are only four available bases rather than 10 digits as in UPC barcodes, a DNA sequence only a few hundred nucleotides in length is enough to provide billions of possible combinations.

Not all positions in a **gene** sequence are equally free to vary, because changing them can alter the **amino acid** specified in the **genetic code** and adversely affect the resulting **protein**. Nevertheless, DNA sequences do change over time because of the accumulation of **mutations**, leading to differences among species that are roughly proportional to how closely related they are and how long they have been genetically separate. Not all genes evolve at the same rate, however, because some are highly constrained by **natural selection**. The key to using DNA as a "barcode" is to identify a stretch of DNA that varies enough to provide a unique identifier for each species but not so much that there is a confusing amount of variability among individuals within a species. In addition, the sequence of choice must also be found in all species of interest, and it must be relatively easy to extract, amplify, and sequence.

In 2003, Paul Hebert of the University of Guelph proposed that a portion of the *cytochrome c oxidase subunit I* (*COI* or *COX1*) gene fulfilled these criteria, at least for animals (Hebert et al., 2003). The *COI* gene is located within the **mitochondria** of **eukaryotic** cells, **organelles** that are descended from formerly free-living **bacteria** and that retain a small number of genes in their own **chromosomes**. It so happens that, across animals, the *COI* gene exhibits the "Goldilocks" amount of variation necessary for a DNA barcode: not too little across species and not too much within species—in fact, the amount is just right. Also, because mitochondrial genes are present in thousands of copies per cell (versus two for a typical gene in the **nucleus**), they can be recovered from tiny amounts of tissue or even from museum specimens that are decades old.

Some of the key factors that had previously been missing for a feasible DNA-based identification system included a mechanism for easily reading the DNA barcode sequence and an accessible database that could be used to connect barcode sequences with the names and characteristics of species. Thus, Hebert, along with a rapidly growing number of researchers from around the world, has set out to create both a rapid, inexpensive system for reading DNA barcode sequences and a comprehensive database of DNA barcode records linked to detailed species information. The ultimate goal of this global effort is nothing less than a complete catalogue of all living things that can be accessed easily by anyone.

Barcoding the Biosphere

As you can imagine, creating a resource containing DNA barcodes for 10 to 100 million species is a daunting task. For one thing, organisms tend to be reluctant to give up samples of their DNA. Fortunately, the choice of high-copy mitochondrial DNA means that only a minute amount of tissue is needed—an insect leg, say, or a feather—and that the vast collections of specimens held in museums can be tapped as sources of barcode sequences. Existing collections do not cover all species, of course, which means that sampling in the field is also very important. Experts in various taxonomic groups from around the world are now busy acquiring samples for DNA barcoding. The Biodiversity Institute of Ontario at the University of Guelph even has a "Bio Bus," a modified recreational vehicle that travels around North America with teams of biologists and students engaged in specimen-collecting missions (see Photo B).

Of course, obtaining a tissue sample is only the first step. The key to DNA barcoding, and what sets it apart from more traditional uses of genetic data in taxonomy, is the stringent standardization it entails and the massive scale at which it is being implemented. Once collected, every specimen must be properly identified, catalogued, photographed, and preserved as a **voucher**. Information on where and when it was collected and by whom it was identified, along with photographs and any other relevant data, must be entered into the Barcode of Life Data Systems (BOLD), the global database of DNA barcodes developed and hosted at the Biodiversity Institute of Ontario (Ratnasingham and Hebert, 2007; www.barcodinglife.org). DNA must then be extracted from the tissue sample, the *COI* gene amplified by **polymerase chain reaction** (PCR), and the sequence of As, Gs, Ts, and Cs read using a **DNA sequencer**. These steps can be carried out in most molecular biology labs, but the Canadian Centre for DNA Barcoding in Guelph has expanded this to an industrial scale. There, robotic systems are used for

PHOTO B. What it takes to barcode the world's biodiversity.
The Biodiversity Institute of Ontario (BIO), which opened in 2006 at the University of Guelph, is the global hub of DNA barcoding. Collaborations with researchers and museums around the world supply much of the material needed for DNA barcoding, but scientists and students from BIO perform their own field collections as well, including on trips around North America in the "Bio Bus," a mobile specimen collecting and processing lab.
Source: Biodiversity Institute of Ontario.

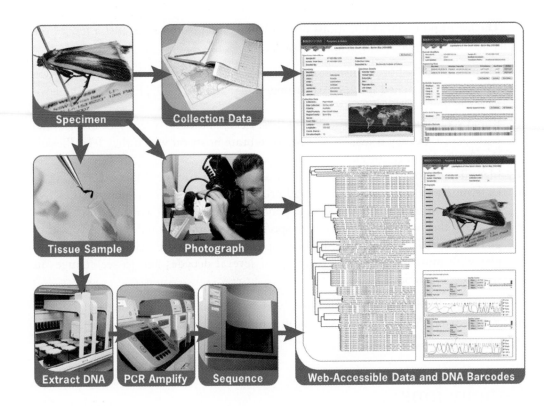

FIGURE 1. DNA barcoding workflow.
This schematic diagram shows the workflow used for high-throughput DNA barcoding at the Canadian Centre for DNA Barcoding, University of Guelph. All DNA barcode sequences are accompanied by additional information about the specimens from which they were taken and are added to the Barcode of Life Data Systems (BOLD) database.
Source: Biodiversity Institute of Ontario.

several of the steps and a large team of research scientists, photographers, computer programmers, students, and technicians are able to generate upwards of 500 000 sequences per year (see Figure 1).

As noted, "only" about 2 million species have been named to date, which means that in many cases, DNA sequences will not only provide a label for a known species, but also identify one that is in need of expert taxonomic description. Genetic data can highlight major genetic separation among potential species, which greatly facilitates the job of describing the morphological, ecological, geographical, and other differences among them. DNA sequence data can also reveal **cryptic species** that were thought to have been well described, but which actually represent complexes of closely related species that are difficult to tell apart visually. This was the case with an early DNA barcoding study of a complex of skipper butterflies that had been known by the single name *Astraptes fulgerator* since 1775. DNA barcodes, combined with information about the morphology and feeding behaviours of the caterpillars, revealed that the name *A. fulgerator* actually refers to 10 species whose adults are physically indistinguishable (Hebert, 2004).

Benefits of Barcoding

The enormous contributions that an ability to easily and accurately identify species would make to biological research are relatively obvious, including rapidly enumerating the members of particular ecosystems or linking adults and eggs/larvae/juveniles or males and females of the same species that might be very different in appearance. But how might this new-found capability have a broad impact on society? As an exercise, you may contemplate how being able to identify any species you encounter might change the way you interact with the biodiversity around you. What might a hike in a forest be like if you had in your backpack a hand-held "DNA barcoder" along with your GPS and digital camera?

The list of potential applications of DNA barcoding is immense. Just a few of the many notable examples include the following:

- Identification by border inspectors and conservation officers of endangered, invasive, pest, or poached species (Armstrong, 2005; Steinke, 2009; Eaton, 2010; Naro-Marciel, 2010).
- Rapid screening of mosquitoes, blackflies, ticks, and other vectors of disease, the pathogens that they transmit, and the vertebrate hosts on which they feed (Besansky, 2003; Alcaide, 2009).
- Identification of bird species involved in strikes with aircraft (Marra, 2009).
- Determination of the identity of food products even after processing, such as fish filets or canned goods, for food safety and to prevent fraud (Wong, 2008).
- Tracking the movement or decline of species in the face of climate change (Bucklin, 2010). With DNA barcoding, it is even possible to compare newly collected samples with museum specimens from up to several decades ago to see changes in species composition.

Undoubtedly, many other applications will arise as the DNA barcode database continues to expand. You may have several in mind already that could materialize in the years to come.

Conclusions

We are surrounded by biodiversity, but we remain unable to access even the most basic information about the vast majority of the species with which we share the Earth. This ignorance has consequences for our ability to protect other species or, indeed, to protect ourselves from other species. Scientists have named nearly 2 million species over the past 250 years, but this surely represents only a minority of the diversity that exists in nature. Thus, we are faced with major challenges related not only to identifying the species we know, but also in discovering and describing the millions that we do not yet know. Modern DNA-based methods can greatly assist us in overcoming these obstacles. The worldwide DNA barcoding initiative, which began in Canada, aims to generate unique identifiers for every species based on one or a few standard gene sequences. This ambitious project is poised to revolutionize the way in which we interact with biodiversity, but it will not reach its objective without the sustained and dedicated efforts of biologists from around the world—and from the next generation.

Critical Thinking Questions

1. In what significant ways do DNA barcodes differ from commercial (UPC) barcodes?
2. Why would the DNA barcoding initiative place an emphasis on using as few genes as possible?
3. Using a mitochondrial gene for the DNA barcode region in animals has several advantages, but what disadvantages might it also have?

Further Research Question

Based on the species that have been described so far, which groups of animals are the most diverse? How do vertebrates compare with other animal groups? Within vertebrates, how are the major groups ranked in terms of species diversity?

References

Alcaide M, Rico C, Ruiz S, Soriguer R, Munoz J, Figuerola J. 2009. Disentangling vector-borne transmission networks: a universal DNA barcoding method to identify vertebrate hosts from arthropod bloodmeals. *PLoS ONE.* 4:e7092.

Armstrong KF, Ball SL. 2005. DNA barcodes for biosecurity: invasive species identification. *Philos Trans R Soc London [Biol].* 360:1813–1823.

Besansky NJ, Severson DW, Ferdig MT. 2003. DNA barcoding of parasites and invertebrate disease vectors: what you don't know can hurt you. *Trends Parasitol.* 19:545–546.

Brown SA. 2001. A history of the bar code. EH.net Encyclopedia [cited 2010 Apr 13]. Available from: http://www.eh.net/encyclopedia/brown.bar_code.php

Bucklin A, Hopcroft RR, Kosobokova KN, Nigro LM, Ortman BD, Jennings RM, Sweetman CJ. 2010. DNA barcoding of Arctic Ocean holozooplankton for species identification and recognition. *Deep-Sea Research II,* in press.

Eaton MJ, Meyers GL, Kolokotronis SO, Leslie MS, Martin AP, Amato G. 2010. Barcoding bushmeat: molecular identification of Central African and South American harvested vertebrates. *Conserv. Genet.,* in press.

Hebert PDN, Cywinska A, Ball SL, deWaard JR. 2003. Biological identifications through DNA barcodes. *Proc. Roy. Soc.* B 270:313–321.

Hebert PDN, Penton EH, Burns JM, Janzen DH, Hallwachs W. 2004. Ten species in one: DNA barcoding reveals cryptic species in the neotropical skipper butterfly *Astraptes fulgerator.* PNAS. 101:14812–14817.

Marra PP, Dove CJ, Dolbeer R, Dahlan NF, Heacker M, Whatton JF, Diggs NE, France C, Henkes GA. 2009. Migratory Canada geese cause crash of US Airways Flight 1549. *Front Ecol. Environ.* 7:297–301.

Naro-Marciel, E, Reid B, Fitzsimmons NN, Le M, DeSalle R, Amato G. 2010. DNA barcodes for globally threatened marine turtles: a registry approach to documenting biodiveristy. *Mol. Ecol. Res.* 10:252–263.

Ratnasingham S, Hebert PDN. 2007. BOLD: The Barcode of Life Data System (www.barcodinglife.org). *Mol. Ecol. Notes.* 7:355–364.

Steinke D, Zemlak TS, Hebert PDN. 2009. Barcoding Nemo: DNA-based identifications for the ornamental fish trade. *PLoS ONE.* 4:e6300.

Wong, EH-K, Hanner RH. 2008. DNA barcoding detects market substitution in North American seafood. *Food Res. Int.* 41:828–837.

Biofuels:
What Will We Do When We Run Out of Oil?

David Bird
Mount Royal University

Introduction

When your car is low on gas, you pull into a gas station and fill the tank. This gas is derived from a finite supply of petroleum, a non-renewable resource. Some people (e.g., Goodstein, 2004) have predicted that within the next 10 to 50 years, we will reach the peak rate of oil extraction, after this, they suggest, oil production will irreversibly decline. The increasing demand and price for fossil fuels, along with the danger of climate change caused by greenhouse gas (GHG) emissions, has been driving the development of alternative sources of energy. One proposed solution to the looming oil crisis has been to use plant and/or agricultural products and waste for fuel, that is, to produce so-called **biofuel**. Such fuels, produced from the **biomass** generated from agriculture, are very attractive in that their production could provide farmers with a reliable income and help reduce overall carbon dioxide emissions. But there are also possible negative effects of using biomass to power our society. Many of the biofuels are derived from crops that also serve as food, which, in the last few years has contributed to food shortages and increasing food prices. Furthermore, the inputs, in terms of water, fertilizer, and the expanded use of land mass, for agriculture to meet the growing demands for both food and energy will inevitably have environmental impacts. Are biofuels the answer to power our cars? Before answering this question, let's look at what biofuels are, their potential benefits, their negative effects, and the possible solutions that have been considered to mitigate these effects.

> **KEY CONCEPTS**
>
> - Carbohydrates serve as fuel and building material.
> - Fats are energy-rich molecules.
> - Energy transformations are governed by the laws of thermodynamics.

What Are Biofuels?

Whereas **fossil fuels** are the petrochemicals formed from ancient deposits of animals and plants, biofuels are derived from crops, plant matter, or sometimes food and agricultural waste.

Ethanol and Diesel Fuel from Crops

Currently, most biofuels that are commercially produced use existing food crops. Two major biofuels are being produced today: **bioethanol** and **biodiesel**. Such grains as corn and wheat are rich in starch, which in turn can be hydrolyzed into glucose. Starch hydrolysis is fairly simple, in part because of the molecular arrangement of the glucose monomers (see "Alternatives to Using Agricultural Crops: What Are the Biofuels of the Future?") and also because of the readily available enzyme **alpha amylase**. This enzyme catalyzes the hydrolysis of the glycosidic bonds connecting the glucose monomers, which produces glucose. Microbial ethanolic **fermentation** then transforms the glucose into ethanol. Currently in the United States and Canada, grain crops, particularly corn, are being used extensively to produce ethanol this way. In tropical countries, much of the sugar cane harvest is now fermented into ethanol. Sugar cane, of course, is rich in sucrose and is more efficient to ferment into alcohol compared with grain-based systems that are rich in starch.

Some plants use **triglycerides** (oils) for energy storage instead of starch. The North American crops soybean and canola produce seeds rich in triglycerides. These oils can be converted into methyl esters by the **transesterification** of triglycerides into fatty acid methyl esters (**FAMEs**). This chemical transformation is catalyzed by a caustic substance, sodium methoxide, in the presence of methanol. FAMEs are useful as fuel for diesel engines. When produced from plant oils, the fuel is referred to as biodiesel. In tropical countries, the oil palm, *Elaeis* spp., is now being grown more extensively for the production of biodiesel than for food, and many countries in the southern hemisphere are creating oil palm plantations solely for its production. Recently, such countries as Indonesia and Malaysia have expanded their oil palm plantations, and currently 80 percent of all biodiesel originates from these two countries.

Are Biofuels "Green"?

Biofuels Require Energy Input

The rationale behind biofuels is twofold: to replace—at least in part—our dependence on petrochemicals for fuel and to reduce the *net* amount of greenhouse gas (GHG) emissions. Even though burning biofuels in automobile engines still produces carbon dioxide, this carbon was previously captured by plants used to produce the biofuel. Arguably, this cycle is neutral in net GHG emissions. The production of biofuel from plants, however, requires energy: bioethanol must be distilled from water, and triglycerides must be chemically converted into FAMEs. Furthermore, growing the crops requires additional energy in the form of fertilizers. Harvesting the crops and transporting the bulk material to the processing plants also requires energy. To be GHG-neutral, a biofuel must meet two conditions: First, it must provide more energy than is used to make it. Second, producing the biofuel must not cause excessive GHG emissions. The degree to which existing biofuels meet these conditions varies (see Figure 1).

Biofuels Can Cause Greenhouse Gases and Other Environmental Concerns

Of course, plants need sunlight, water, and nutrients to grow. Modern agriculture uses fertilizer extensively; the runoff from agriculture fields gives rise to **eutrophication** of rivers and lakes, causing more environmental concerns. Caused by high levels of nutrient input into aquatic ecosystems, eutrophication promotes the growth of algae and plankton, which choke out the growth of aquatic plants, leading to further problems in the ecosystem. Furthermore, soil bacteria convert some of the nitrogen in applied fertilizers into nitrous oxide, a GHG that is hundreds of times more intense than carbon dioxide. The demand for biodiesel production is driving the expansion of oil palm plantations in such countries as Indonesia and Malaysia, where swampland and forests rich in peat are being cleared to create new plantations. These wetlands are drained, and the peat is burned to clear the land. Peat is the accumulation of partially decayed plant matter. In wetlands or rainforests, it accumulates over thousands of years because the waterlogged

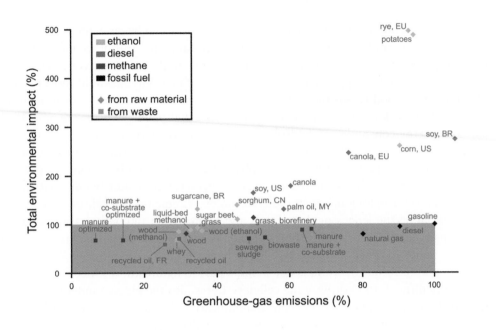

FIGURE 1. **Greenhouse gas emissions plotted against overall environmental impacts of 29 transport fuels, scaled relative to gasoline.**
The origin of biofuels produced outside Switzerland is indicated by country codes: Brazil (BR), China (CN), European Union (EU), France (FR), Malaysia (MY), and the United States (US). Fuels in the shaded area are considered advantageous in both their overall environmental impacts and greenhouse gas emissions.
Source: Scharlemann JPW, Laurance WF. 2008. Environmental science— How green are biofuels? Science 319(5859): 43–44. Supplemental figure S1. Reprinted with permission from AAAS. Adapted from R. Zah et al., Ökobilanz von Energieprodukten: Ökologische Bewertung von Biotreibstoffen (Empa, St. Gallen, Switzerland, 2007).

soils inhibit decomposition. Thus, clearing these forests not only leads to a loss of biodiversity but also releases tremendous amounts of carbon dioxide through the oxidation of thousands of years of accumulated carbon (UNEP, 2009).

Food versus Fuel

Finally, we must consider if there is enough agricultural land to support both food and fuel sufficient for the world's population. The answer is not clear; while agricultural yields per hectare continue to improve, they are doing so at increasingly slower rates. Meanwhile, the amount of arable land per person is decreasing as the global population increases (UNEP, 2009). As a result, due to limited resources for land and water, a trade-off between food and fuel begins to emerge. For example, more than 25 percent of the U.S. corn yield was converted into ethanol in 2008, contributing to the rising cost of food worldwide and food shortages in much of the developing world (Runge and Senauer, 2007).

Alternatives to Using Agricultural Crops: What Are the Biofuels of the Future?

Biofuels are not necessarily derived from agricultural crops. Methods exist that produce ethanol from waste materials, such as wood chips, or from so-called energy crops that would be grown on land not amenable to normal agriculture. Fast-growing plants, such

PHOTO A. **Agricultural land and water are limited resources.**
Using agricultural land to produce fuel may create a food versus fuel conflict for land and water use, particularly in the developing world.
Source: Reuters/Landov.

as switchgrass and poplar, are rich in **cellulose**. Cellulose can be fermented into ethanol using a process similar to starch-based ethanol production. Still other methods have been proposed to produce gasoline-equivalent fuel from the same sources using chemical conversions. These approaches are still in their infancy, but they hold some promise of avoiding the food versus fuel debate caused by biofuel production from agricultural crops. A drawback to these approaches, however, is that plant cell walls are more difficult and energy-consuming to hydrolyze than starch for two main reasons. First, the structure of cellulose is different from starch. While both are a polymer of glucose, starch is made of glucose monomers linked by **alpha-1,4-glycosidic bonds**, making the polymer helical in structure, while cellulose is linked by **beta-1,4-glycosidic bonds**, making the polymer linear. The long linear strands of cellulose bundle together through hydrogen bonds all along the length of the strands and form strong fibres that are difficult to break apart. Second, the cellulose fibres in plant cell walls are often cross-linked through covalent bonds to other compounds, such as **lignin**, an aromatic polymer. The notable strength and resiliency of wood is due in large part to **lignification**. Once lignified, it is even more difficult to hydrolyze the cellulose fibres into the glucose monomers necessary for fermentation or further chemical modification. Future uses of wood or agricultural waste for fuel will have to overcome these challenges.

Another experimental approach being developed is to grow oils in algal cultures. Some species of algae can accumulate as much as 50 percent of their dry weight in storage triglycerides. Algal production of biodiesel has the potential of requiring less land, since much more energy per hectare can be produced using this method. Still, the environmental cost of water use and nutrient inputs must be balanced. Some have suggested a solution that addresses both problems of water and nutrient demand: using waste effluent from high-intensity animal farming or city waste water and converting an environmental problem into sustainable fuel for the future (Clarens et al., 2010).

The Second Law of Thermodynamics and Automobiles

A group of scientists have recently suggested that ethanol will never sustainably replace gasoline. Biologist John Ohlrogge and others have argued that driving using internal combustion engines, even when using biofuels, is simply too inefficient to be feasible in the long term (Ohlrogge et al., 2009). Less than 20 percent of the energy stored in the fuel of an internal combustion engine is converted into kinetic energy to move the vehicle; the rest is lost as heat. No matter how we may be able to improve the efficiency of the automobile engine, we can't escape the second law of thermodynamics. In every energy conversion, entropy increases. Instead, biomass could be used in electric generators directly to produce electricity. Such generators are more efficient than automotive engines, and vehicles driven by electric engines are much more efficient than internal combustion engines. Furthermore, such electricity plants also produce heat, which can be used for heating water and buildings, significantly raising the overall use of the energy stored in biomass. This approach is being used in an innovative way by an Alberta company. Alberta is famous for its cattle industry, and most of the cattle are raised in high density on feedlots. Feedlots produce large volumes of animal waste in a concentrated form. Treating this waste as a resource, Highmark Renewables has patented a technology that generates methane by microbial fermentation of the manure. In turn, the methane is used as a fuel to drive electrical generators. What remains of the manure as a by-product after microbial fermentation is rich in plant nutrients and sold as fertilizer.

Conclusions

All forms of energy production will have costs and benefits. Scientists are taking into consideration the environmental life cycle of existing and proposed biofuels in order to make better decisions for the future. Many different biofuels have been proposed, and bioethanol and biodiesel production have burgeoned into large industries. Initially, many of these approaches appeared to be good solutions for the future, but subsequent studies that considered, for example, the full cycle of corn-ethanol production have questioned these solutions. Sustainable energy will take innovative thinking and careful consideration of the impact of any potential production system.

Critical Thinking Questions

1. Starch and cellulose are both plant polysaccharides made up of glucose. Is one more readily converted into glucose for fermentation than the other? Why or why not?
2. For every kilogram of starch, how many moles of glucose are present? How many moles of ethanol can be produced from a kilogram of starch?
3. There is a by-product of the production of FAMEs from animal or oils. Based on your knowledge of the chemical structure of oils, what is this by-product? Estimate, by mass, how much of the by-product is produced for each gram of FAMEs produced from oils.

Further Research Question

Is the by-product of biodiesel good for anything? What uses have been suggested for it?

References

Clarens AF, Resurreccion EP, White MA, Colosi LM. 2010. Environmental life cycle comparison of algae to other bioenergy feedstocks. *Environ. Sci. Technol.* 44(5):1813–1819.

Goodstein DL. 2004. *Out of gas: the end of the age of oil.* New York: W.W. Norton & Company.

Ohlrogge J, Allen D, Berguson B, DellaPenna D, Shachar-Hill Y, Stymne, S. 2009. Driving on biomass. *Sci.* 324:1019–1020.

Runge CF, Senauer B. 2007 May/June. How biofuels could starve the poor. *Foreign Affairs.* 86.

Scharlemann JPW, Laurance WF. 2008. Environmental science: how green are biofuels? *Sci.* 319(5859):43–44.

[UNEP] United Nations Environment Programme. 2009. Towards sustainable production and use of resources: assessing biofuels [report on the Internet]. Paris (FR): UNEP. [cited 2010 Apr 9]; Job No.: DTI/1213/PA. Available from: http://www.unep.org/pdf/Assessing_Biofuels-full_report-Web.pdf

Biotechnology and Human Health:
Producing Therapeutic Protein in Transgenic Plants

Ron Wilen

University of the Fraser Valley

Introduction

The old saying "an apple a day keeps the doctor away" has taken on a new meaning with the development of genetic engineering. Imagine eating a banana that would vaccinate you against hepatitis B or a tomato that could prevent you from developing Alzheimer's disease (see Photo A). Is this science fiction or reality? Well, bananas expressing hepatitis coat proteins and tomatoes producing amyloid proteins do exist (Kong, Richter, Yang, Arntzen, Mason, and Thanavala, 2001; Jung Won Youm, Jeon, Kim, Kim, Ko, Joung, and Kim, 2008), and soon eating fruits and vegetables will be a way to be vaccinated. Maybe the saying will be changed to "an apple a day keeps the needle away."

Medical Uses of Plants

Plants have been used for medicinal purposes since the beginnings of recorded history. The Renaissance era was known as the age of herbal medicine, with plant extracts being used to treat most ailments. Today herbal medicine is still widely used around the world.

KEY CONCEPTS

- The genetic code is universal: human proteins can be made in plants.
- Genetic engineering and recombinant DNA (rDNA) technology can provide substantial health benefits to society.
- The characteristics of the structure and function of protein aid in protein isolation.

PHOTO A.
Perhaps one day you will need only to eat a banana to get a vaccination.
Source: Siberia/Dreamstime. com/Getstock.com and 350jb/ Dreamstime.com/Getstock.com

In modern medicine, purified plant metabolites are used in the treatment of numerous diseases. Paclitaxel, digitoxin, quinine, and morphine are just a few of the drugs that use plant metabolites. However, many human ailments are caused by the failure of the body to produce a specific protein or metabolite, and these diseases cannot be cured with a drug, whether from plants or elsewhere. For example, in type 1 diabetes, the pancreas fails to synthesize insulin, and in hemophilia, a functional clotting factor fails to be produced. These are just two of the many diseases for which the treatment requires a protein.

Today, these proteins are produced by a variety of techniques that include extraction from tissues of cadavers, chemical synthesis, or the use of recombinant DNA (rDNA) technology and fermentation. Each method has limitations and problems, including ethical concerns, functionality, and cost. rDNA technology relies on the use of bacterial hosts to produce a human protein through fermentation, which requires extensive purification to isolate the protein of interest. In addition to the issue of purification is the fact that bacterial proteins do not undergo **post-translational processing** (reactions that alter a protein's covalent structure, such as phosphorylation, glycosylation, and proteolytic cleavage), which is necessary for the function of many human proteins. A solution to the latter issue is to use a eukaryotic host cell to produce the recombinant protein.

Of the eukaryotic organisms that have been proposed for producing human proteins, plants have received the most attention. Numerous model systems that use seeds, roots, and tubers as production vessels have been developed (Vandekerckhove et al., 1989; Haq, Mason, Clements, and Arntzen, 1995). Several characteristics make plants ideal model systems for producing human proteins: (1) they undergo translational processing that is similar to that in humans, (2) they have no potential to be contaminated with human viruses, which could happen when using animal systems, and (3) the cost of production is infinitely lower than with any other method. The downside to using plants is purification. Like all living organisms, the transgenic plants will accumulate numerous other proteins that will share physical and chemical properties with the recombinant human protein. Because biochemical purification techniques generally exploit differences in the chemical properties, isolating the single protein of interest from the host is a challenge.

Oleosin Protein Technology

A technology used by SemBioSys Genetics, a biotechnology company based in Calgary, Alberta, may provide a solution to the purification problem. Maurice Moloney is the chief scientific officer and founder of the company. The technology was developed in Moloney's laboratory when he was professor of plant biology at the University of Calgary. While studying gene expression during seed development in canola (*Brassica napus* L.) (Van Rooijen, Wilen, Holbrook, and Moloney, 1992; Wilen, Van Rooijen, Pearce, Paris, Holbrook, and Moloney, 1991), researchers in Moloney's laboratory noticed a family of proteins that accumulated late in seed development. These proteins displayed the unusual property of remaining with the oil fraction when seeds were crushed in an aqueous solution. With a simple centrifugation and wash, it is now possible to purify these proteins from the rest of the seed proteins.

These proteins are called **oleosins**, and they display a unique tertiary structure. The protein consists of three domains: a hydrophilic N-terminus, a C-terminus, and an extremely hydrophobic central domain. They are synthesized on the endoplasmic reticulum and embedded into an organelle called an **oleosome** (or oilbody). The oleosome is the **triacylglyceride** (three fatty acids attached to a glycerol) storage organelle in plant seeds. At maturity the **cytoplasmic face** (the side facing away from the cell membrane) of the oleosome is completely coated in oleosins, with the hydrophilic domains on the

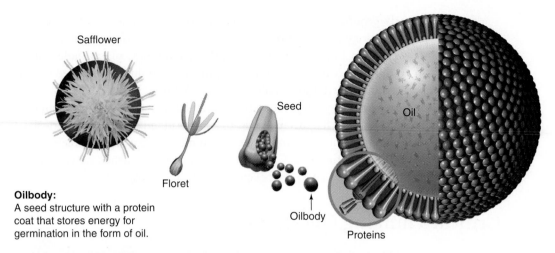

Safflower

Seed

Oil

Floret

Oilbody:
A seed structure with a protein coat that stores energy for germination in the form of oil.

Oilbody

Proteins

FIGURE 1. From flower to recombinant protein.
Seeds are produced in the ovary of a flower. Within the seed, the oil accumulates in discrete organelles called oleosomes or oilbodies. The oleosomes are coated with proteins called oleosins. Through the use of rDNA techniques, oleosin can be modified to produce a fusion protein that will stay embedded in the oleosome to facilitate its isolation.
Source: Courtesy of SemBioSys Genetics.

exterior and the hydrophobic central domain firmly embedded in the triacylglycerides core of the oleosome. The anchorage into the oleosome permits the oleosins to remain with the oil fraction when the crushed seeds are centrifuged (see Figure 1).

How could researchers take advantage of this simple purification step? The answer was to produce a fusion protein. Through the use of **rDNA** (recombinant DNA) techniques, the gene for the protein of interest would be **ligated** (attached) to the oleosin gene. To test whether this technique would work, Moloney's group fused the gene for hirudin to the 3′ end of an oleosin gene isolated from the model plant *Arabidopsis thaliana* (Van Rooijen, Terning, and Moloney, 1992). Hirudin is a medically important anticoagulant that is produced by leeches. After transforming canola plants with the oleosin-hirudin construct, the researchers were able to demonstrate that the new fusion protein inserted into developing oleosome, with the hirudin portion of the fusion exposed to the cytoplasm. When these transgenic seeds were subjected to homogenization in an aqueous buffer and then centrifuged, the oleosin-hirudin fusion protein partitioned with the oil fraction.

The next problem was how to separate the hirudin protein as an isolated protein rather than as a fusion protein. The researchers designed a short piece of linker DNA to place between the oleosin and hirudin gene sequences in the fusion construct. The linker DNA encoded a **Factor Xa** protease-recognition sequence. Factor Xa is an enzyme that will cleave any protein that contains this unique amino acid sequence. The isolated oleosomes from transgenic plants expressing this construct were then resuspended in an aqueous buffer, and the Factor Xa protease was added. Following incubation, the mixture was then centrifuged again, and the aqueous fraction was examined. Western blot analysis with a hirudin antibody demonstrated that the majority of the hirudin protein was present in the aqueous fraction and was of the correct molecular mass when analyzed by mass spectroscopy.

The last question was whether the isolated hirudin was functional. Hirudin binds to the blood-clotting protein thrombin and inhibits the formation of clots. When the hirudin from the transgenic plant was added to blood samples, clotting did not occur. This showed the recombinant protein was fully functional and demonstrated the feasibility of the technology (Parmenter, Boothe, van Rooijen, Yeung, and Moloney, 1995; Kühnel, Alcantara, Boothe, van Rooijen, and Moloney, 2003). The results of these studies show that recombinant proteins can be simply and cost-effectively isolated from the rest of the cellular components by using the oleosome technology.

Since these early proof-of-concept experiments, researchers at SemBioSys Genetics have refined the technology and are currently using safflower (*Carthamus tinctorius*) as the host plant for protein production. By using this technology, plant-made human insulin was shown to be equivalent to recombinant insulin (Humulin) produced via fermentation in bacteria in phase 1 and 2 clinical trials (Nykiforuk, Boothe, Murray, Keon, Goron, Markley, and Moloney, 2006). SemBioSys Genetics is also now producing the protein Apo A1$_{Milano}$, which has been shown to reduce plaque build-up in arteries.[1] This product is in the pre-clinical testing stage, which means we won't be able to use it for many years. In the meantime, the Canada Food Guide recommends we eat 7 to 10 servings of fruits or vegetables every day, even if they aren't transgenic.

Critical Thinking Questions

1. Genetically engineered plants with genes from humans, leeches, and other plants produce functional proteins. What basic biological concept is demonstrated by this?
2. What are the advantages of linking a medicinal protein to an oleosin protein?
3. What are some of the potential problems with eating a banana that contains a vaccine?

Further Research Question

If you wanted to produce a protein that was very hydrophobic in a transgenic plant, how would you modify the oleosin separation strategy?

References

Haq TA, Mason HS, Clements JD, Arntzen CJ. 1995. Oral immunization with a recombinant bacterial antigen produced in transgenic plants. *Sci.* 268:714–716.

Jung Won Youm JW, Jeon JH, Kim H, Kim YH, Ko K, Joung H, Kim HS. 2008. Transgenic tomatoes expressing human beta-amyloid for use as a vaccine against Alzheimer's disease. *Biotechnol. Lett.* 30:1839–1845.

Kong Q, Richter L, Yang YF, Arntzen CJ, Mason HS, Thanavala Y. 2001. Oral immunization with hepatitis B surface antigen expressed in transgenic plants. *PNAS.* 98:11539–11544.

*Kühnel B, Alcantara J, Boothe J, van Rooijen G, Moloney M. 2003. Precise and efficient cleavage of recombinant fusion proteins using mammalian aspartic proteases. *Protein Eng.* 16:777–783.

Nykiforuk CL, Boothe JG, Murray EW, Keon RG, Goron, HJ, Markley NA, Moloney MM. 2006. Transgenic expression and recovery of biologically active recombinant human insulin from *Arabidopsis thaliana* seeds. *Plant Biotechnol. J.* 4:77–85.

*Parmenter DL, Boothe JG, van Rooijen GJH, Yeung EC, Moloney MM. 1995. Production of biologically active hirudin in plant seeds using oleosin partitioning. *Plant Mol. Biol.* 29:1167–1180.

Van Rooijen GJH, Terning LI, Moloney MM. 1992. Nucleotide sequence of *Arabidopsis thaliana* oleosin gene. *Plant Mol. Biol.* 18:1177–1179.

Van Rooijen GJH, Wilen RW, Holbrook LA, Moloney MM. 1992. Regulation of accumulation of mRNAs encoding a 20kDa oil-body protein in microspore derived embryos of *Brassica napus*. *Can. J. Bot.* 70:503–508.

---

[1] WO 05/047455: "Methods for the production of apolipoproteins in transgenic plants" (US Patent Application).

Vandekerckhove J, Damme JV, Lijsebettens MV, Botterman J, DeBlock M, Vandewiele M, De Clercq A, Leemans J, Van Montagu M, Krebbers E. 1989. Enkephalins produced in transgenic plants using modified 2S seed storage proteins. *Biotechnol.* 7:929–932.

Wilen RW, Van Rooijen GJH, Pearce DW, Paris RP, Holbrook LA, Moloney MM. 1991. Effects of jasmonic acid on embryo-specific processes in *Brassica* and *Linum* oilseeds. *Plant Physiol.* 95:399–405.

Bitter Taste:
Genetics and Plant Secondary Compounds

Sharon L. Gillies
University of the Fraser Valley

Introduction

You are not going to get any dessert until you eat all your vegetables! Many of us heard that admonition when we were young. We all know vegetables are good for us. Packed full of nutrients, low in calories, and high in fibre, you could say vegetables are the perfect food. But what if they taste bitter to you? Some of us find broccoli unpalatable, while others have no problem eating it. Why this difference?

Our tongues have 25 different bitterness receptors that allow us to detect thousands of bitter compounds. A lot of bitter flavours are plant secondary compounds that have no direct role in plant growth and development but function as defenses against herbivores and pathogens. Along with bitterness to deter animals, some of these compounds are also highly toxic. Identifying bitter flavours and distinguishing between them is important to our survival. Our ability to taste bitter is more complex than our ability to distinguish the

KEY CONCEPTS
■ The sense of taste uses chemoreceptors, which can detect the presence of particular molecules.
■ Inheritance patterns are often more complex than predicted by simple Mendelian genetics.
■ Plants respond to attacks by herbivores and pathogens by producing bitter and toxic compounds.

PHOTO A. **Eat your veggies.** It is likely that this child is a bitter taster. It is not going to be easy to get him to eat his broccoli.
Source: Monkeybusinessimages/ Dreamstime.com/Getstock.com

other flavours: sweet, sour, salty, and **umami** (the taste of glutamate, an amino acid). This level of discrimination may allow us to distinguish between a bitter flavour from a toxin and the bitterness we might like in some foods, such as beer and cheese.

Genetics of Bitter Taste

Our ability to taste bitterness is due to a family of 25 genes called *TAS2R* genes (*TAS* stands for taste receptor gene). Some of these genes code for taste receptors sensitive to a wide variety of different bitter chemicals, others are highly selective. They are located in clusters on chromosomes 5, 7, and 12. Each of the 25 bitter genes may have several different **alleles** (alternative forms of the gene). The resulting genetic complexity of our ability to taste bitterness means that saccharin may leave you with a bitter aftertaste, but spinach and broccoli taste great. Researchers are using the ability to taste bitter PTC (phenylthiocarbamide) and PROP (6-n-propylthiouracil) as a research tool. The bitterness of PTC and PROP is based on **thiourea** (contains the functional group N—C=S), which is not found in food but is similar enough structurally to naturally occurring bitter-tasting chemicals to use in studies. The gene for this variability in PTC/PROP sensitivity is the *TAS2R38* gene found on chromosome 7. But *TAS2R38* has been found to be only 60 to 85 percent responsible for the **phenotypic variation** (taster or non-taster).

Biologists originally thought the ability to taste PTC/PROP was determined by simple Mendelian genetics with only two alleles: one dominant and one recessive. In order to test for tasters and non-tasters, researchers commonly use the **threshold level** (a very tiny amount is increased until it is either tasted or not) of PTC or PROP. Using this technique, researchers found that about 70 percent of Canadians are PTC/PROP tasters and 30 percent are non-tasters. If you received even a single copy of the dominant allele called PAV, you are most likely a taster. If you received two copies of the recessive allele called AVI, you are probably a non-taster. While the majority of people do have only these two alleles, determining the ability to taste bitter is not that simple. Recent studies have identified a total of seven different alleles that cause a range of abilities to taste PTC/PROP. Most of these alternative alleles are rare, and some are found only in sub-Saharan Africa.

In other studies, when subjects were asked to rate how bitter PTC or PROP tasted to them, the results were different. The same 30 percent of Canadians were found to be PTC/PROP non-tasters, 45 percent were medium-tasters, and 25 percent were very sensitive super-tasters. It has therefore been hypothesized that inheritance of this gene may be due to **incomplete dominance** (the heterozygote is intermediate in character). Most super-tasters are **homozygous** (have two copies of PAV) for the taster allele; medium-tasters are **heterozygous** (with one copy of the taster allele PAV and one copy of the non-taster allele AVI); and non-tasters are homozygous for the non-taster allele (two copies of AVI); however, some research suggests that super-tasters may use additional bitter receptors and have more taste buds on their tongues. Not only are super-tasters more sensitive to bitter, they are also super sensitive to sweet and salty. There is also the unusual occurrence of non-taster parents producing taster children, which also suggests that inheritance does not follow simple Mendelian genetics. The mode of inheritance for the *TAS2R38* gene is still not clear.

In general, PTC/PROP tasters find caffeine and many vegetables more bitter than non-tasters. Some studies have discovered that tasters and super-tasters find broccoli, Brussels sprouts, cabbage, kale, asparagus, spinach, grapefruit, grapefruit juice, and soy products more bitter than non-tasters. Can you blame your genes if you hate broccoli? The link between the ability to taste PTC/PROP bitterness and food choice is actually weak in adults. The lack of relationship between food choice and being a PTC/PROP

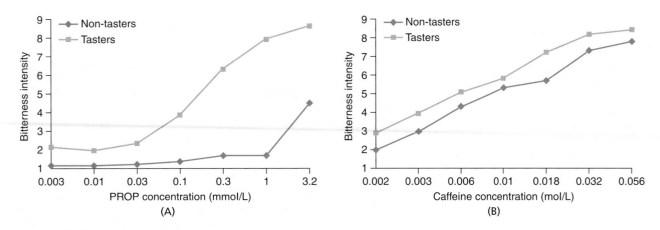

FIGURE 1. PROP tasters versus non-tasters.
(Left) Mean bitterness intensity for PROP solutions by PROP tasters and non-tasters. (Right) Mean bitterness intensity for caffeine solutions by PROP tasters and non-tasters.
Source: Ly A, Drewnowski A. 2001. PROP (6-n-Propylthiouracil) tasting and sensory responses to caffeine, sucrose, neohesperidin dihydrochalcone and chocolate. Chem. Senses 26:41–47, 2001, Fig. 3, p. 44, © 2001, by permission of Oxford University Press on behalf of the Chemical Senses Journal.

taster might be because tasters use more sweeteners than non-tasters. Take a look around the next time you buy your coffee. If you see someone putting a lot of sugar and cream in his or her cup, they just might be a taster.

Bitter Compounds in Plants

Each year, moulds and fungus destroy crops that could have fed 300 million people. An estimated 20 percent of all crops are unharvestable because of insect pests. Plants produce many bitter and toxic compounds to deter herbivores and protect against **pathogens** (e.g., moulds, fungus, bacteria, and viruses that cause disease). Plant defenses can be constitutive, which means that the compounds are produced all the time. This is energetically expensive to the plant. Alternatively, when a plant is injured, it can induce the production of various toxic secondary compounds.

Plants produce some well-known bitter alkaloid poisons. Members of the nightshade plant family (Solanaceae) produce atropine, scopolamine, and hyoscyamine. These compounds are **anticholinergics** (inhibit neurological transmitters) and can cause hallucinations, convulsions, coma, and even death. Some edible examples of this family are peppers, tomatoes, and potatoes. If you leave your potatoes in the light, they will turn green and begin to produce a bitter and toxic glycoalkaloid.

If you have ever tasted bitter celery, you are familiar with furanocoumarins. As well as being bitter, these compounds are **mutagenic** (cause DNA damage) and **carcinogenic** (promote cancer), and also cause **contact dermatitis** (skin rash) in humans. Celery breeding programs have given us celery with a reduced ability to produce furanocoumarins. Without this ability, celery is unable to defend itself against some pathogens, such as the mould *Fusarium*. Soil-borne *Fusarium* is found in areas of the Fraser Valley and other agricultural regions of Canada. Because of the increase in *Fusarium* disease in celery plants in the 1990s, researchers developed a resistant variety. Unfortunately, this type of celery was resistant because researchers bred the ability to produce large amounts of furanocoumarins back into it. This bitter variety didn't stay in people's mouths or on the market for long.

Broccoli and other members of the **Brassica family** (e.g., cauliflower, Brussels sprouts, cabbage) are one of the most disliked vegetable groups in our diets. The compounds in broccoli responsible for the bitter taste are a group of secondary compounds

FIGURE 2. The bitter taste of broccoli and other members of the Brassica family may protect us from eating large amounts of toxic compounds. *Source: Reprinted from Spiteller D. 2008. Plant Defense Strategies, in Jorgensen, SE and Fath, B, eds. Encyclopedia of Ecology. Academic Press, Oxford, pp. 2798–2811; Figure 11, p. 2806. © 2008 with permission from Elsevier.*

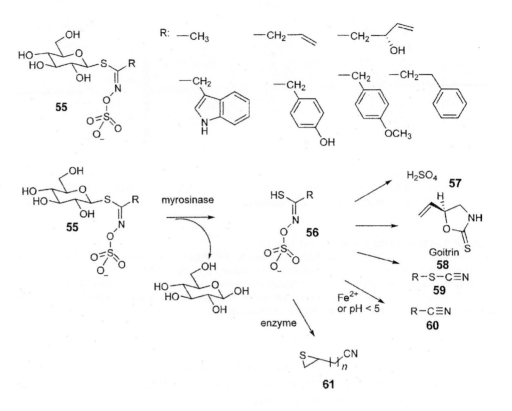

called glucosinolates (see Figure 2). Some glucosinolates can interfere with the thyroid's iodine function and can cause **goiter** (enlarged thyroid). Other glucosinolates are beneficial with some anti-cancer effects. The *TAS2R38* receptor is highly sensitive to glucosinolates, and PTC/PROP tasters rate these vegetables as 60 percent more bitter than non-tasters. The ability to taste the bitterness of these compounds may protect us from consuming a dangerous amount of glucosinolate.

Researchers are still looking to create the perfect broccoli, one low in glucosinolates and high in sugar that everyone will like. Plant breeders have developed different broccoli **varieties** (plants with different characteristics produced by selective breeding) that vary in their concentration of glucosinolates and sugars, but there is a trade-off. Lowering gluconsinolate levels to reduce bitterness could also reduce the anti-cancer activity of these vegetables.

Ahmed El-Sohemy from the University of Toronto is leading a research project on **nutrigenomics** (genetic basis of food preferences). He states:

> Nutrigenomics is the science that explores how nutrients and food **bioactives** (components of food that can affect health) interact with the genome to impact human health. Common genetic variations can explain why some individuals respond differently from others to the same dietary factors. Variations in genes that code for taste receptors on the surface of the tongue can also affect our sensitivity to different tastants. For example, some individuals are much more sensitive to the bitter taste of broccoli and may, therefore, avoid consuming it. (2010 email to the author; unreferenced)

El-Sohemy and his colleagues are looking at how individual differences in taste can influence our diet selection and affect our nutrition. In extreme cases, aversion to bitter food, such as vegetables, can result in nutrition-related chronic diseases. He found that such factors as age, sex, and ethnicity can modify your PTC/PROP taste perception. Researchers from his lab found that the elderly are more willing to try and accept new foods, regardless of the genetics of their taste receptors.

Conclusions

It can be a problem to get some children to eat their vegetables. Studies show that children who are tasters and super-tasters reject bitter-tasting food. Genetics is therefore the main factor in the food choice of children. Scientists are now searching for compounds that can block the bitter receptors in the tongue. This may increase the acceptability of bitter vegetables and even medicines. Fortunately, our ability to taste bitterness and other flavours decreases as we age; therefore, even if you hated your vegetables as a child, you may develop a taste for them as you get older.

Critical Thinking Questions

1. Why do we need 25 bitter receptors and genes?
2. If the inheritance of *TAS2R38* is incomplete dominance, using a Punnett square, what is the chance that a super-taster and a medium taster will produce a super-taster child? How would this differ if the inheritance is due to simple dominant and recessive alleles?
3. Plant breeding programs are attempting to produce varieties of vegetables without bitter compounds. How might that affect the plants and agriculture?

Further Research Question

How have animals evolved to cope with a variety of toxic plant secondary compounds in their diets (see Dearing et al., 2005)?

References

Acamovic T, Brooker JD. 2005. Biochemistry of plant secondary metabolites and their effects in animals. *Proc. Nutr. Soc.* 64:403–412.

Behrens M, Foerster S, Staehler F, Raguse J, Meyerhof W. 2007. Gustatory expression pattern of the human TAS2R bitter receptor gene family reveals a heterogenous population of bitter responsive taste receptor cells. *J. Neurosci.* 27:12630–12640.

*Dearing MD, Foley WJ, McLean S. 2005. The influence of plant secondary metabolites on the nutritional ecology of herbivorous terrestrial vertebrates. *Annu. Rev. Ecol. Evol. Syst.* 36:169–189.

EI-Sohemy A, Stewart L, Khataan N, Fontaine-Bisson B, Kwong P, Ozsungur S, Cornelis, MC. 2007. Nutrigenomics of taste—impact on food preferences and food production. *Nutrigenomics.* 60:176–182.

*Garcia-Bailo B, Toguri C, Eny KM, El-Sohemy A. 2009. Genetic variation in taste and its influence on food selection. *Integr. Biol.* 13:69–80.

Gillies SL, Cliff, MA, Toivonen PMA, King MC. 1997. Effect of atmosphere on broccoli sensory attributes in commercial MAP and microperforated packages. *J. Food Qual.* 20:105–115.

Hayes JE, Bartoshuk LM, Kidd JR, Duffy VD. 2008. Supertasting and prop bitterness depends on more than the TAS2R38 gene. *Chem. Senses* 33(3):255–265.

Howel GA, Jander G. 2008. Plant immunity to insect herbivores. *Annu. Rev. Plant Biol.* 59:41–66.

Karban R, Myers JH. 1989. Induced plant responses to herbivory. *Annu. Rev. Ecol. Syst.* 20:331–48.

Kim UK, Drayna D. 2004. Genetics of individual differences in bitter taste perception: lessons from the PTC gene. *Clin. Genet.* 67:275–280.

Kuiper HA, Kleter GA. 2003. The scientific basis for risk assessment and regulation of genetically modified foods. *Trends Food Sci. Technol.* 14:277–297.

Navarro-Allende A, Khataan N, El-Sohemy A. 2008. Impact of genetic and environmental determinants of taste with food preferences in older adults. *J. Nutr. Elderly.* 27:267–276.

Schonhof I, Krumbein A, Bruckner B. 2004. Genotypic effects on glucosinolates and sensory properties of broccoli and cauliflower. *Nahrung/Food.* 48:25–33.

Spiteller D. 2008. Plant defense strategies. In: Jorgensen SE, Fath B, editors. *Encyclopedia of ecology.* Oxford: Academic Press. p. 2798–2811.

Tepper, BJ. 2008. Nutritional implications of genetic taste variation: the role of prop sensitivity and other taste phenotypes. *Annu. Rev. Nutr.* 28:1–22.

Bubbles in Foods:
Softness, Sweetness, and Light

Martin G. Scanlon
University of Manitoba

Introduction

Have you ever bitten into a peeled raw potato? Why not? You wouldn't hesitate to bite into a raw banana or apple, and yet, we have become accustomed to consuming certain foods only when they are cooked. In fact, the softening of food materials by cooking is surmised to have played a pivotal role in hominid development. Digesting raw foods is an energy-intensive process, but before cooking, it was the only option. Thus, pre-hominids expended a lot of energy just on metabolizing food. When some groups discovered fire and began to cook their food, this energy was redirected and used in other metabolically costly yet advantageous processes, such as increasing brain size—a key step toward becoming hominids. Other than through cooking, food can be softened by substituting a volume fraction of solid materials with air or other gases. This process decreases the toughness and strength of the food, softening it and making it easier to digest. This practice is part of the massive industry of food science, which is involved in the research and design of new, tasty, and safe food products. The discovery in Egypt, some 5000 years ago, that an ascomycete, *Saccharomyces cerevisiae*, could generate carbon dioxide and ethanol in a ground cereal slurry and that the ensuing gas-filled (leavened) material could be solidified by baking marks the start of food softening by bubbles and the start of the story of bread.

Today, many foods and beverages, made in small quantities in the kitchen or in huge quantities in large manufacturing facilities, have a significant volume fraction of bubbles. Some examples of gas-filled foods are shown in Figure 1, where you can see that bread is situated toward the higher end of this gas fraction continuum. Foods with a lower bubble volume fraction are bubbly liquids with isolated bubbles. More compressed bubbles that pack tightly have higher bubble volume fractions (0.6 or higher) and are classified as foams.

KEY CONCEPTS

- Bubbles soften foods to make them more palatable.
- Bubbly foods and foams are an important part of the food industry.
- Protein molecules are good foaming agents because of their amphiphilic nature.

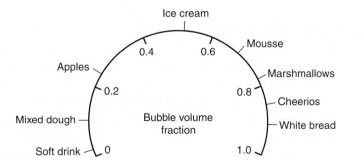

FIGURE 1. Classification of some common foods and beverages according to their volume fraction of gas.

FIGURE 2. **Cross-sections of loaves prepared from doughs mixed with fine oat bran at different levels of substitution.**
Source: Courtesy of Dr. Grant Campbell, The University of Manchester.

FIGURE 2. **Cross-sections of loaves prepared from doughs mixed with fine oat bran at different levels of substitution.**
Source: Courtesy of Dr. Grant Campbell, The University of Manchester.

Carbon Dioxide

Carbon dioxide is the gas most commonly used to create aerated food. This by-product from the anaerobic respiration of yeast (*Saccharomyces cerevisiae*) is still the means of bubble softening in bread and many other baked products. Yeast is also the means for carbonating some beverages, such as beer and champagne. In other carbonated beverages, the headspace of the beverage container is filled with industrially derived carbon dioxide under pressure.

Bubbles are also part of the solution to getting a larger segment of the population to make healthful food choices and so limit diet-related disease. Because taste and other quality attributes govern consumer purchasing decisions, food has to taste good, no matter how compelling its nutritional advantages. Bran, flaxseed, or other healthful components added to dough usually impair bubble creation or growth and hence affect the quality of the bread (see Figure 2). Therefore, manufacturers trying to create nutritious, enriched baked products need to devise processing strategies that reduce or eliminate the disruption of the bubble structure and maintain the quality of the baked product that is critical to consumer appreciation.

Bubbles in Pop

Many beverages rely on bubbles to impart a sense of quality and pleasure. However, some aspects of pleasure derived from bubbles are somewhat surprising. In a chapter in the book *Bubbles in Food* (the proceedings of the first international conference on the subject), Earl Carstens of the neurobiology section at the University of California (Davis) performed some neat experiments to find out why carbonated drinks, such as champagne and cola, tingle on the tongue. One thought was that when bubbles of carbon dioxide burst on the tongue, we sense it mechanically and this imparts a pleasurable sensation. However, Carstens and his colleagues showed how the tingle sensation arises not because of an interaction of bubbles with the tongue's mechanoreceptors but because our pain receptors are stimulated. The carbon dioxide dissolved in the drink gives rise to a weak acid, carbonic acid, and it is this acid that elicits a response from your oral pain receptors. Therefore, it seems that masochism is an essential element in the allure of carbonated beverages.

Bubbles in Beer

Another carbonated beverage in which bubble creation and retention is essential to product quality is beer. Ideally, beer should produce a steady stream of bubbles throughout its lifetime. For some beers, these bubbles should give rise to a substantial head of foam on the top of the beer. Guinness stout is probably the archetypal example, where the white, bubble-filled head contrasts distinctively with the opaque black liquid. Attaining this desired composite by using a draught dispenser is not difficult in a bar, but when the drink originates from a bottle or a can, creating this structure is much harder.

In the late 1980s, Guinness Breweries saw the development of a canned product that would mimic its draught product as the key to increasing market share. Guinness recognized that to achieve this goal, it needed to generate millions of tiny bubbles as the consumer depressurized the can during opening and so create the distinctive white head on the top of the stout. The solution came from inserting a "widget" into the can so that the depressurization step expelled a small amount of the beer through a tiny orifice in the widget. This formed the bubbles that became the creamy head whose consistency was similar to that of the draught product. This innovation in packaging technology paid big dividends to Guinness; the company essentially fashioned a new market out of a flat canned beer sector, won awards around the world for the invention, and reaped huge profits from sales of the new canned draft beer.

Bubbles in Medicine

Bubbles with short lifetimes are directly involved in certain medical diagnoses. When bubbles reside in fluids, such as blood or water, they make the fluid more compressible. Injecting very small bubbles (thousandths of a millimetre) into the bloodstream near suspected critical tissue damage (e.g., in the heart muscle circulatory system) allows the flow pattern of the blood in this damaged region to be readily imaged by ultrasound. This visualization is made possible because the ultrasonic pulses from which the images are constructed are pressure waves, and they are powerfully scattered by the bubbles that have been injected into the bloodstream. Doctors are then able to evaluate whether critical regions of the heart tissue are getting enough blood flow. Thus, the success of these non-invasive diagnoses of heart function in critical-care situations relies on the interesting properties of these medical microbubbles.

Foam

In foams, the bubbles are more compressed and so they press into each other and are no longer spherical. Foams are interesting materials since they are made up of matter in two states, usually an aqueous liquid and a gas. With this combination, they should flow, yet they exhibit the capacity to resist shear stresses, a defining characteristic of materials that are solid. The smaller the bubbles in the foam, the more it can resist shear stresses, making the foam stiffer. This stiffening principle is put to good use in recipes for soufflés and angel cakes, for which it is essential to create a stiff foam by mixing long enough to get the mean bubble size small enough so that the foam can withstand the stresses of mixing in the additional ingredients.

In making soufflés and cakes, and a number of other foods, such as ice cream, the aeration process does not make use of yeast and carbon dioxide; instead, the mechanical action of mixing incorporates air into the batter. More air is drawn in the longer the batter is mixed, and the air bubbles are repeatedly divided into smaller and smaller bubbles, causing the foam to stiffen. One of the world's foremost experts in the science of ice cream, Doug Goff, works at the University of Guelph. He remarks that getting the correct amount of air into the freezing ice cream mix to produce ice cream at the rate of one litre per second is a demanding process, requiring the precise dosing of minor ingredients and the precise incorporation of sterile air (sterile to eliminate food safety hazards). Failure to achieve the correct amount of air in the product can ruin its quality or cause havoc on the process line as plant personnel attempt to fit 2.1 litres of over-bubbled ice cream into a two-litre container. Proteins, frequently from egg or dairy sources, are the main components that help foams solidify and stabilize. Proteins are effective in both tasks because they are **amphiphilic** molecules (a molecule that has both hydrophilic and hydrophobic parts). As a result, the protein molecules are able to orient themselves so that hydrophilic regions of the protein molecule can reside in the aqueous phase, and the hydrophobic regions can orient toward the air phase of a bubble. Proteins stabilize foam because they are cohesive at the surface and undergo a conformational change in their β-sheet structure. When the proteins change shape, they form multiple bonds. This creates a network that holds the incorporated air in place and is responsible for the structure and stiffness of the foam. Different proteins, such as whey, egg, or soy proteins, all have different foaming power; substituting one for another in a recipe may produce unexpected results. Furthermore, pH and the presence of sugars, salts, and fats will all influence how well foam will form.

Conclusions

The incorporation of bubbles and foam into our foods helps soften them and make them more palatable. This fact has led to the introduction of many aerated foods, and the manufacture of food products is big business. Understanding the properties of foods, their chemical makeup, and their structure is the field of food science. A lot of money goes in to ensuring that we have foods that are safe, look tasty, and have an appealing flavour and an alluring texture. Bubbles aren't just for bath time anymore.

Critical Thinking Questions

1. Assuming that all the carbon dioxide in a bottle of champagne comes from fermentation of glucose, how many grams of glucose are consumed by yeast in creating a pressure of 5 atm in the bottle? Henry's law constant for CO_2 in champagne at 8°C is 2.23 kg m^{-3} atm^{-1} and the bottle contains 75 cL of champagne, with a 25 mL headspace [$c = K_{HP}$].
2. Meringues are made by beating egg whites with sugar. Why does the meringue not form properly if the whole egg is used?
3. In a food foam, why do proteins preferentially locate at the interface between bubbles?

Further Research Question

How would changes in the ionic environment brought about by the addition of metal ions or protons affect the properties of proteins as foam-stabilizing ingredients? (Consult the studies by Sagis et al., 2001, and Liang and Kristinsson, 2007.)

References

Campbell GM, Webb C, Pandiella SS, Niranjan K (Eds.). 1999. *Bubbles in Food*. St. Paul, MN: Eagan Press.

Fennema OR, editor. 1996. *Food chemistry*. 3rd ed. New York: Marcel Dekker.

Liang Y, Kristinsson HG. 2007. Structural and foaming properties of egg albumen subjected to different pH-treatments in the presence of calcium ions. *Food Res. Int.* 40:668–678.

Sagis LMC, de Groot-Mostert AEA, Prins A, van der Linden E. 2001. Effect of copper ions on the drainage stability of foams prepared from egg white. *Colloids Surf., A.* 180:163–172.

The Burgess Shale and the Cambrian Explosion:
Evolution in the Rear-View Mirror

Heather Jamniczky
University of Calgary

Introduction

Humans are just one of a huge number of diverse animals that inhabit this planet. In a stroll down the block for coffee you will likely see or hear different types of birds, cats, dogs, and squirrels. A hike in the woods or a scuba dive around a tropical reef would reveal hundreds more species. How did all this diversity arise? What did Earth's animal population look like millions of years ago? Can we find out?

A **UNESCO World Heritage Site**,[1] the **Burgess Shale** provides a window into an ancient world. On a ridge connecting Mount Wapta and Mount Field, high above the tiny town of Field, British Columbia, lies one of Canada's most fascinating fossil localities. There, in 1909, Charles Doolittle Walcott of the Smithsonian Museum discovered the Burgess Shale. Over the next 15 years, he collected more than 65 000 fossil specimens. Others, most notably Royal Ontario Museum scientists, have since worked the site and collected more specimens. What makes the Burgess Shale so special is the unsurpassed preservation of the soft bodies of organisms that swam in Earth's oceans millions of years ago, during a geological time called the **Cambrian period**. Representatives of every major animal group present on Earth today, as well as others that are extinct, are preserved here. But the Burgess Shale is more than just a place of exceptional preservation; this locality provides a way for us to see the outcome of a critical period in the evolution of the animal form. In the Cambrian period, animal-body plans were being established, and both external and internal forces were driving the generation of diversity at unprecedented rates. This time, known as the **Cambrian explosion**, has been a source of vigorous debate among scientists.

The Burgess Bestiary

Approximately 505 million years ago, near the base of a large reef called the Cathedral Escarpment, the Burgess animals were living on and above a reasonably warm, shallow, muddy sea floor. Similar habitats exist in warm oceans around the world today. The Burgess Shale environment was teeming with marine life of all descriptions: predators and prey, plant eaters and filter feeders all lived in close proximity and formed an active

> ### KEY CONCEPTS
> - The Burgess Shale provides a snapshot of a diverse Cambrian ecological community.
> - Several possible drivers are behind the evolution of animal diversity.

---

[1]The United Nations Educational, Scientific and Cultural Organization identifies and encourages the protection of cultural and natural heritage sites worldwide. Learn more at http://whc.unesco.org/.

FIGURE 1. **A reconstruction of the ecological community preserved in the Burgess Shale fossil locality.**
Source: Publiphoto/Photo Researchers, Inc.

ecological community (see Figure 1). But sudden mudslides would trap the animals, burying them instantly, protecting the remains from oxygen and scavengers, and supporting the animals' soft tissues during the long fossilization process.

The animals that lived in this region and became the fossils of the Burgess Shale are both like and unlike the animals of today, and they present a tantalizing evolutionary puzzle. Many are **arthropods**, a group of animals that includes familiar creatures, such as butterflies, shrimp, and crabs. But the preserved arthropods are very different. *Marrella* (see Figure 2, A and B), for example, is the most abundant organism in the Burgess Shale. It had a unique head shield, feathery gills, and legs along the sides of its body. It was very small, ranging in length from 2 to 20 mm. Despite clear similarities to modern arthropods, nothing quite like it lives in the oceans today. Another oddity, and likely a top predator in the Cambrian oceans at more than 1 m long, was *Anomalocaris* (see Figure 2, C), which exhibited long frontal appendages and a fearsome radial jaw. These body parts were once thought to belong to separate animals. The classification of *Opabinia* (see Figure 2, D), with its five eyes and flexible terminal appendage, has been a source of considerable debate among scientists: Is it even an arthropod? The rarity of this animal in the Burgess Shale has made the classification process even more difficult.

What about other types of animals? The Burgess Shale also contains molluscs, worms of various sorts, sponges, and even animals related to our vertebrate ancestors. The Burgess Shale fauna is remarkably diverse, and the fossils record the existence of a very complex ecosystem.

Most of the Burgess Shale animals are exceptionally well preserved, allowing scientists to examine minute details of their anatomy. Most fossils consist of only the hard parts of animals, such as bones, teeth, and shells, but in the Burgess Shale fossils, soft structures, such as gills and digestive tracts, were also preserved. The animals found here are nearly complete, allowing stronger inferences to be made about how they lived

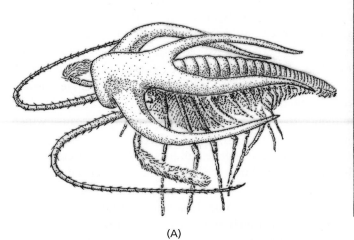
(A)

(B)

(C)

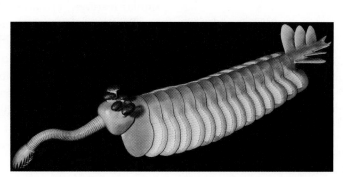
(D)

FIGURE 2. **Burgess Shale animals.**
A. *Marrella*, the most abundant animal in the Burgess Shale. Note the large head shield and feathery gills. B. A photograph of a *Marrella* specimen. C. *Anomalocaris*, the terror of the Cambrian seas. The circular mouth and anterior appendages were once thought to belong to separate animals. D. *Opabinia*, an alien-looking Burgess animal with five eyes.
Source: A. © National Museum of Natural History/Smithsonian Institution. B. O. Louis Mazzatenta/National Geographic Stock. C. De Agostini Picture Library/Getty Images. D. Chase Studio/Photo Researchers, Inc./First Light.

and interacted. These remains are rare in the fossil record, and they are extremely valuable as we attempt to understand how life on Earth evolved. Fossil sites that preserve soft anatomy are called *Lagerstätten*.

The Cambrian Explosion: An Evolutionary Conundrum

The first appearance of multicellular animals with hard body parts in the fossil record has been called the Cambrian explosion. In the early Cambrian period, approximately 540 million years ago, it appears that animal diversity increased extremely quickly. The Burgess Shale preserves records from just after this event and provides insight into the composition of diverse animal communities. When they were first discovered, and in several subsequent reinterpretations, many of the Burgess animals appeared to belong to groups that no longer exist, giving the impression that animal diversity was greater in the Cambrian period than it is today. It has been proposed that the Cambrian explosion was a time in which unprecedented experimentation in animal body forms was occurring and that, in fact, more *types* of animal-body plans existed then than at any other time in Earth's history. Proponents of this hypothesis, called the contingency hypothesis, argue further that the composition of the fauna we see today was dictated by which members of particular Burgess Shale animal groups survived extinction events and which did not. In other words, if a different set of animals had survived, life as we know it would be completely different. In fact, the human species might not even exist. This argument gives strong prominence to the role of chance in evolution because which individuals survive and which perish is due mostly to luck.

In contrast, more recent studies using newer techniques and reinterpretations of older work have revealed that many of the Burgess Shale animals are related to earlier fossils. In fact, they belong to lineages leading to modern animal groups and are therefore not nearly the wonders they first appeared to be. This account argues that the number of animal-body plans has remained relatively stable over evolutionary time. Several scientists have argued that evolution is not a game of chance. Instead, animals will tend to respond in parallel ways to similar selective pressures, resulting in the appearance of similar animals under similar circumstances. This viewpoint relies heavily on a phenomenon known as **convergent evolution**, in which two distantly related organisms evolve similar features in response to similar selective pressures.

Which of these interpretations is more likely correct? Evaluating these alternative scenarios is not easy. As with the debate over the cause and intensity of the Cambrian explosion, the answer to how we arrived at the animals we see today remains a fascinating mystery. Other Cambrian fossil deposits around the world have revealed analogous communities for comparison and have added to the evidence available for analysis. For example, recent fossil discoveries in Greenland and China have pushed the date of the Cambrian explosion further back.

Regardless of which evolutionary scenario you favour, what remains is the relatively quick appearance of all these animal forms in the fossil record. Is this real, or is it an artifact of fossil preservation? How quickly did these animals evolve? What evolutionary pressures drove them? What role did the action of natural selection on different genomes (another fascinating area of research not covered in this essay) play in this? These and related questions have provided fertile ground for scientific investigation for many years.

What Drove the Cambrian Explosion?

Many theories have been proposed to explain the apparent explosion of animal-body plans in the early Cambrian period, which can be condensed to two alternative viewpoints. The first posits that a geochemical driver was behind animal-body plan divergence: the presence of increased levels of atmospheric oxygen allowed larger animals and more complex food chains to evolve. The second suggests that the cause of the relatively rapid evolution of animals was ecological: new feeding styles, such as predation, and increased mobility expanded the complexity of interactions among community members, introduced new selective pressures, and allowed animals to begin to occupy new niches. The debate about which alternative is correct continues today, and we are depending on future fossil discoveries to help us better understand the physiology and community structure of these ancient animals. Whatever the outcome of this work, the Burgess Shale opens a window into an exciting period of animal evolution.

Conclusions

The amazing fossils of the Burgess Shale are an interesting evolutionary puzzle. Was the Cambrian explosion a real event? How did we arrive at the collection of animal-body plans we see today? These questions nicely illustrate the foundational difficulty in many evolutionary studies: when we look at the fossil record, we are looking back at evolutionary history. Exceptionally well-preserved fossils provide us with many tantalizing clues, but they often lead to different interpretations. Clarity is achieved as scientists examine, re-examine, and debate, and as each new fossil discovery adds another piece to the puzzle of life on Earth.

Critical Thinking Questions

1. What is special about the preservation of fossils in the Burgess Shale? How do these fossils enhance our understanding of evolution?
2. What is meant by the term *convergent evolution*? How does this hypothesis about animal evolution differ from the contingency hypothesis?
3. Describe two alternative theories about the causes of the Cambrian explosion. Why might the same geological evidence lead to different theories about causes?

Further Research Question

Pikaia is a chordate found in the Burgess Shale, a type of animal thought to be related to our vertebrate ancestors. What features of *Pikaia* have led paleontologists to classify it as a chordate? Which features are missing? What living animal does *Pikaia* most closely resemble?

References

Briggs DEG, Fortey RA. 2005. Wonderful strife: systematics, stem groups, and the phylogenetic signal of the Cambrian radiation. *Paleobiol.* 31:94–112.

Collins D. 2009. Misadventures in the Burgess Shale. *Nat.* 460:952–953.

Conway MS. 1998. *The crucible of creation: the Burgess Shale and the rise of animals.* New York: Oxford UP.

Gould SJ. 1989. *Wonderful life: the Burgess Shale and the nature of history.* New York: Norton.

Butterfly Hearing:
Wings Aren't Just for Flying

Sarah Hewitt
Mount Royal University

Introduction

"Did you hear that?" your friend whispers frantically behind you. You pause mid-stride to listen. You can hear the wind in the trees on the hillside and the splatter of raindrops as they hit the puddles on the ground. You faintly hear the rumble of thunder in the distance. Maybe this wasn't the best day for a hike. Then you hear it—the distinct crack of a branch breaking in the forest behind you. And then you hear a low, guttural growl. The hairs on the back of your neck stand up at the sound of an angry bear.

In this situation, your auditory system would be the last thing on your mind, but in those brief seconds, you deciphered the different sounds made by your friend, the wind, the rain, the thunder, the branch cracking, and the bear. Not only did you pick out different sounds, but you also knew from which direction each sound originated. In humans, and other mammals, the first step in sound reception involves the mechanical vibration of the tympanic membrane in the ear. This vibration is transmitted to the fluid-filled cochlea, where it is converted to a neural impulse by the organ of Corti (the sensory organ of hearing). The auditory centres in our brain process this neural impulse, and we perceive it as a sound. Because the different segments of the cochlea respond to different frequencies, humans can hear a wide range of sounds. All auditory sensory systems, whether in mammals or invertebrates, rely on sensing the vibrations created by sound waves. The ability to detect sounds evolved independently across unrelated species, which has led to the diverse array of hearing mechanisms in living species today.

Insects have particularly diverse hearing mechanisms. Like us, they use auditory signals for many reasons, such as communicating, finding mates, and detecting predators and prey. Many insects detect sounds with their antennae or with fine hairs on their bodies that vibrate in response to specific frequencies. Other insects use something similar to what we think of as an ear. The most complex and best described of the insect hearing organs are **tympanal ears**. Tympanal ears consist of a **tympanal membrane** stretched across a frame in front of an air-filled space (which allows the membrane to vibrate and move in response to sound waves) and one or more **chordotonal** organs, a specialized mechanoreceptor unique to insects. The chordotonal organ converts the vibration to a neural impulse and transmits the signal to the insect's brain. Researchers believe tympanal ears may have evolved independently at least 17 times in insects, and they can be located on almost any part of the insect body, including the mouth region, thorax, legs, and wings (see Figure 1).

KEY CONCEPTS

- Auditory mechanisms are diverse across species.
- Structural features of auditory sensory mechanisms determine what sounds can be heard.

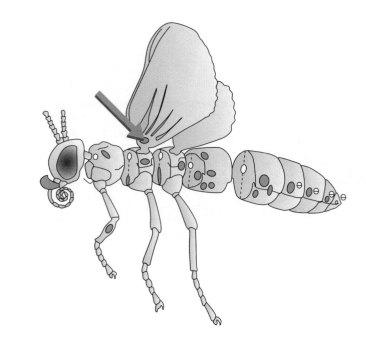

Dr. Jayne Yack from Carleton University studies how different insect species, including a species of tropical butterfly called *Morpho peleides*, detect sounds. This butterfly
has a unique tympanic membrane. Yack's team examined which frequencies of sound
cause the membrane to vibrate, thus revealing which frequencies *M. peleides* can hear.

The insect order Lepidoptera includes about 120 000 species of butterflies and
moths. Moths are generally **nocturnal** (active at night), while butterflies are predomi-
nantly **diurnal** (active during the day). Hearing in moths is well documented: they use
tympanal ears to detect echolocation calls from predatory bats. In butterflies, the senses
of vision, taste, and smell (for finding food and for orientation) are well described. Less
is known about their sense of hearing, however, and it was once thought that butterflies
were deaf. We now know that tympanal membranes are not only widespread but also
diverse in structure throughout butterfly species.

Research Question

How does the unique morphology of the tympanal membrane in the tropical
butterfly species *M. peleides* affect the tuning properties of the butterfly ear?

In different types of butterflies, the tympanal membrane varies in its thickness, size,
shape, and surface topography. *M. peleides* is of particular interest because of the unique
structure of its tympanal membrane. It has an outer oval-shaped region, with a distinct
dome in the middle. These are termed the outer and inner membranes, respectively. Yack
wondered if the inner and outer membranes are sensitive to different frequencies of sound.

Hypothesis

The inner and outer segments of the tympanal membrane vibrate in response to
different frequencies of sound.

Methods and Results

Yack's team examined the morphology of the inner and outer tympanal membranes, and
then compared how each region responded to a range of sound frequencies. After cap-
turing the butterflies, the researchers removed the forewings and viewed the tympanal
membrane by using light microscopy and scanning electron microscopy (see Figure 2).

FIGURE 2. **Location and external morphology of the ear in *M. peleides*.**
A. *M. peleides* in a natural resting position. The tympanal ear on the forewing is indicated by the red arrow.
B. Scanning micrograph of the ear structure in *M. peleides*.
Source: Adapted with permission from Figure 1 of Lucas KM, Windmill JF, Robert D, Yack JE. 2009. Auditory mechanics and sensitivity in the tropical butterfly Morpho peleides (Papilionoidea, Nymphalidae). Journal of Experimental Biology *212(Pt 21): 3533-3541. © The Company of Biologysts Ltd.. http://jeb. biologists.org/*

This examination revealed that the dome-like inner membrane is slightly thicker than the surrounding outer membrane.

To measure the vibrational properties of the inner and outer membranes, Yack and her team used a technique called laser vibrometry. The tympanal membrane was dissected from the wing and positioned perpendicularly in front of a speaker. Sounds with different frequencies projected from the speakers would then strike the tympanal membrane. As the membrane vibrated in response to the sound waves, the vibrometer measured the magnitude of deflection of the membrane. The deflection of both the inner and the outer membranes was measured across a range of sound frequencies, and the researchers could determine whether one region vibrated more within a particular range of frequencies. They found that at lower frequencies (1 to 5 KHz), the outer membrane vibrated, but when the frequency was increased (5 to 20 KHz), both the inner and the outer membranes vibrated together. The different regions of the membrane are innervated by separate sensory chordotonal organs, which means that the butterfly can likely differentiate incoming sound signals of high or low frequency based on which portion of the membrane (the outer membrane or both membranes) is vibrating.

Conclusions

The tympanal membranes of different species have different shapes, allowing animals to hear specific frequencies and, as is the case for *M. peleides*, enabling them to differentiate between two ranges of frequencies. But why might different species be attuned to specific frequencies? Studies in moths and nocturnal butterflies show that they use ultrasonic hearing to avoid becoming dinner for hungry bats. When moths and butterflies hear the ultrasonic echolocation calls of bats, the insects use flight manoeuvres to help them avoid capture. Yack proposed that the ears of *M. peleides* may be specialized to detect the lower-frequency sounds emitted by this diurnal butterfly's main predator: birds. The flight sounds of birds have a low frequency, within the ranges that *M. peleides* can detect. The sensitivity of *M. peleides* to two different ranges of frequencies could mean that the butterfly can detect two important predator noises: bird flight sounds and birdsong, either of which may tell the butterfly that it is in danger of becoming a meal.

Future Directions

Yack has no shortage of ideas for the future direction of her work. "The things that interest me include the taxonomic and functional diversity of butterfly ears, as well as the evolutionary origins of hearing in butterflies. Which species possess ears, and which do not, and why do some need to hear while others don't? How do ears differ structurally and how are these structural differences reflected in their physiological responses to sound? (2010 email from Yack to author; unreferenced)

Understanding the diverse hearing mechanisms across species gives us better insight into how selection processes have shaped the ears of animals so they can hear one another and their predators, and your ears so you can hear the thunder and rain, and the bear approaching behind you.

Critical Thinking Questions

1. What does the human auditory system have in common with an insect auditory system?
2. What is the function of the chordotonal organs?
3. Why is the structure of the tympanal membrane in *M. peleides* important for its function?

Further Research Question

What behavioural test might be performed to examine whether *M. peleides* changes its behaviour in response to bird predators?

References

Lane KA, Lucas KM, Yack JE. 2008. Hearing in a diurnal, mute butterfly, *Morpho peleides* (Papilionoidea, Nymphalidae). *J. Comp. Neurol.* 508(5):677–686.

*Lucas KM, Windmill JF, Robert D, Yack JE. 2009. Auditory mechanics and sensitivity in the tropical butterfly *Morpho peleides* (Papilionoidea, Nymphalidae). *J. Exp. Biol.* 212(Pt 21):3533–3541.

Yack JE, Dawson JW. 2008. *Insect ears: the senses—a comprehensive reference.* Vol. 3. San Diego (CA): Academic Press. pp. 35–54.

*Yack JE, Fullard JH. 2000. Ultrasonic hearing in nocturnal butterflies. *Nat.* 403(6767):265–266.

2010 personal communication between J. Yack and author unreferenced.

Cancer Biomarkers:
What Are They, and How Do We Use Them to Personalize Cancer Treatment?

Graham Dellaire*
Dalhousie University

Introduction

By the time we reach university age, most of us know a relative, friend, or colleague that has had cancer or is fighting the disease. Stories about cancer survivors, cancer deaths, new causes of cancer, and new cancer treatments bombard us every day from television, newspapers, and the internet. Although heart attacks and strokes kill more people each year than cancer, the World Health Organization (WHO) is predicting that cancer rates will spike by 30 percent, surpassing heart disease as the number one killer, by 2030 (WHO, 2010). Even now, your chance of developing cancer in your lifetime is approximately 1 in 2.5 (40 percent). For both males and females, lung cancer accounts for the majority of cancer-related deaths, followed by prostate cancer for males and breast cancer for females; colorectal cancer is the number three cancer killer for both males and females (Canadian Cancer Society, 2009). These statistics are similar for all Western countries and are linked to both a demographic shift in age, as most cancers develop in later life, and increasing obesity rates, caused by the sedentary lifestyle of urban living and the high-fat/low-fibre diets in Western countries. The medical systems of all Western countries have become increasingly taxed by the need to diagnose, treat, and provide care for cancer patients.

> ### KEY CONCEPTS
> - Cancer results from genetic changes that affect cell cycle control.
> - Hormones and other signalling molecules bind to target receptors, triggering specific response pathways.

DNA Damage Signalling and Repair Play an Important Role in the Development of Cancer

A very simple way to think about the development of cancer is that most arise from a series of genetic mutations that result in unregulated cell proliferation. The important genes for cancer development are classified as either tumour-promoting *oncogenes* or *tumour-suppressor* genes (Corn and El-Deiry, 2002). In general, mutations that promote cancer enhance the activity of the oncogenes and inhibit the activity of the tumour-suppressor genes. Although some people have a genetic predisposition to the early development of certain cancers, such as breast or colon cancer (Cole et al., 1996), most cancers arise only in older individuals because of the accumulation of random mutations in their DNA that occur from inappropriate or aberrant DNA repair (Jackson and Loeb, 2001).

*The research of the author is supported by grants from the Canadian Breast Cancer Foundation—Atlantic and the Canadian Institutes of Health Research.

How well your body repairs damaged DNA, and how often your DNA is damaged, therefore, will have a great impact on your chances of developing cancer. Diet, on the one hand, can also play an important role in the development of cancer, because the food we ingest can contain carcinogens that damage our DNA. On the other hand, some foods, such as the cruciferous vegetables, contain chemicals that detoxify these carcinogens in our diets. Even with a careful diet, free radicals continually damage the genetic material within our cells on a daily basis. These free radicals are produced by our mitochondria during oxidative metabolism (Jackson and Loeb, 2001). Furthermore, epithelial cells lining our lungs, stomach, and colon are continuously dividing to replace damaged and dying cells, and the replication of DNA in these cells can also produce mutations. As one might predict, the hereditary predisposition to cancers, including breast and colon cancer, often involves the mutation of genes involved in cell cycle control and/or DNA damage signalling and repair (Cole et al., 1996). Fortunately, we have evolutionarily conserved DNA repair mechanisms that can keep genetic damage in check and prevent mutations. Even if cancer should arise, cell cycle checkpoints keep those cells from proliferating out of control by triggering a dormant state known as senescence or by programmed cell death known as apoptosis (Bartek and Lukas, 2007). In addition, our immune system plays an important role in the surveillance of cancer cells, destroying them before they can form a tumour (Raulet and Guerra, 2009).

Traditional cancer therapy is based on diagnostic, surgical, and therapeutic treatments that serve to detect and treat the average cancer patient. The outcome of this generic approach to therapy is that a minority of patients have their cancer detected early and respond to treatment very well. A significant number of patients receive inefficient or inappropriate treatment, resulting in reduced survival and adverse side effects from radiation or chemotherapy (Duffy and Crown, 2008). It is unlikely, therefore, that one "cure" will be developed to treat the collection of malignancies known as cancer. As a result, the concept of personalized therapy has arisen to meet the challenge of not only treating cancer more effectively but also decreasing the toxicity of cancer therapy.

What Are Biomarkers?

Personalized medicine is made possible by the use of specific biological markers, referred to as biomarkers, that can help diagnose a disease as well as predict its therapeutic outcome (Duffy and Crown, 2008). These biomarkers can exist in several different forms. A biomarker can be a specific genetic change; an example of this is the fusion of two chromosomes (i.e., translocation) that underlies the development of certain leukemias, such as translocation between chromosome 9 and 22, which is associated with chronic myelogenous leukemia (CML) (Mauro and Druker, 2001). Other biomarkers are specific proteins that are expressed at high levels in cancer tissue, such as the Ki-67 antigen (Dowsett and Dunbier, 2008), or expressed at low levels, such as the promyelocytic leukemia protein (PML) (Gurrieri et al., 2004). A further class of biomarkers is based on the expression of a group of genes, referred to as gene signatures, which are used to predict positive responses (i.e., to predict clinical outcomes) to hormone therapy in breast cancer (Duffy and Crown, 2008; Dowsett and Dunbier, 2008).

How Do We Use Biomarkers?

The main types of biomarkers are classified by their use as diagnostic, prognostic, or predictive/therapeutic, and are summarized in Table 1 and Figure 1 (Duffy and Crown, 2008; Dowsett and Dunbier, 2008).

Diagnostic markers are used in the detection of cancer and include markers for highly proliferative cells used in the analysis of biopsies (e.g., the Ki-67 protein). Other

TABLE 1. Types of Cancer Biomarkers*

Type of Marker	Biomarker Name	Cancer Type	Notes
Diagnostic			
	Alpha-foetoprotein (AFP)	Liver cancer	Serum marker
	Breast cancer antigens 1 (BRCA1) and 2 (BRCA2) mutations	Breast and ovarian cancer	Genetic markers that encode DNA repair proteins
	Cancer antigen (CA)15-3	Breast cancer	Serum marker
	Cancer antigen (CA)-125	Ovarian cancer	Serum marker
	Carcinoembryonic antigen (CEA)	Gastric and colon cancer	Serum marker
	Chromosomal translocations (e.g., t[9;22])	Leukemias (i.e., chronic myelogenous leukemia [CML])	Genetic marker, translocation creates an oncogene
	Ki-67	Solid tumours of multiple tissues	Tissue/protein marker of proliferating cells
	Promyelocytic leukemia (PML)**	Solid tumours of multiple tissues	Tissue/protein marker; low levels indicate tumour formation
	Prostate-specific antigen (PSA)	Prostate cancer	Serum marker
Prognostic			
	Estrogen receptor (ER) Progesterone receptor (PR) Human epidermal growth factor receptor (HER2)	Breast cancer	Tissue/protein marker; triple-negative (ER-, PR-, HER2-) tumours are highly aggressive forms of breast cancer
	Ki-67	Multiple cancers	Tissue/protein marker, where high levels correlate with more malignant cancer
	Oncotype DX	Breast cancer	Gene signature marker, which predicts the chance of metastasis of stage I or II, lymph node negative and ER+ breast cancer
	Urokinase plasminogen activator to plasminogen activator inhibitor 1 ratio (uPA/PAI-1)	Breast cancer	A high uPA/PAI-1 ratio indicates a more malignant cancer likely to metastasize
Predictive/ Therapeutic			
	EGFR	Lung cancer	Predicts response to kinase inhibitors gefitinib and erlotinib
	ER/PR	Breast cancer	Predicts response to hormone therapy
	HER2	Breast cancer	Predicts response to anti-HER2 antibody therapy, as well as positive response to kinase inhibitor lapatinib
	Ki-67	Multiple cancers	Proliferation marker
	Oncotype DX	Breast cancer	Predicts response or ER+ breast cancers to hormone therapy
	Topoisomerase IIa (Topo2A)	Breast cancer	High levels predict positive response to anthracyclines

Source: *Collated from Duffy and Crown, 2008, and Dowsett and Dunbier, 2008.
**Gurrieri et al., 2004.

FIGURE 1. Types of cancer biomarkers.
Cancer biomarkers can be classified as diagnostic (red), prognostic (green), or predictive/therapeutic (blue). Some markers, such as the estrogen (ER), progesterone (PR), and human epidermal growth factor receptor 2 (HER2), are both prognostic and predictive/therapeutic biomarkers. Ki-67, a cell proliferation marker, is a biomarker that fits into all three classes. Table 1 describes these and other biomarkers in more detail. *Source: Adapted from Duffy, MJ and J. Crown. 2008. A personalized approach to cancer treatment: How Biomarkers can help. Clinical Chemistry 54:1770–1779; and Dowsett M and Dunbier AK. 2008. Emerging biomarkers and new understanding of traditional markers in personalized therapy for breast cancer. Clinical Cancer Research 14:8019–8026.*

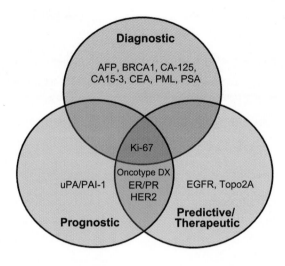

diagnostic biomarkers include genetic mutations, such as mutations in the BRCA1 and BRCA2 genes, associated with the early onset of specific cancers, which predispose women to both ovarian and breast cancer (Cole et al., 1996). These markers are used to determine which individuals will need special surveillance and screening at a young age to help prevent cancer because of their increased risk. The last type of diagnostic markers are the "serum" markers, which are proteins whose levels are elevated in the blood serum of individuals with specific cancers, including alpha-foetoprotein (AFP; liver cancer), cancer antigen (CA)-125 (ovarian cancer), CA15-3 (breast cancer), carcinoembryonic antigen (CEA; gastric and colon cancer), and prostate-specific antigen (PSA; prostate cancer). Together, these markers are used for population screening for early detection of cancer as well as for monitoring cancer recurrence in survivors. For example, elevated levels of serum PSA or CEA may signal the recurrence of prostate or colon cancer, respectively.

Prognostic markers are perhaps the largest class of cancer biomarkers and are used to determine the probable outcome of a particular cancer with or without treatment, usually expressed as either disease-free or overall survival. Traditional prognostic markers include tumour size, location, involvement of lymph nodes, and whether the cancer has metastasized. In general, smaller tumours that remain within the organ or tissue region (i.e., in situ) offer the best prognosis with a good chance of full remission. Although the prognosis-based classification or "staging" of a patient's cancer can differ from cancer to cancer, the most common system involves the use of stages 0 and I to IV, where an increase in stage signifies a decreased chance of survival. For example, in breast cancer stage 0 signifies a tumour that is in situ or confined to the mammary duct or lobule (i.e., for ductal or lobular carcinoma, respectively). It offers the best chance of survival (see http://www.cancer.ca). Stage I breast cancer signifies that the tumour is 2 cm or smaller in size and has spread beyond the mammary duct or lobule, invading the surrounding tissue, but has not left the breast. Stage II breast cancers are larger (2 to 5 cm in size) and, in addition to invading the surrounding tissue, may have spread to the lymph nodes. Stage III breast tumours have spread to the lymph nodes and may also involve the invasion of nearby tissues outside the breast, including skin and muscle. Finally, stage IV signifies a breast tumour that, in addition to the criteria for stage III, has moved, or metastasized, to distant sites in the body, including the lungs, liver, kidneys, and brain. In addition, biomarkers are also used to "grade" cancers based on how likely they are to grow rapidly and spread. For example, grade 1 and 2 breast cancers have a low and a moderate chance of spreading rapidly (respectively), and grade 3 breast cancers would be the most likely to spread (Canadian Cancer Society, 2009). Grading is often done by using such tissue protein markers as Ki-67, where more tissue staining signifies higher grade, as well as by analyzing the morphology of cell nuclei in the tumour, where small or multiple nuclei of aberrant shape per cell are consistent with a higher grade of tumour.

Additional biomarkers are used for breast cancer prognosis based on the presence or absence of three important growth factor receptors: the estrogen receptor (ER) alpha, the progesterone receptor (PR), and the human epidermal growth factor receptor (HER2). These hormones can induce the expression of important genes controlling the cell cycle and can trigger rapid proliferation of the cancer in the presence of the hormone. The ER, for example, is perhaps the most important biological factor for the clinical outcome of breast cancer because it helps predict both the prognosis of the cancer and the most appropriate choice of therapy (i.e., it can act as a therapeutic marker, which we will discuss in detail later). Breast tumours that do not express ER, PR, and HER2, which are referred to as triple-negative, are more likely to be very aggressive and difficult to treat. These receptors are also used to classify breast tumours as being either luminal (i.e., ER-positive [ER+]), which are the easiest to treat; HER2-like (HER2+ and mainly ER–); or basal-like (ER–, PR–, and HER2–). Usually PR+ tumours are also ER+, as the progesterone receptor gene is regulated by the estrogen receptor. Examples of ER and HER2 positive and negative tumours are shown in Figure 2. Another serum and tissue marker used as a prognostic biomarker in breast cancer is the ratio of the urokinase plasminogen activator (uPA) to plasminogen activator inhibitor 1 (PAI-1). PAI-1 inhibits the ability of uPA to digest the protein "meshwork" surrounding the tumour called the extracellular matrix, which normally prevents cancer cells from metastasizing. A high ratio of uPA versus PAI-1 signifies a highly malignant cancer that has a strong likelihood of spreading throughout the body (i.e., metastasizing) and thus should be treated aggressively. Finally, multigene expression profiles, or signatures, can be used to predict the possible outcome of cancer and tumour response to treatment. One of the most widely used gene signatures is the Oncotype DX that measures the expression level of 21 genes (i.e., 16 cancer-associated genes and 5 control genes). The Oncotype DX gene signature was developed to predict the chance of distant metastasis occurring for stage I and II, lymph node–negative, ER+ breast cancer. The Oncotype DX expression profile for a given tumour is expressed as a recurrence score (RS) in which the higher the RS score, the greater the chance of metastasis (Duffy and Crown, 2008).

Predictive/therapeutic markers, the last type of marker we will discuss, are used in the selection of a particular cancer therapy and the prediction of the outcome of a particular therapy. With respect to breast cancer, many of the prognostic biomarkers are also valuable therapeutic biomarkers, making tests for these markers doubly important

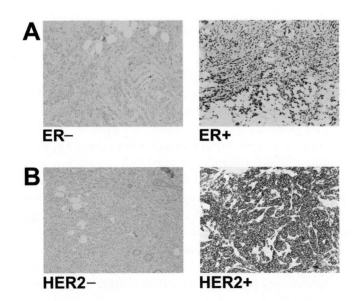

FIGURE 2. Examples of ER and HER2 positive and negative breast tumour biopsies.
Tumour biopsies were processed for the immunhisto-chemical detection (brown) of the estrogen receptor (ER) (A) or the human epidermal growth factor receptor 2 (HER2) (B). Breast tumours positive and negative for ER and HER2 are indicated. *Source: Images courtesy of Dr. P. Barnes, Dept. of Pathology, Dalhousie University.*

in patient care. These dual-duty biomarkers include ER, PR, and HER2. For example, ER+ breast tumours are the most likely to respond favourably to hormonal therapy using anti-estrogen drugs, such as tamoxifen, that block the binding of estrogen to the receptor, and/or aromatase inhibitors, such as anastrozole, that block estrogen production. In addition, metastatic breast cancer that is ER+ and PR+, rather than just ER+ alone, has the highest probability of remission through antihormonal therapy. Similarly, the Oncotype DX gene signature can be used to classify the chances of relapse of breast cancer in patients with lymph node negative, ER+ tumours treated with tamoxifen. Similar to the versatility of the hormone receptors as biomarkers, Ki-67 can be used not only as a diagnostic and prognostic marker but also as a predictive/therapeutic marker to predict a positive response to chemotherapy that targets rapidly dividing cells, such as the anthracycline antibiotics.

Receptor status, however, does not always correlate positively with therapeutic outcome based on the treatment type. For example, ER– tumours often respond much better to chemotherapy that uses the anthracycline class of drugs, such as doxorubicin (also known as adriamycin), in part because of the higher proliferation rate associated with these tumours (Dowsett and Dunbier, 2008). HER2 status can also predict sensitivity to anthracyclines, whereas HER2+ breast cancers are more responsive to doxorubicin, with the degree of sensitivity correlating positively with increasing gene expression or gene amplification. HER2+ breast tumours are also more likely to respond well to drugs that target cells in mitosis, such as the microtubule inhibitor paclitaxel (Taxol) (Dowsett and Dunbier, 2008). Often, other genes on the same chromosome are duplicated during the amplification of the *HER2* gene, including *topoisomerase IIA (Topo2A)*. The Topo2A protein is involved in the transcription and replication of DNA and is inhibited by anthracycline drugs, causing lethal breaks in the cell's DNA. Thus, the amplification of the *HER2* gene often results in the co-amplification of *Topo2A*; increased levels of Topo2A also correlate with an increased sensitivity to anthracyclin drugs and may in part account for the observed sensitivity of HER2+ cancers to treatment with doxorubicin.

Finally, the growth of breast tumours expressing HER2 can also be inhibited with antibody therapy by using antibodies directed against HER2. Trastuzumab, which goes by the trade name Herceptin, is one such antibody. The HER2 receptor is of the tyrosine kinase type, and HER2+ breast cancer tumour growth can be retarded with the tyrosine kinase inhibitor lapatinib. Similarly, lung cancer cells expressing the epidermal growth factor receptor (EGFR or HER1) are also sensitive to the tyrosine kinase inhibitors gefitinib and erlotinib (Duffy and Crown, 2008).

Conclusions

Cancer is a collection of malignancies induced by genetic mutations that promote the activity of oncogenes and inhibit the activity of tumour suppressor genes that normally work together to regulate cellular proliferation. Our DNA is continually being damaged by internal and external sources, including the food we eat. Potentially cancer-causing mutations can arise when DNA damage is not repaired appropriately. Because of the random nature of these mutations in our DNA, no two people have exactly the same cancer, making it a very personal disease; therefore, the success of individual patients' cancer treatments has been recognized to benefit from personalized therapy adapted to the specific characteristics of their cancers. Biomarkers are genetic mutations, proteins, and gene expression signatures that aid in the diagnosis of cancer (i.e., diagnostic markers), the prediction of how aggressive a cancer will be to treat (prognostic markers), as well as the cancer's appropriate treatment or therapy (predictive or therapeutic markers). Thus, biomarkers have become an invaluable aid in the improvement of cancer treatment by facilitating personalized therapy. Through the use of biomarkers, cancer is detected earlier, and treatment is safer and more affective.

Critical Thinking Questions

1. What role does DNA damage play in the development of cancer?
2. Why are predictive or therapeutic biomarkers important? In addition, name two such markers that are important in treating breast cancer.
3. If you were a governmental or non-profit funding agency, what type of cancer biomarker research study would you fund and why?

Further Research Question

Why is the promyelocytic leukemia (PML) protein considered a tumour suppressor, and how did researchers determine that the PML protein was a biomarker for cancer (see Gurrieri et al., 2004)?

References

*Bartek J, Lukas J. 2007. DNA damage checkpoints: from initiation to recovery or adaptation. *Curr. Opin. Cell Biol.* 19:238–245.

Canadian Cancer Society [Internet]. modified 2010; 2009 [cited 2010 Apr 10]. Available from: http://www.cancer.ca

Cole DE, Gallinger S, McCready DR, Rosen B, Engel J, Malkin D. 1996. Genetic counselling and testing for susceptibility to breast, ovarian and colon cancer: where are we today? *Can. Med. Assoc. J.* 154:149–155.

Corn PG, El-Deiry WS. 2002. Derangement of growth and differentiation control in oncogenesis. *BioEssays.* 24:83–90.

*Dowsett M, Dunbier AK. 2008. Emerging biomarkers and new understanding of traditional markers in personalized therapy for breast cancer. *Clin. Cancer Res.* 14:8019–8026.

*Duffy MJ, Crown J. 2008. A personalized approach to cancer treatment: how biomarkers can help. *Clin. Chem.* 54:1770–1779.

*Gurrieri C, Capodieci P, Bernardi R, Scaglioni PP, Nafa K, Rush LJ, Verbel DA, Cordon-Cardo C, Pandolfi PP. 2004. Loss of the tumor suppressor PML in human cancers of multiple histologic origins. *J. Natl. Cancer Inst.* 96:269–79.

*Jackson AL, Loeb LA. 2001. The contribution of endogenous sources of DNA damage to the multiple mutations in cancer. *Mutat. Res.* 477:7–21.

Mauro MJ, Druker BJ. 2001. Chronic myelogenous leukemia. *Curr. Opin. Oncol.* 13:3–7.

Raulet DH, Guerra N. 2009. Oncogenic stress sensed by the immune system: role of natural killer cell receptors. *Nat. Rev. Immunol.* 9:568–580.

[WHO] World Health Organization [Internet]. Geneva (Switzerland): Cancer; c2010 [cited 2010 Apr 10]. Available from: http://www.who.int/topics/cancer/en/

Choline Metabolism and Transport:
The Sunny Side of Eggs

Vera Michel and Marica Bakovic
University of Guelph*

Introduction

For many of us, eggs were a staple part of our diet when we were young. Our parents told us that eating eggs would help us grow up healthy and strong. Aside from minerals and proteins, what do eggs contain that makes them so beneficial for development? The answer is *choline*, a nutrient of which few people have heard. Choline is a component of and a precursor for many crucial compounds. It cannot be adequately synthesized in the body, which makes it an essential nutrient that we need to get from food.

Eggs contain the lipid lecithin, which is actually a mixture of closely related phospholipids called phosphatidylcholines. Phospholipids have two **hydrophobic** (lipid-soluble) fatty acid tails and one **hydrophilic** (water-soluble) phosphate group. Choline, a small hydrophilic molecule, is attached to the phosphate group of phosphatidylcholine (see Figure 1).

Phosphatidylcholines make up more than 50 percent of lipids in the plasma membrane, the bilayer surrounding each cell in the body. This role is quantitatively choline's most important one and is the reason that it is such a crucial nutrient for all our tissues. In addition to this structural function, choline also has specific roles in certain tissues. It is a component of the neurotransmitter acetylcholine, which is necessary for the transmission of signals from motor neurons to muscle cells and for some neuron-to-neuron communication. Choline plays a further role in the nervous system, forming the head group of the lipid **sphingomyelin**, which is abundant in the **myelin sheaths of axons**

KEY CONCEPTS

- Lipids are a diverse group of hydrophobic compounds.
- Choline is an essential nutrient for phospholipid synthesis and methylation.
- Choline is a precursor of betaine, which is produced in mitochondria.
- Choline requires transport proteins to cross membranes.

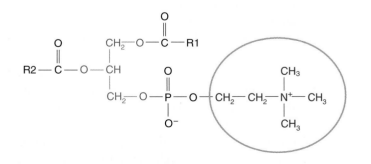

FIGURE 1. Chemical structure of phosphatidylcholine. Phosphatidylcholine is a phospholipid with two fatty acid tails, a phosphate group, and the small molecule choline (circled) makes up its polar head.

*The research described in this essay was funded by NSERC and Ontario Ministry of Agriculture and Food.

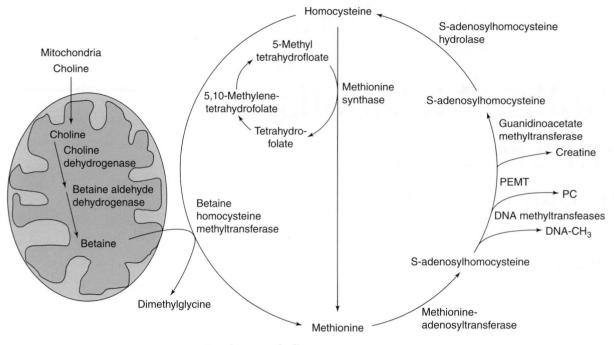

FIGURE 2. Betaine metabolism.
Choline is oxidized to betaine in the mitochondria of kidney and liver cells. Betaine leaves the mitochondria and participates in the methylation of homocysteine to methionine, thus contributing to the formation of S-adenosylmethionine, an important methylating agent.

(an insulating material that surrounds part of a neuron). Choline plays a crucial role in the assembly of very-low-density lipoproteins (VLDL), proteins that are necessary for transporting cholesterol and fats from the liver to the blood and tissues, where they can be broken down and metabolized.

Finally, choline is important in the production of a molecule called **betaine** (see Figure 2). In the mitochondria of liver and kidney cells, choline is oxidized to form betaine (trimethylglycine), a key player in the process of fluid balance. Once betaine is synthesized, it leaves the mitochondria and enters the cytosol. Betaine functions as an organic **osmolyte** in the kidney, regulating the fluid content inside and outside the kidney cells to ensure a proper balance between inorganic and organic cations and water. Betaine can also be converted to S-adenosylmethionine, which then donates the methyl group to methyltransferases for DNA methylation.

Egg lecithin is one of the best-known dietary sources of choline, but beef liver and pork liver also contain choline in the form of lipid-soluble lecithin. Other foods, including legumes (soybean), wheat bran, wheat germ, and spinach, contain different forms of choline. These foods are all good sources of water-soluble choline compounds, such as free choline, phosphocholine, and betaine. Free choline is absorbed in the upper small intestine, across the mucosal brush border, and enters the circulatory system. Because lecithin or phosphatidylcholine is lipid soluble, it is transported in the body in **lipoproteins** (a protein with a lipid component used for transporting lipids in the blood). In fact, most circulating choline in the body is found as phosphatidylcholine in lipoprotein particles, which supply choline directly to the tissues, along with fatty acids for the metabolism of **triglyceride** (a fat with three fatty acids bound to a glycerol).

The recommended intake for choline is 550 mg/day for men and 425 mg/day for women. If choline is insufficiently supplied by the diet, the lack of phosphatidylcholine synthesis prevents the correct assembly and release of VLDL in the liver. As a consequence, triglycerides accumulate in the liver, causing damage and fatty liver disease. Most healthy individuals meet or exceed the recommended intake for choline; however, certain population groups are at risk of becoming choline deficient: pregnant and lactating women, developing fetuses, formula-fed infants, older adults, and people dependent on **parenteral** (intravenous) nutrition.

In some tissues, such as the liver and kidneys, choline can be oxidized to a structurally similar compound, called a betaine. Choline has to cross the mitochondrial membrane because the enzymes for choline oxidation (choline dehydrogenase and betaine aldehyde dehydrogenase), are localized on the inner side of the mitochondrial membrane and in the mitochondrial matrix, respectively. Mitochondrial membranes form an efficient barrier against charged compounds, such as choline.

Research Question
How does choline cross mitochondrial membranes?

Research from Marica Bakovic's lab had previously looked at the transport of choline across the plasma membrane. Transporter proteins are needed to translocate choline from the extracellular space into the cytosol. The solute transport protein called solute carrier 44A1 (SLC44A1) was identified as a plasma membrane choline transporter (Fullterton, Wagner, Yuan, and Bakovic, 2006), and the researchers suspected that it might also transport choline across the mitochondrial membrane.

Hypothesis
The solute transport protein SLC44A1 may be involved in the transport of choline across the mitochondrial membranes and into the mitochondrial matrix.

Methods and Results

Antibodies were designed to specifically bind to the SLC44A1 protein. These antibodies were detected with a secondary antibody coupled to a fluorescent marker. If the SLC44A1 protein was expressed in the mitochondrial membrane, the antibody would bind to it. When viewed with a confocal laser scanning microscope, the fluorescent markers would allow the researchers to actually see and measure how much of the protein was present. Cells were grown on glass coverslips and exposed to these antibodies (see Photos A and B). By using the confocal microscope, the researchers then determined the level of SLC44A1 protein expression in these cells.

Next, choline uptake into isolated mitochondria was measured twice: first when the SLC44A1 protein transporter was functional, and then in the presence of the specific inhibitor hemicholinium-3.

The choline-transporter-like protein SLC44A1 was found in the mitochondrial membrane (see Photo C). When the transport mediated by this protein was blocked with the specific inhibitor hemicholinium-3, choline uptake into the mitochondrial matrix was very low (see Figure 3), suggesting that SLC44A1 mediates mitochondrial choline transport.

Mitochondrial and plasma membrane choline transport is mediated by the choline transport protein SLC44A1. Several different types of choline transporters can be present in the same cell, and each seems to transport choline for a specific purpose. SLC44A1, for example, is present in most tissues, which implies that this protein transports choline for a ubiquitous process, such as phosphatidylcholine synthesis. This transporter is present in the mitochondrial membrane of cells that are functionally very different, including muscle and epithelium cells. The enzymes for betaine synthesis are, however, only significantly active in liver and kidneys, which means that SLC44A1 might have another purpose in addition to supplying choline for betaine metabolism.

PHOTO A, B, C. Live cells were stained, and colocalization was analyzed with confocal laser scanning microscopy.
A. Mitochondria were stained red by using MitoTracker Red. B. SLC44A1 was stained green with fluorescent-tagged antibodies. C. Photo A and B are overlaid. This photo shows that SLC44A1 is present in mitochondrial membranes.
Source: Michel V, Bakovic M (2009). The solute carrier 44A1 is a mitochondrial protein and mediates choline transport. FASEBJ Aug; 23(8);2749–58, p. 2753. © 2009 by FASEB. Reproduced with permission of The Federation of American Societies for Experimental Biology. Permission conveyed through © Clearance Center, Inc.

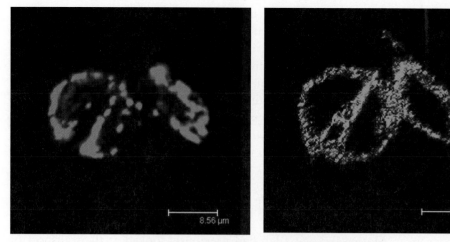

(A)

(B)

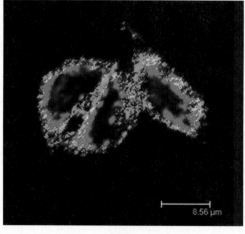

(C)

FIGURE 3. Mitochondrial choline transport is mediated by the choline transport protein SLC44A1.
Mitochondrial choline transport is decreased when SLC44A1 is inhibited by using a 500 µM solution of the specific inhibitor hemicholinium-3 (HC-3).
Source: Michel V, Bakovic M (2009). The solute carrier 44A1 is a mitochondrial protein and mediates choline transport. FASEBJ Aug; 23(8);2749–58, p. 2754. © 2009 by FASEB. Reproduced with permission of The Federation of American Societies for Experimental Biology. Permission conveyed through © Clearance Center Inc.

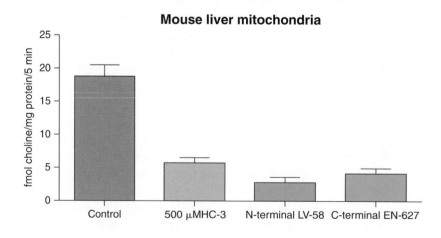

Conclusions

SLC44A1 is a recently discovered transporter that mediates choline transport at the plasma membrane. In liver and kidney cells, however, choline is oxidized to betaine in the mitochondria and must first pass through the mitochondrial membrane. We have now discovered that this transporter is also expressed in the mitochondrial membrane of mouse and human cells and tissues, and we have demonstrated that inhibition of SLC44A1 in isolated mitochondria causes a dramatic decrease in mitochondrial choline uptake. Once betaine is synthesized, it leaves the mitochondria and enters the cytosol. We also have some preliminary data showing that the loss of this transporter in humans may lead to impaired betaine metabolism, but future studies need to find and explain a direct link between SLC44A1 and betaine synthesis.

Choline is an essential nutrient and plays numerous vital roles in the body, from forming the structure of the cell membrane to carrying out a wide variety of cellular processes. Therefore, hardboiled, scrambled, or sunny side up, eggs help make us strong, help us keep it together, and help us think on our feet.

Future Directions

An exciting topic for future research will be establishing a connection between choline and epigenetics. Epigenetics is a new field of study investigating how DNA and gene expression can be modified without altering the underlying genetic sequence. These modifications can involve methylation of the DNA. Recent studies have found that betaine can be converted to S-adenosylmethionine, which then donates the methyl group to methyltransferases, enzymes that mediate DNA methylation. It will be interesting to see whether future studies can establish a link among choline transport (via the SLC44A1 transporter), betaine production, and DNA methylation. Thus, in addition to its already numerous roles in the body, choline may soon be receiving another job: altering our very DNA.

Critical Thinking Questions

1. Why is choline an important nutrient? What are its functions in the body?
2. Why would choline require a transport protein to cross a membrane?
3. What symptoms might someone who is deficient in choline display over the short term and long term? Would the symptoms be different if the individual was a child?

Further Research Question

What would the phenotype of an organism lacking SLC44A1 (e.g., an SLC44A1-knockout mouse) look like?

References

Craig SA. 2004. Betaine in human nutrition. *Amer. J. Clin. Nutr.* 80(3):539–549.

Fullterton MD, Wagner L, Yuan Z, Bakovic M. 2006. Impaired trafficking of choline transporter-like protein-1 at plasma membrane and inhibition of choline transport in THP-1 monocyte-derived macrophages. *Am. J. Physiol. Cell Physiol.* 290:C1230–C1238.

Li Z, Vance DE. 2008. Phosphatidylcholine and choline homeostasis. *J. Lipid Res.* 49(6):1187–1194.

Michel V, Bakovic M. 2009. The solute carrier 44A1 is a mitochondrial protein and mediates choline transport. *J. Fed. Am. Soc. Exp. Biol.* 23(8):2749–2758.

Niculescu MD, Zeisel SH. 2002. Diet, methyl donors and DNA methylation: interactions between dietary folate, methionine and choline. *J. Nutr.* 132:2333S–2335S.

USA Institute of Medicine, Standing Committee on the Scientific Evaluation of Dietary Reference Intakes. 1998. *Dietary reference intakes for folate, thiamin, riboflavin niacin, vitamin B12, panthothenic acid, biotin and choline.* Vol 1. Washington (DC): National Academic Press.

Zeisel SH, Mar MH, Howe JC, Holden JM. 2003. Concentrations of choline-containing compounds and betaine in common foods. *J. Nutr.* 133:1302–1307.

CO_2 Levels and Plants:
What's So Wrong with a Greenhouse?

Sharon L. Gillies
University of the Fraser Valley

Introduction

If you have ever enjoyed a locally grown tomato in November or bought a poinsettia in December, these plants were most likely grown in greenhouses. Greenhouses give us the ability to grow plants during seasons in which they would not otherwise grow. With glass walls and ceilings that trap infrared radiation (heat), greenhouses are an ideal environment in which to grow many different kinds of plants. In fact, some greenhouse growers even increase the CO_2 levels in their greenhouses to help their plants grow faster. But do we really want to impose this environment on the whole planet?

Human activities have increased atmospheric CO_2 levels in recent history. It is possible that we have have had an impact on CO_2 levels since we began clearing forests in Europe and cultivating rice in China 5000 to 8000 years ago. CO_2 levels were estimated at below 200 ppm (parts per million) during the last glacial maximum, approximately 20 000 years ago. The levels increased at the beginning of the Holocene to about 280 ppm, between 12 000 and 10 000 years ago. Current CO_2 levels are about 385 ppm (see Figure 1) and are predicted to increase to 550 ppm by the year 2050.

The **greenhouse effect** is caused by CO_2, water vapour, and other greenhouse gases present in the atmosphere. These gases absorb much of the infrared radiation Earth emits and reflects some of it back (the same way a greenhouse does), keeping the average temperature from dropping and preventing our planet from turning into a giant snowball. This natural greenhouse effect is very important to every living organism on Earth. But too much of a good thing can be a problem. As the concentration of atmospheric CO_2 and other greenhouse gases increases, global temperatures rise, with the greatest warming occurring in the polar regions. This regional disparity is similar to the warming event seen during the Holocene Climate Optimum between 9000 and 5000 years ago. Researchers estimate that during the Holocene Climate Optimum, the increase in Arctic and Antarctic temperatures was about 4°C as opposed to the estimated increase of 1°C in the tropics.

Rolf Matthews from Simon Fraser University and Francine McCarthy from Brock University are investigating post-glacial climate change in Canada using **palynology**, the study of the deposition of pollen, spores, and other particulate organic matter that accumulate over time in sediment, such as on lake bottoms. Changes in the distribution of plant species over time can be inferred by the pollen and spore record and may be attributable to changes in climate. This type of research is a form of paleoclimatic reconstruction.

KEY CONCEPTS

- The accumulation of greenhouse gases is increasing.
- The Calvin cycle uses ATP and NADPH to convert CO_2 to sugar.
- Alternative mechanisms of carbon fixation have evolved in hot, arid climates.
- Human activities now dominate most chemical cycles on Earth.

FIGURE 1. The yearly average atmospheric CO$_2$ levels for Nunavut, Canada.
The data in this graph were collected at Alert, Nunavut. The yearly average atmospheric CO$_2$ levels in 1975 was 334 ppm. This increased to 387 ppm in 2008.
Sources: Meteorological Service of Canada, Environment Canada, and Earth System Research Laboratory, Global Monitoring Division.

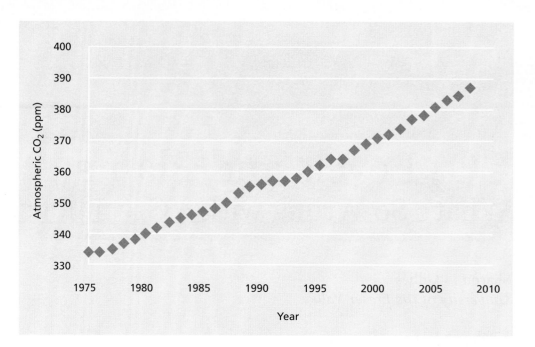

Global warming causes greater temperature increases in polar regions for four main reasons. First, as polar snow and ice melts, darker land and ocean surfaces lose their reflective covering and absorb more solar energy. With more land exposed, a greater proportion of solar energy will go directly into warming land masses. Second, in polar regions, the atmospheric layer must warm before the surface does. Because the atmosphere is shallower there, the surface will warm more quickly than in other regions. Third, the ocean surface is exposed as sea ice retreats, and the solar heat absorbed by the oceans is more easily transferred to the atmosphere. Fourth, predicted changes in atmospheric and oceanic circulation could also increase warming by bringing warmer currents and air masses further north to the Arctic and further south to the Antarctic.

The Canadian Boreal Forest

The boreal forest of Canada functions as a major **carbon sink** by extracting and storing a lot of carbon in its biomass—primarily in its trees. The boreal forest is continuing to grow and is actively removing CO$_2$ from the atmosphere through photosynthesis. With

PHOTO A.
The Canadian boreal forest.
Source: © Dale Wilson/ Masterfile.

increased temperatures in northern Canada, we have recently seen the expansion of the boreal forest into adjacent tundra zones; however, since the 1990s, data from remote sensing has shown an increase in the losses of stored carbon in the Canadian boreal forest because of disturbances by fires and insects. Werner Kurz and his colleagues from the Canadian Forest Service suggest that the Canadian boreal forest may change from a carbon sink to a **net carbon source**, releasing more CO_2 into the atmosphere if climate change increases the intensity and frequency of forest fires, the damage from insects, and the respiration of soil-dwelling organisms.

What effect will an increase in atmospheric CO_2 have on the boreal forest? One prediction is that photosynthesis in the boreal forest will increase as CO_2 levels increase, resulting in the absorption of even more CO_2. This could happen because carbon from CO_2 is the essential building block of organic molecules produced by photosynthesis. Increased CO_2 should mean increased photosynthesis, right? Not necessarily. Experiments at Free Air Carbon Dioxide Enrichment (FACE) found that plant growth rates can increase with elevated atmospheric CO_2, but the growth is less than predicted. The reduced growth is due to a lack of nitrogen, an essential nutrient for plants. As a result, increases in plant growth from elevated CO_2 may be limited by nutrient availability.

Increased CO_2 Will Affect C_3 and C_4 Plants Differently

With sufficient nutrients, the plants in the boreal forest, which are almost all C_3 plants, could increase their photosynthetic activity with increased atmospheric CO_2. **C_3 plants** directly fix atmospheric CO_2 in the Calvin cycle using the enzyme RuBisCO. Most studies indicate C_3 carbon fixation can be increased by elevated CO_2. This is not the same for plants that use the alternative C_4 photosynthetic pathway. **C_4 plants** use the enzyme PEP carboxylase to fix atmospheric CO_2 into a four-carbon organic acid first, and then the enzyme RuBisCO uses this organic acid as its carbon source in the Calvin cycle.

Adapted to hot, dry climates, C_4 plants are rare in cool climates because of their poor photosynthetic performance at low temperatures relative to C_3 species. In hot, dry conditions, C_4 plants lose less water through transpiration than C_3 plants. During the stress of drought and high temperatures, plants normally close most of their stomata, and the concentration of CO_2 in the plant becomes extremely low. The unique **kranz anatomy** of C_4 plants (the enzyme RuBisCO is found only in bundle-sheath cells, special cells that form a ring around the vascular bundles in the leaves) allows CO_2 to be concentrated around RuBisCO, even when stomata are closed, and photosynthesis keeps going. By contrast, under similar conditions of drought and high temperatures, C_3 plants experience photorespiration. Photorespiration occurs when RuBisCO uses oxygen as an alternate substrate to carbon, which severely reduces the photosynthetic rates in C_3 plants; therefore, C_4 plants have a competitive advantage under conditions of drought, high temperature, and low CO_2. So, while elevated CO_2 increases photosynthesis in C_3 plants under most conditions, C_4 plants benefit from elevated CO_2 only when under drought stress (see Figure 2).

As CO_2 levels increase, temperatures in Canada are predicted to increase, which will also affect photosynthesis in plants. Because increased atmospheric CO_2 decreases photorespiration in C_3 plants even during heat stress, C_3 plants may have a competitive advantage over C_4 plants in a warmer climate with high CO_2 levels. In the C_3-dominated boreal forest, competition between C_3 and C_4 plants may not be an issue; but, the Canadian prairies are a mix of C_3 and C_4 grasses that constantly compete with one another for resources. The predicted changes in temperature and CO_2 levels may change the

FIGURE 2. Temperature and CO_2 influences the predicted superiority of different photosynthetic pathways.
Modelled CO_2 uptake for C_3 and C_4 plants as a function of atmospheric CO_2 concentrations: upper bar is 550 ppm CO_2—the predicted levels we will have by 2050 (and those seen during the Miosine), current CO_2 concentrations (middle bar), and CO_2 levels of 200 ppm estimated at last glacial maximum (lower bar).
Source: Adapted with kind permission from Springer Science + Business Media: Ehleringer JR, Cerling TE, and Helliker BE. 1997. C4 photosynthesis, atmospheric CO_2, and climate. Oecologia 112(3):285–299. Copyright © 1997, Springer Berlin/Heidelberg.

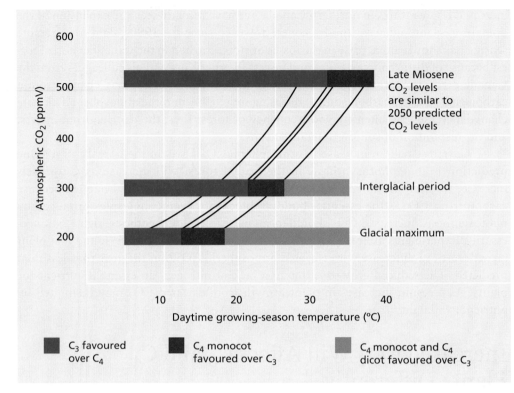

distribution of C_3 and C_4 plants as certain plants out-compete others. Increased CO_2 levels will also have an impact on agriculture in Canada, with C_3 weeds possibly gaining a competitive advantage over C_4 crops, such as corn. Canada thistle (*Cirsium arvense*) is an example of a noxious weed that grows more roots when CO_2 levels are increased, which makes herbicides less effective.

Conclusions

The complexity of the interactions between organisms and their environment makes it difficult to be sure how all the different ecosystems in Canada will respond to the predicted increases in atmospheric CO_2. Biologists continue their efforts to better understand how a future hotter planet will affect life everywhere.

Critical Thinking Questions

1. Why is it difficult for scientists to predict the rate of warming that Arctic regions will experience?
2. Why are C_4 plants considered to be adapted for hot, dry conditions?
3. How will increases in atmospheric CO_2 alter the distribution of C_3 and C_4 grasses in the Canadian prairies?

Further Research Question

How could changing CO_2 levels—from their low level during the last ice age to the high levels predicted by the year 2050—affect C_3 and C_4 plants (see Ward et al., 2008)?

References

*Ainsworth EA, Long SP. 2005. What have we learned from 15 years of free-air CO_2 enrichment (FACE)? a meta-analytic review of the responses of photosynthesis, canopy properties, and plant production to rising CO_2. *New Phytol.* 165:351–372.

Archambault DJ, Li X, Robinson D, O'Donovan JT, Klein KK. 2001. The effects of elevated CO_2 and temperature on herbicide efficacy and weed/crop competition [Internet]. Final Report Prepared for the Prairie Adaptation Research Collaborative. [cited 2010 Apr 12]. Available from: http://www.parc.ca/pdf/research_publications/agriculture2.pdf

Bonan GB. 2008. Forests and climate change: forcings, feedbacks, and the climate benefits of forests. *Sci.* 320:144–1449.

Ehleringer JR, Cerling TE, Helliker BR. 1997. C_4 photosynthesis, atmospheric CO_2, and climate. *Oecol.* 112:285–299.

Kubien DS, Sage RF. 2004. Low-temperature photosynthetic performance of a C_4 grass and a co-occurring C_3 grass native to high latitudes. *Plant Cell Environ.* 27:907–916.

Kurz WA, Stinson G, Rampley G. 2008. Could increased boreal forest ecosystem productivity offset carbon losses from increased disturbances? *Philos. Trans. R. Soc. Biol.* 363:2259–2268.

Leakey ADB. 2009. Rising atmospheric carbon dioxide concentration and the future of C_4 crops for food and fuel. *Proc. R. Soc. Biol.* 276:2333–2343.

Logan AJ, Régnière J, Powellet JA. 2003. Assessing the impacts of global warming on forest pest dynamics. *Front Ecol. Environ.* 1(3):130–137.

Wang D, Heckathorn SA, Barua D, Joshi P, Hamilton EW, LaCroix JL. 2008. Effects of elevated CO_2 on the tolerance of photosynthesis to acute heat stress in C_3, C_4, and CAM species. *Am. J. Bot.* 95:165–176.

*Ward JK, Myers DA, Thomas RB. 2008. Physiological and growth responses of C_3 and C_4 plants to reduced temperature when grown at low CO_2 of the last ice age. *J. Integr. Plant Biol.* 50:1388–1395.

Connecting Salamander Habitat in Waterton Lakes National Park:
Building Tunnels to Love

Niki Wilson and Barbara Johnston
Parks Canada

Introduction

What would you do for sex? Would you crawl down a wet, muddy hill in the pouring rain? Would you risk being attacked by dangerous predators? Would you dodge cars on a wet highway in the dark, even if it meant a vehicle might kill you? If you were a long-toed salamander in Waterton Lakes National Park (WLNP), that's exactly what you would do—until now. The recent installation of amphibian tunnels under the roads in WLNP has now made salamander sex a whole lot safer.

> **KEY CONCEPTS**
>
> - Seasonal migration occurs in many species.
> - The disruption of habitat connectivity can endanger migrating animals.

Why Did the Salamander Cross the Road?

Adult long-toed salamanders (*Ambystoma macrodactylum*; see Figure 1) live in forested areas where they feed on small worms and insects. They spend the majority of their time underground, where it is moist and they are safe from predators. They are nocturnal, elusive, and most likely to be seen during three seasonal migrations that are critical for their survival. The first migration occurs on cold, wet spring nights in late April, as soon as the snow and ice have begun to melt. Long-toed salamanders absorb water and oxygen through their skin and need to travel in wet, dark conditions to prevent dehydration. They migrate en masse to the shallow waters of ponds and small lakes, with the males arriving slightly ahead of the females. They spend two to four weeks breeding and laying eggs. The second migration occurs once the eggs are laid, when the adults return to their non-breeding

FIGURE 1. **Long-toed salamander.**
Source: © Parks Canada.

FIGURE 2. Non-breeding habitat, Entrance Road and Linnet Lake.
Source: © Parks Canada.

FIGURE 2. Non-breeding habitat, Entrance Road and Linnet Lake.
Source: © Parks Canada.

habitat. After the adults have gone, the eggs hatch into larvae that play an important ecological role as carnivores at the top of the aquatic food chain. As the larvae grow, they metamorphose into juvenile salamanders. The third migration occurs in September and October, when the juveniles find their way to the same non-breeding habitat as the adults.

In WLNP, one population of long-toed salamanders migrates from its non-breeding habitat to Linnet Lake to breed (see Figure 2). Although the distance is not far, the journey is perilous because it forces the salamanders to cross the main road (Entrance Road) into the park.

The issue was first raised by one of the park's staff in 1991 when he noted unusually high numbers of dead salamanders along Entrance Road (see Figure 2). It became apparent that the mortality was, in part, the result of a new sidewalk that had been built two years earlier for park visitors who were walking to and from the Visitor Reception Centre and Linnet Lake. The right-angle curb of the sidewalk was too steep for the salamanders to climb, leaving them stranded on the road where they were killed by cars and predators.

Following this observation, park scientists commissioned research on the salamanders to learn more about the impact of the road. Volunteers from the community of WLNP assisted the salamanders during their April migration by physically lifting them over the curb. The right-angled curb was soon retrofitted to a sloped curb to allow the salamanders easy crossing.

Despite community efforts and improvements to the curb, monitoring from 1994 to 2001 showed that between 10 and 44 percent of the long-toed salamanders that attempted to cross the road were killed by vehicles. One researcher noted that highway traffic in the months of April, May, September, and October (when salamanders are migrating across the roadway) increased by 52, 17, 18, and 20 percent, respectively, between 1989 and 2000. Increased traffic volume is shown in many studies to result in increased wildlife mortality.

A Species at Risk

In Alberta, long-toed salamander distribution is limited to the western margin of the province. They are listed as a species of special concern, meaning that without human intervention, the provincial population may become threatened with extinction. Like many amphibians, their survival is challenged by multiple factors: vehicle-caused mortality, loss of habitat, disease, and climate change. The introduction (both natural and human caused) of predatory fish into breeding sites has also likely resulted in the disappearance of salamanders through predation and competition.

The effect of all these factors on the Linnet Lake long-toed salamander population is not well understood. However, Parks Canada is mandated to protect ecological processes, such as seasonal migrations, and to take measures to protect species at risk. Knowing that mortality on Entrance Road was something it could mitigate, Parks Canada aimed to control vehicle-caused mortality as a potential stress on the population.

Mitigating Road Mortality with Crossing Structures

In 2008, park managers made the decision to install amphibian tunnels *under* the road at critical locations. Four tunnels were installed between May and June (see Figure 3).

Each 1 m section is made of polymer concrete with air slots to allow air, moisture, and light into the tunnel (see Figures 4 and 5). This creates an acceptable, enticing environment for the amphibians to enter. These segments were then placed together and set in concrete to span the width of the road (see Figure 6). Each tunnel is like a box culvert that is 600 mm wide by 520 mm high.

A series of small fences intercept the animals during their migration and direct them to the tunnels.

Are the Tunnels Working?

The use of the tunnels was monitored intensely in the first two years after installation (2009 and 2010). In 2009, researchers conducted daily visual surveys by walking the 500 m along the Entrance Road (i.e., the length that parallels Linnet Lake) and identifying each amphibian encountered. The surveys showed amphibians are using the tunnels, and vehicle-caused mortality has been substantially reduced since the installation. A

FIGURE 3. Location of amphibian crossing tunnels across Entrance Road.
Source: © Parks Canada.

FIGURE 4. Amphibian tunnels as they appear on the road.
Source: © Niki Wilson.

FIGURE 5. Holes allow moisture into the tunnels.
Source: © Niki Wilson.

FIGURE 6. Car crossing over amphibian tunnel.
Source: © Parks Canada.

series of remote cameras at each tunnel entrance and exit documented use by at least 10 other species, including snowshoe hares, raccoons, garter snakes, and tiger salamanders. Some of these animals had not previously been detected in this part of WLNP, and tunnel monitoring provided an opportunity to further understand what animals are using the area.

Conclusions

As for all amphibians in WLNP, survival of the long-toed salamander is threatened by a number of factors. One of the factors Parks Canada tried to control was vehicle-caused mortality as a stress on the population; thus far, the mitigation measures appear to have been successful. Monitoring will continue, and scientists do not yet know whether the decrease in road mortality will have an effect on the population as a whole.

Critical Thinking Questions

1. Why do long-toed salamanders migrate when it's damp or raining?
2. Describe the seasonal migrations of long-toed salamanders. Why were these a challenge for them in Waterton Lakes National Park?
3. Why is it difficult for scientists in Waterton Lakes National Park to determine whether or not the amphibian tunnels will have an effect on the Linnet Lake population of long-toed salamanders?

Further Research Question

The study of the interaction among roads, animals, and the natural environment is called *road ecology*. Describe this emerging science.

References

Fukumoto J. 1995. Long-toed salamander (*Ambystoma macrodactylum*) ecology and management in Waterton Lakes National Park [master's thesis]. Calgary: University of Calgary; [108 p.].

Pagnucco K. 2009. Field report for the Waterton Lakes National Park amphibian study. Waterton (AB): Parks Canada.

Parks Canada. 2000. Waterton Lakes National Park of Canada management plan: A portion of Waterton-Glacier International Peace Park. Edmonton (AB): Author.

Pearson KJ. 2002. Linnet Lake long-toed salamander (*Ambystoma macrodactylum*) road kill prevention and population estimation project summary report, Waterton Lakes National Park, 2001 [unpublished technical report]. Waterton (AB): Parks Canada Agency, Waterton Park; [27 p.].

Sustainable Resource Development [Internet]. Edmonton (AB): Government of Alberta; c1995–2010. Long-toed salamander (*Ambystoma macrodactylum*); 2009 Oct 24 [cited 2010 Apr 19]. Available from: http://www.srd.alberta.ca/BioDiversityStewardship/WildSpecies/Amphibians/Salamanders/LongtoedSalamander.aspx

Waterton Lakes National Park of Canada [Internet]. Edmonton (AB): Parks Canada; c2010. Wildlife: saga of the salamander; 2009 Sept 23 [cited 2010 Apr 19]. Available from: http://www.pc.gc.ca/eng/pn-np/ab/waterton/natcul/natcul1/w.aspx

Waterton Lakes National Park, Western and Northern Service Centre, Calgary [unpublished technical report]. Waterton (AB): Parks Canada Agency, Waterton Park, AB; [5 p.].

Epigenetics:
You Inherit More than Your Genes

Samantha A. Beck
University of British Columbia

Introduction

The double helix structure of DNA has become an iconic symbol in pop culture (see Figure 1). From *X-Men* to *Jurassic Park* to *CSI*, we are used to seeing scientists studying this double-stranded molecule. But why is that structure so important? Why has it captured the imagination of the public and scientists alike? The idea that all the organisms on Earth can be described by a simple alphabet of As, Cs, Ts, and Gs is tantalizing and controversial, but for biologists and researchers in many fields there is another reason to respect the elegant structure of DNA: inheritance.

From classical genetics and the ideas of Gregor Mendel to evolutionary theory, inheritance is a fundamental biological concept. When Watson and Crick published their structure of DNA in 1953 they made the simple yet incredibly powerful statement "It has not escaped our notice that the specific pairing we have postulated immediately suggests a possible copying mechanism for the genetic material." They meant that the structure of DNA explained what biologists had understood conceptually for hundreds of years: that a mechanism must exist for the duplication of genetic information when cells divide. With its two strands and paired bases—A always with T and G always with C—each strand can function as a template for the synthesis of the other strand.

> ### KEY CONCEPTS
> - When cells divide, gene expression patterns are inherited along with the genes themselves.
> - One mechanism guiding this inheritance is the methylation of symmetrical DNA sequences.

FIGURE 1. The iconic structure of the double helix.
This staircase at the BC Cancer Research Centre was built to mimic the iconic structure of DNA.
Source: Photographer: Nic Lehoux/Architect: Henriquez Partners IBI Group Architect in Joint Venture.

When cells divide to produce an exact replica of themselves via the process of mitosis, the genome of the cell must first be duplicated through the production of two identical **sister chromatids** during the stage of the cell cycle known as the **synthesis phase**, or **S phase**. We now understand the genetic basis of inheritance and the important role the double helix structure plays in this. But is the genetic sequence the only thing that is duplicated? Do the identical daughter cells produced through the process of mitosis inherit more than just a genome? Interestingly, scientists have now uncovered a completely new layer of inheritance beyond the well-described DNA replication process. **Epigenetics** is a relatively new field of research into the inheritance of the "decisions" a cell makes regarding which parts of its huge genome it uses.

Division of a specialized cell in your body, such as a skin cell, produces two daughter cells that are also skin cells. A skin cell will never divide to produce a liver cell, just as a liver cell will never divide to produce a skin cell. This is true despite the fact that, with few exceptions, all the cells in your body share the *same DNA sequence*. Daughter skin cells are different from daughter liver cells because they inherited something more than just the DNA sequence.

Human development begins from a single cell with one diploid DNA sequence, but the human body contains more than 200 different cell types. All these different cell types can be made from a single DNA sequence because different cells use different genes to synthesize proteins important for their individual functions. For example, skin cells express high levels of the protein keratin, which makes skin tough and waterproof. Specialized liver cells, however, do not produce keratin but do produce such enzymes as alcohol dehydrogenase, which breaks down alcohol in the blood. Each cell type expresses a unique subset of genes in the genome while ignoring other genes. A **gene expression pattern** is the specific combination of genes that are "turned on" and genes that are "turned off" in a particular cell at a particular time. Liver cells and skin cells each have their own unique gene expression pattern.

During the developmental progression from a single cell to many cells with specialized functions, some genes are turned on and others, off. These changes will be inherited as cells divide. When a skin cell divides, both of the daughter cells produced will express the same subset of genes as the original cell. But how do these genes "remember" whether they were on or off in the original cell? Researchers in the field of **epigenetics** are trying to answer this question.

One part of the answer, at least in mice and humans, is a mechanism that Watson and Crick would surely find elegant. Scattered throughout the genome, and usually found near the beginning of genes, are symmetrical nucleotides with the sequence 5′-CG-3′ that can be covalently modified by enzymes called **DNA methyltransferases**. When these enzymes are activated, a methyl group is added to the 5′ cytosine in this sequence and to the complementary strand (see Figure 2). When the sequence replicates, the result is two **hemi-methylated** daughter strands. This means that one cytosine in each daughter strand is methylated, but one is not. Another group of similar enzymes, called **maintenance methyltransferases**, recognize this hemi-methylated state, and fill in the missing methyl group (see Figure 2). In this way, the two methyl groups can each act as a template for the methylation of the newly synthesized cytosine, just as the two strands of DNA in the double helix can each act as a template for synthesis of the complementary strand.

Generally, genes marked with this methylation pattern are turned off. Genes that a skin cell does not need to express, such as alcohol dehydrogenase, could be marked through methylation of 5′ cytosine residues, while genes that a skin cell expresses, such as keratin, would not be methylated in this cell type. Each time the cell divides, the methylation marks are inherited along with the DNA sequence through the action of the maintenance methyltransferases. In this way, methylation marks are part of a large and complex "epigenetic code" allowing cells to remember which genes should be "on" (unmethylated) and which genes should be "off" (methylated).

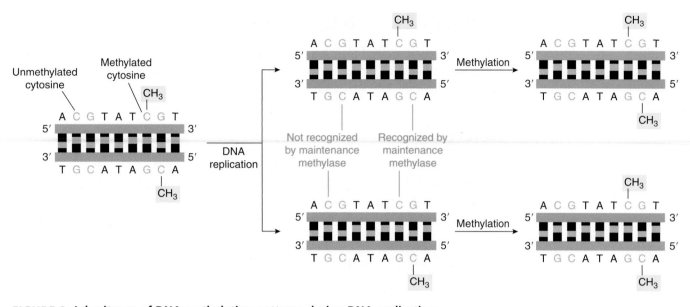

FIGURE 2. Inheritance of DNA methylation patterns during DNA replication.
Source: Bruce Alberts, Alexander Johnson, Julian Lewis, Martin Raff, Keith Roberts, Peter Walter. Molecular Biology of the Cell, 5th ed. Garland Science Textbooks © 2002 From Molecular Biology of the Cell 4E by Alberts et al. Reproduced by permission of Garland Science/Taylor and Francis LLC.

Conclusions

The field of epigenetics is still in its infancy, and researchers have yet to fully break the epigenetic code. At the University of British Columbia's Life Sciences Institute, a group of scientists called the Molecular Epigenetics Group tackle further questions about the epigenetic code in an ideal arrangement. They share a common lab space, and despite the fact that they use different organisms, including yeast, the fruit fly *Drosophila melanogaster*, as well as mice and other mammals, their exchange of ideas is valuable. Epigenetics and the need to decide which genes are used by which cells is a basic cellular process critical to all multicellular organisms and even single-celled organisms, such as yeast. The collaborative environment of the Molecular Epigenetics Group means that researchers can rapidly translate ideas about how things are done in one organism into other model organisms. A wealth of knowledge and a unique perspective is always just down the hall.

The fruit fly is especially interesting to this field because methylation of cytosine residues does not play a role in this organism's epigenetic inheritance. Instead, it is likely the proteins non-covalently associated with DNA that direct epigenetic inheritance in fruit flies. Many of the genes encoding these proteins are highly similar to those found in other organisms, and different labs within the Molecular Epigenetics Group study the same proteins in different organisms. Because similar proteins suggest similar function, it will be interesting to determine how these mechanisms compare in organisms with cytosine methylation and organisms without. New experimental results from one organism can often lead researchers who study a different organism down a new path. This inspiration is what makes collaborative environments that facilitate the inheritance of ideas so important.

Critical Thinking Questions

1. How are the structures of DNA and methylated DNA important to the concept of inheritance?
2. Why is information regarding a biological process in one organism relevant to a researcher examining the same biological process in a different organism?
3. When we think of inheritance, we often think of what is passed from parents to offspring. Do you think epigenetic information is passed from parents to offspring?

Further Research Question

DNA is wrapped around histones in the nucleus. Histones can be post-translationally modified with methyl and acetyl groups. What effects do these types of histone modifications have on the DNA that surrounds them?

References

Beck SA, Faradji F, Brock H, Peronnet F. 2009. Maintenance of *Hox* gene expression patterns. In: Deutsch J, editor. Hox *genes studies from the 20th to the 21st century.* Austin (TX): Landes Biosciences.

Klose RJ, Bird AP. 2006. Genomic DNA methylation: the mark and its mediators. *Trends Biochem. Sci.* 31:89–97.

The Evolution of the Vertebrate Jaw:
How Would You Eat without One?

Julia C Boughner
University of Saskatchewan

Introduction

Imagine that you had no upper and lower jaws. How would you chew your food or talk? If you were a wild animal, how would you capture your supper or prevent yourself from becoming a meal? The evolution of jaws in vertebrates was a monumental change because it led to a never-before-seen tool to exploit new ecological niches.

Jaws help vertebrates—animals with a spinal cord protectively encased in a **vertebral column** (Janvier, 1997)—to hunt and eat, as well as to defend themselves. Jaws also help such vertebrates as humans to vocalize (talk). Today, jaws are so pervasive among living vertebrates that you might not realize that not *all* of them actually have jaws. Jawless vertebrates are called **agnathans**, which is Latin for "no jaws." Lampreys are the sole living members of this group. These eel-like aquatic vertebrates attach to and suck the blood of live prey with their rasping tooth-ringed mouths (see Figure 1, A). Hagfish resemble lampreys (in that they lack jaws), but they also lack a vertebral column and for this reason are not considered true vertebrates. That said, these classifications remain somewhat controversial (Forey and Janvier, 1993; Janvier, 2007). All other jawed vertebrates are called **gnathostomes**, where *gnathos* (pronounced with a silent *g*) is Latin for "jaw" and *stoma* for "mouth" (see Figure 1, B).

KEY CONCEPTS

- Selection processes favoured the evolution of diverse forms of jaws in vertebrates.
- The field of evolutionary developmental biology investigates which genes and molecules are important for the development and evolution of new and different body parts.

(A)

FIGURE 1. Jawless vertebrate (Agnathans) and jawed vertebrates (Gnathostomes).
A. In profile (middle right), a lamprey looks innocuous; but, when seen from below, its tooth-filled mouth is positively intimidating!
Source: Wikipedia: Lamprey, http://en.wikipedia.org/wiki/File: Diversas_lampreas.1_-_Aquarium_Finisterrae.jpg, accessed 22 January 2010.

FIGURE 1. (*continued*)
B. Placoderms, an extinct group of armoured fish, were among the first gnathostomes. The largest known placoderm fish, *Dunkleosteus*, is no less frightening than the lamprey!
Source: Jon Hughes/Bedrock Studios © Dorling Kindersley.

(B)

What Defines a Vertebrate Jaw?

In general terms, the word *jaw* can refer to any animal's mouthpart. Think of insect mandibles: these are called jaws, too. But in vertebrates, a jaw is a hinged complex of upper and lower mouthparts made of soft and hard **connective tissues**, including cartilage and bone. Muscle action around the jaw joint (where the lower jaw attaches to the skull) moves the jaw skeleton. Movements can be strictly vertical (think of a shark clamping down on prey) or involve rotation (think of a cow chewing cud). Jaw structure and function can be highly specialized. For example, the "hollow" lower jaw of the northern stoplight loosejaw fish (see Figure 2) is attached to the upper jaw only at its hinge and by a single modified tongue bone!

Upper and lower jaws form from **dermal bone**. During development, dermal bone forms directly from cell condensations, unlike other types of bone, which grow from a cartilage template. Even though the lower jaw (also called the mandible) forms from dermal bone, it is a strange exception to this rule. In vertebrates, the mandible forms around a special rod of cartilage called **Meckel's cartilage**, which is found only in the lower jaw. Meckel's cartilage persists into adulthood in some vertebrates, including birds, but is resorbed (broken down and dissolved) in others, including primates.

FIGURE 2. **Strange but true: The jaw of the northern stoplight loosejaw fish.**
An artist's rendition of the northern stoplight loosejaw (*Malacosteus niger*), a deep-sea dwelling fish found many places worldwide, including off of Canada's east coast. This predatory fish scans the dark for food by using bioluminescence. The open structure of the lower jaw reduces water resistance, helping the fish to quickly snap its jaws shut on prey.
Source: © Alex Ries 2007.

Vertebrate jaws typically hold rows of **teeth**, which evolved before jaws. For functional reasons, tooth size, morphology, number, and location vary dramatically across vertebrate groups, as does the structure of tooth attachment to the jaws. Because of this advantageous potential for variation, teeth as well as jaws have evolved to help different animals process many different shapes and textures of plant and animal foods.

The Evolutionary Origins of Vertebrate Jaws

The earliest record of vertebrate jaws is from the **Devonian period**, named for the rocks in Devon, England, where the first fossils were found. During this "Age of Fishes," which spanned about 416 million to 359 million years ago (mya) in the Paleozoic era, all major fish lineages diversified dramatically. Some freshwater lobe-finned fish began the transition to land as the first **terrestrial tetrapods** (meaning "four-footed") (Forey and Janvier, 1993; Raff, 2007). For unknown reasons, the Devonian ended with a mass extinction bigger than the one that killed the dinosaurs at the end of the Cretaceous about 65 mya. Many jawless fish species became extinct. In contrast, jawed fish survived well. (It's important to note that these fish evolved other structures, such as paired fins, in addition to jaws, that made them able to exploit ecological niches and rapidly grow in number of species.) Resources were probably harder to come by in the post-extinction environment. Jaws were surely an advantage in that they better equipped the survivors to successfully compete for food and territory (see Figure 1, B). Under such harsh conditions, agnathans would be hard-pressed to out-compete gnathostomes, and it is probably for this reason that so few agnathans persist today.

Variation in Jaw Morphology

Because living jawed vertebrates descended from the first gnathostomes, they share some bony and cartilaginous jaw elements. That is to say, these elements are **homologous**. Body parts are considered homologous if they are similar because of shared ancestry. Shared ancestry can but does not necessarily include shared developmental processes. Human arms, whale fins, and bat wings are made of the same three bones—the humerus, radius, and ulna—because the common ancestor of these mammals had the same bones. However, important group-specific differences have also evolved, and jaws are one example of such a change. Compared with mammalian jaws, reptilian jaws—particularly mandibles—are made up of many more bones, such as the quadrate, pterygoid, angular, splenoid, and dentary.

The jawbones of birds, turtles, and amphibians are more similar to those of reptiles than to those of mammals. (Recall that birds are considered a subgroup of reptiles; birds are the descendants of some dinosaurs.) This similarity is a result of the ancestral relationships shared by these groups. Because mammals diverged from the reptile line very early on, mammals share fewer ancestral traits. For instance, instead of several smaller bones, the mammalian mandible is made of a large **dentary** bone, which holds the teeth and connects directly to the skull base at the jaw joint.

The Evolution of the Mammalian Ear

Some of the jawbones found in reptiles were lost in mammals through evolution. Of the reptilian jawbones that were not lost, some became something else, as was the case with mammalian ear evolution. In your middle ear, you have three **ear ossicles**, or ear bones, called the stapes, incus ("anvil"), and malleus ("hammer"). These tiny bones

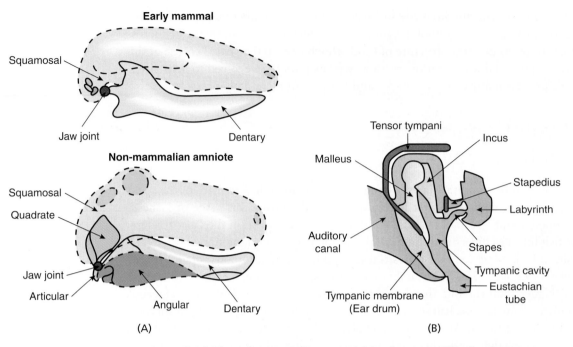

FIGURE 3. Evolution of mammalian ear ossicles from reptilian jawbones.
A. The quadrate (blue) and articular (pink) bones in a reptilian jaw (top) compared with the incus and malleus bones of a mammal (bottom). B. The structure of a mammalian ear.
Source: A. Based on Wikipedia: Mammalian and non-mammalian jaws, http:// en.wikipedia.org/wiki/ File:Jaw_joint_-_mammal_n_non-mammal.png, accessed 22 January 2010. B. Based on Wikipedia: Middle ear, http://en.wikipedia.org/wiki/Middle_ear, accessed 22 January 2010.

conduct sound waves from the eardrum into the inner ear. Reptiles have only one ear ossicle: the stapes ("stirrup"). The other two ear bones associated with the mammalian middle ear are named the quadrate and the articular (see Figure 3, A). In reptiles, these two bones remain part of the jaw joint. The quadrate, found in the upper jaw, became the incus in the mammalian ear. The articular, a lower jawbone in reptiles, became the malleus. Over evolutionary time, these three bones changed location, size, and shape to become part of the mammalian auditory complex (see Figure 3, B) (Raff, 2007).

The "Evo-Devo" Biology of the Jaw

You may still be wondering how jaws evolved from seemingly nothing. Unfortunately, at this time it's not directly possible to study what changes extinct animals went through in their developmental stages or how they evolved. But there may be a solution to this problem.

In the last few decades, a new research area called **evolutionary developmental biology** (or "evo-devo") has developed. Evo-devo biologists study how living animals form their body parts in order to understand how these body parts evolved (Raff, 2007). When you think about it, if there is natural selection for a given **phenotype**, such as long legs, then there is also selection for the developmental processes that grew that phenotype. The information about these processes is held in the animal's genes, or **genotype**. In the case of jaws, evo-devo studies of the processes behind jaw development have started to give insight into the processes by which jaws evolved.

Hox genes are a special group of genes that play a key role in determining what major body parts—such as legs, antennae, wings, and vertebrae—go where. These important patterning genes probably had a lot to do with the origin of jaws. In vertebrate embryos, *Hox* genes are *not* expressed in the head tissues that become the upper and lower jaws (see Figure 4) (Shigetani et al., 2002). Based on this knowledge, the first gnathostomes may have gained jaws because *Hox* expression was lost in the embryonic

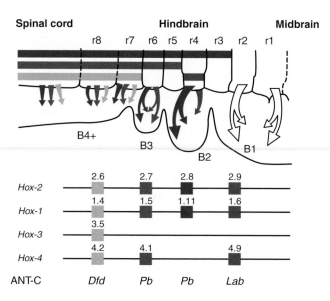

FIGURE 4. Lack of *Hox* gene expression in the tissues that will become the jaw.
Early in embryo development, *Hox* genes are not expressed in the parts of the head (r1, r2) that later become the tissues (B1) that form the jaws.
Source: Reprinted by permission by Macmillan Publishers Ltd: Figure 4b, 863. Hunt P, Gulisano M, Cook M, Sham MH, Faiella A, Wilkinson D, Boncinelli E, Krumlauf R. 1991. A distinct Hox code for the branchial region of the vertebrate head. Nature 353:861–864. © 1991 Nature Publishing Group.

head parts that form jaws (Cohn, 2002), although this theory remains controversial (Takeo et al., 2004). If losing *Hox* activity in these tissues somehow rewrote the gnathostomes' genetic instructions to become jaws, this local deletion must have been via a genetic mutation that didn't compromise the rest of the animal's healthy development and growth.

Even the way in which jaws evolve to look so different might be explained by similar developmental events. Jaw tissues form via similar processes that first instruct cells to become, or to differentiate into, cartilage or bone, and then tell cells to form the distinct shape of each skeletal part. Each bone develops from its own cluster of cells. The precise way in which cells behave once they differentiate—including multiplying or dying—produces a species-specific jaw or different numbers of bones.

Conclusions

Vertebrate jaws first evolved hundreds of millions of years ago. This many years later, jaws remain a critical evolutionary adaptation that allows vertebrates to successfully exploit new ecological niches. You might not notice it, but jaw evolution continues today as Earth's environments shift and the ecological pressures on species change. I'm excited and confident that future evo-devo findings will help us to better understand the morphological changes that led to contemporary vertebrate jaws.

Critical Thinking Questions

1. Especially in light of the mass extinction at the end of the Devonian, explain the process of natural selection that spurred the widespread evolution of jaws from the very first jawed fish.
2. How would having jaws have made it more likely for some species of fish to be the first animals to transition to land?
3. How might different jawbone shapes and numbers form during an animal's development?

Further Research Question

Describe different ways in which the teeth attach to the jaws across vertebrate groups, and discuss the functional purposes of these attachment types.

References

Cohn MJ. 2002. Lamprey *Hox* genes and the origin of jaws. *Nat.* 416:386–387.

Forey P, Janvier P. 1993. Agnathans and the origin of jawed vertebrates. *Nat.* 361:129–134.

Janvier P. 1997. Vertebrata. Animals with backbones. In: Tree of Life Web Project [Internet]. (under construction) [modified 1997 Jan; cited 2010 Jan 22]. Available from: http://tolweb.org/

Janvier P. 2007. Homologies and evolutionary transitions in early vertebrate history. In: Anderson JS, Sues HD, editors. *Major transitions in vertebrate evolution.* Chap. 2. Bloomington (ID): Indiana UP. p. 57–121.

Raff RA. 2007. Written in stone: fossils, genes and evo–devo. *Nat. Rev. Genet.* 8:911–920.

Shigetani Y, Sugahara F, Kawakami Y, Murakami Y, Hirano S, Kuratani S. 2002. Heterotopic shift of epithelial-mesenchymal interactions in vertebrate jaw evolution. *Sci.* 296:1316–1319.

Takeo Y, Pasqualetti M, Kuraku S, Hirano S, Rijli FM, Kuratani S. 2004. Lamprey *Hox* genes and the evolution of jaws. *Nat.* 429.

Forensic Entomology:
Using Insects to Solve Crimes

Gail S. Anderson
Simon Fraser University

Introduction

Forensic science has been quietly involved in helping the police solve crimes for more than a century; however, with the recent popularity of several television shows, forensic science has suddenly come to the forefront of the public's attention. Forensic science, as portrayed on television, is glamorous and sexy and always solves the crime in less than 60 minutes, including commercial breaks. Most people realize that much of what they see in such shows is for entertainment purposes only, but how much is truth and how much is fiction?

Using insects to solve crimes may seem to be one of the more far-fetched sciences, developed purely for television but, in actual fact, forensic entomology is one of the oldest forensic sciences used in real criminal investigations today. Forensic entomology is the use of insects in legal investigations. The more specific terms, *medico-legal* or *medico-criminal entomology*, refer to analyzing the insects associated with a body to estimate a minimum post-mortem interval (Byrd and Castner, 2009). Although the science behind medico-criminal entomology has advanced in leaps and bounds in the last few decades, its use in criminal investigations goes back to the tenth century (Greenberg and Kunich, 2002). In that case, a woman claimed that her husband's death was due to a house fire, but the flies present indicated a major head wound, so the woman confessed to her husband's murder (Greenberg and Kunich, 2002).

Insects colonizing a body can give a trained forensic entomologist a great deal of information about the time of death, whether the remains have been moved or disturbed after death, the pattern of injuries, whether the victim used drugs or was poisoned, and, in the case of a living victim, when an injury occurred or when a person last received medical attention (Anderson, 2009a).

Estimating Elapsed Time since Death

Insects are ubiquitous and are animals with a long evolutionary history. Several families of insects, called carrion insects, have adapted to exploit carrion or dead animals (including humans). Carrion insects include primarily insects from the orders Diptera, or true flies, and Coleoptera, or beetles. Not all Diptera and Coleoptera are associated with carrion, but certain specialized groups utilize dead animals at some or all stages of their life cycle. Their association with carrion is a normal part of their lives, and by

---

KEY CONCEPTS

■ The rate of insect development is dependent on the external environment, temperature in particular.

■ The assemblage of species found in a biological community changes over time and is primarily a function of climate and chance historical events.

PHOTO A.
Maggot mass of third instar
Calliphoridae larvae feeding
on a pig carcass. Note the red
crops, which indicate food
material in the crop or the
food storage organ.
Source: Gail Anderson.

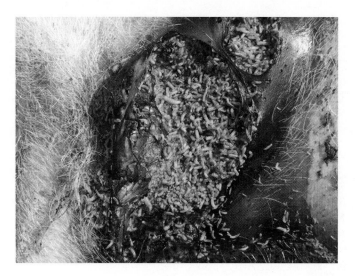

understanding the relationships among the insects colonizing the remains, the environment, and the remains themselves, a forensic or medico-criminal entomologist can interpret the insect evidence and give investigators a great deal of information about a death.

The main question asked of a forensic entomologist is "When did the victim die?" There are two entomological methods used to estimate elapsed time since death. The first method utilizes maggot age and development. When environmental conditions are appropriate, insects will begin to colonize a body immediately after death, usually arriving within minutes in the presence of blood (Anderson and VanLaerhoven, 1996; Nuorteva, 1977). These first colonizers are usually the blow flies or Calliphoridae: large, brightly coloured, shiny flies. These flies are attracted to remains because they are ideal places for flies to lay their eggs, as their young feed on dead animal material. The eggs hatch into first stage or **first instar larvae** (maggots), which feed on liquid protein, such as blood, or at the **mucosal** layers (endodermal tissue that lines the orifices) as they cannot break adult human skin (Erzinclioglu, 1996). After a short period of time, these larvae moult to the second instar and continue to feed, now consuming tissue. They then moult into the third instar, which feed voraciously, removing a lot of tissue and frequently skeletonizing parts of the remains. At this time, the larvae usually form maggot masses (see Photo A). After a period of time, the third instar does not moult but instead undergoes various physiological and behavioural changes, entering a post-feeding or wandering stage. At this point, it leaves the remains, searching for a safe place to pupate (see Photo B). During pupation, the insect metamorphoses into an adult fly, which

PHOTO B.
Wandering or non-feeding
third instar Calliphoridae
larvae leaving a pig carcass in
search of a suitable pupation
medium.
Source: Gail Anderson.

emerges, leaving behind an empty pupal case as evidence that this cycle has occurred (Erzinclioglu, 1996). Insects are cold-blooded animals, so their development is primarily based on ambient temperature. As temperature increases, they develop through their life cycle rapidly, and as temperature decreases, they develop more slowly. Between maximum and minimum threshold temperatures, this relationship is mostly linear, which makes it predictable (Chapman, 1980).

This predictable relationship allows forensic entomologists to estimate how long ago the first insects colonized the remains by first seeing how far through the life cycle the insects have proceeded at the crime scene. The scientists then identify the species of insects involved and find out the temperature at the crime scene based on weather records and datalogger (a data recorder that records temperature) recordings of local microclimate. They then use published data on specific species' development rates to estimate how long it would take the species found to reach the stage of the oldest insects on the body under the given conditions. For instance, if the oldest insects on the body are in the second instar and at the temperature at the crime scene the species present take a minimum of 48 hours to reach this stage, then insects have been on the body for at least two days, which indicates that the victim has been dead for at least two days. The duration could be longer, as this is a minimum, but it could not be less.

The second method used to estimate elapsed time since death is based on insect succession on the body. Blow flies are usually the first to colonize remains, but as the body progresses through biological, chemical, and physical decompositional changes, the nutrient availability of the remains sequentially changes, attracting other insects and repelling earlier colonizers, in a predictable manner. These later colonizing insects primarily include other members of Diptera and Coleoptera. Some of these insects feed directly on the remains, whereas others feed on other insects, developing a complex food web. This sequence of insect colonization is affected by many parameters—including geographical region, season, habitat, and exposure (Anderson, 2009b)—but within these parameters, it is predictable. As long as forensic entomologists have local data for the area, season, and habitat, they can predict the timing of insect succession on the remains. The entomologist can, therefore, conclude a minimum elapsed time since death; for example, under these conditions, this combination of insects is found on a body between two and four months after death. Often when insects colonize, they leave evidence of themselves behind, such as empty pupal cases, cast larval skins, or beetle wing covers (elytra). Even after the remains are no longer attractive to that species, this evidence indicates that it has been present. These data then narrow the range. For instance, a species that is no longer present may colonize under those conditions from one to three months, narrowing the above estimate to three to four months since death. Insects will continue to colonize the remains until there is no food left and the remains are nothing more than dry bones. In some situations, this can take years.

A medico-criminal entomologist is usually asked to give an estimate of elapsed time since death, which can support or refute a suspect's alibi and provide the police with an investigative timeline. In addition to this, insects can tell entomologists other things about a crime, such as whether wounds were present, whether the body has been moved or disturbed, and, in the case of a living victim, the length of time of neglect.

Position and Presence of Wounds

Blow flies do not provide any maternal care to their offspring. Their only role in ensuring their offspring's survival is to lay their eggs where they are most likely to survive. Hence, blow flies are well adapted to locate a cadaver through sight and smell, and then to locate the best **oviposition** (egg-laying) site through taste (using the taste receptors on their feet). Tiny, newly hatched first instar larvae cannot break adult human skin and so require a liquid food source during this stage. This means that flies will generally be attracted to wound sites first to lay their eggs, and if there are no wounds, to the orifices, which are lined with a moist mucosal layer, which is easier than skin to break. The subsequent larvae will form maggot masses in these areas. When a body is found, decomposition, as well as insect activity, may have obscured the wounds, but an examination of the position of maggot masses on the body may indicate a wound pattern. For instance, in a natural death, you would expect maggot masses to be found around the facial orifices and the genitalia, if these remains are exposed. If the remains have maggot masses in the stomach area and hands, however, this would suggest these are the site of wounds, perhaps a stab wound in the stomach and defence wounds in the hands (Lord, 1990). It is important to note that it is not the entomologist who would definitively identify a wound site but instead the forensic pathologist who performs the autopsy; however, the entomologist would indicate that the colonization pattern suggests a possible wound site.

Has the Body Been Moved?

Many insects have adapted to live in very specific habitats or geographic regions. If insects on a body are not those normally found in the environment where the body is found, then it would suggest that the body has been moved from its normal environment to the discovery site. For instance, many species of blow flies are typical of rural areas, whereas others are typical of urban areas (Hwang and Turner, 2005). Blow flies found in rural areas live on naturally found carrion, whereas those in urban areas have become adapted to human habitation and live primarily on human garbage. Many killings occur in urban areas, but in order to avoid discovery, the killer will often move the body to a remote location. If the body is colonized by an urban blow fly species, these eggs will be moved with the remains to the rural dump site. When the body is later discovered, the presence of older, urban species as well as later colonizing rural species, will suggest that the body was moved from an urban area.

Has the Body Been Disturbed?

Killers frequently return to the scene of the crime. If they disturb the body in some way, the insects may be able to indicate when this disturbance took place. For instance, if a body is buried, then exposed and reburied, insects will colonize at each exposure time. Analysis will show not just the time of death but also the time of disturbance (Anderson, 1999a). A killer is likely to have developed an alibi for the killing but is unlikely to have considered one for the time of disturbance, so this sort of information could be very useful in the police investigation.

Estimating Length of Time of Neglect

Carrion insects feed on dead organic material, which usually means a dead animal or person, but living people, such as those with gangrenous wounds, can have **necrotic** (dead) tissue on them. In such cases, when the wound is neglected, or the people are unable or unwilling to look after themselves, insects can colonize these wounds. In such cases, the entomologist is not estimating time of death but the length of time of neglect, which can be valuable in abuse cases (Goff et al., 1991).

Conclusions

Insects are usually the first witnesses to a murder. Insect evidence, when carefully analyzed by a trained forensic entomologist, can be very valuable in a death investigation and the use of entomology in criminal investigations has grown exponentially in the last few years. Research in this area is now being developed in most areas of the world, and new areas are continually being developed, such as its use in poaching (Anderson, 1999b) or animal abuse cases (Anderson and Huitson, 2004). Research in this area has expanded across Canada and into different habitats, such as the marine environment (Anderson, 2008; Anderson and Hobischak, 2004), in order to expand the scope of cases that can utilize forensic entomology.

Critical Thinking Questions

1. How does a forensic entomologist age an insect found on a body?
2. Why would geographical region and environmental habitat have an impact on estimating time of death by using insects?
3. Explain why insects can be used to locate wounds.

Further Research Question

Will climate change affect forensic entomology? Why or why not?

References

Anderson GS. 1999a. Forensic entomology in death investigations. In: Fairgreave S, editor. *Forensic osteological analysis: a book of case studies.* Springfield (IL): Charles C. Thomas. p. 303–326.

Anderson GS. 1999b. Wildlife forensic entomology: determining time of death in two illegally killed black bear cubs: a case report. *J. For. Sci.* 44(4):856–859.

Anderson GS. 2008. *Investigation into the effects of oceanic submergence on carrion decomposition and faunal colonization using a baited camera, part I.* Ottawa (ON): Canadian Police Research Centre.

Anderson GS. 2009a. Forensic entomology. In: James SH, Nordby J, editors. *Forensic science: an introduction to scientific and investigative techniques.* Boca Raton (FL): CRC Press. p. 137–165.

Anderson GS. 2009b. Insect succession on carrion and its relationship to determining time since death. In: Byrd JH, Castner JL, editors. *Forensic entomology: the utility of arthropods in legal investigations.* Boca Raton (FL): CRC Press. p. 201–250.

Anderson GS, Hobischak NR. 2004. Decomposition of carrion in the marine environment in British Columbia, Canada. *Int. J. of Legal Med.* 118(4):206–209.

Anderson GS, Huitson NR. 2004. Myiasis in pet animals in British Columbia: the potential of forensic entomology for determining duration of possible neglect. *Can. Veter. J.* 45(12):993–998.

Anderson GS, VanLaerhoven SL. 1996. Initial studies on insect succession on carrion in southwestern British Columbia. *J. For. Sci.* 41(4):617–625.

*Byrd JH, Castner JL. 2009. *Forensic entomology: the utility of arthropods in legal investigations.* 2nd ed. Boca Raton (FL): CRC Press.

Chapman RF. 1980. *The insects, structure and function.* London (UK): Hodder and Stoughton.

Erzinclioglu Z. 1996. Blowflies. In: *Naturalist's handbooks.* Vol. 23. Slough (UK): Richmond Publishing Co. Ltd.

Goff ML, Charbonneau S, Sullivan W. 1991. Presence of fecal matter in diapers as potential source of error in estimations of postmortem intervals using arthropod development patterns. *J. For. Sci.* 36(5):1603–1606.

*Greenberg B, Kunich JC. 2002. *Entomology and the law: flies as forensic indicators.* Cambridge (UK): Cambridge UP.

Hwang C, Turner BD. 2005. Spatial and temporal variability of necrophagous diptera from urban to rural areas. *Med. Veter. Entomol.* 19(4):379–391.

Lord WD. 1990. Case histories of the use of insects in investigations. In: Catts EP, Haskell NH, editors. *Entomology and death: a procedural guide.* Clemson (SC): Joyce's Print Shop. p. 9–37.

Nuorteva P. 1977. Sarcosaprophagous insects as forensic indicators. In: Tedeschi CG, Eckert WG, Tedeschi LG, editors. *Forensic medicine: a study in trauma and environmental hazards.* Philadelphia: W.B. Saunders Co. p. 1072–1095.

Gender Differences in Children's Toy Preferences:
Biologically Determined or Socially Conditioned?

Evelyn F. Field
Mount Royal University

Introduction

Think back to your childhood—yes, that may be a long time ago for some of you. Did you play with toy fire trucks and trains or with Barbie dolls and dress-up costumes? When you were outside did you prefer to run around, pounce on your friends, and playfight or did you prefer to amuse yourself with tea sets and to create make-believe games where you were a mother telling *your* child what to do? Are you a male or a female? In humans, gender differences in play behaviour and toy preferences have been well documented (Berenbaum and Hines, 1992; Hines, 2004). The scientific explanation for why these differences develop, however, has been a subject of debate for years.

During the last several decades, two major theoretical perspectives have been proposed to explain why male and female children exhibit different patterns of play and toy preferences. The first perspective, often referred to as the **biological theory of gender development,** posits that sex differences in our behaviour are determined by the effects of **androgens** (e.g., testosterone), produced by the testes of the male fetus, on the developing brain. This process of **masculinizing** the brain is called **androgenization**. In contrast, females are often thought of as the default phenotype, because without the effects of androgens, the brain develops in a female-typical manner. The second perspective, often referred to as the **social learning theory of gender development,** argues that gender differences in play behaviour and toy preferences are due to differences in how we socialize male and female children within our specific family or cultural groups. Thus, male and female children play with different toys and exhibit different styles of play behaviour because we, as parents or caregivers, encourage them to do so from birth. From a scientific point of view, these two perspectives leave us with a difficult puzzle to solve. How can we determine whether gender differences in play and toy preferences in human children are driven primarily by innate differences in our biological makeup or by the social environment within which we develop? In humans, it is impossible to demonstrate with complete certainty that the behavioural choices we make from the moment of birth are not influenced by the people who care for us.

> **KEY CONCEPTS**
>
> - Gender differences are evident in behaviour from an early age.
> - In part, gender differences arise because of differences in hormone levels during embryonic development.

Research Question

Are gender differences in toy preferences due to inherent differences in our biological composition, or are they due to differences in how male and female children are socialized?

Gerianne Alexander and Melissa Hines (2002) at City University of London came up with a creative hypothesis to test whether gender differences in toy preferences and play behaviour are due to biology or some, as yet undocumented, process of socialization. They asked the following question: What would the male and female juveniles of another primate species do with human toys that we would consider as masculine or feminine? To answer this question, Alexander and Hines studied the toy preferences of several troops of vervet monkeys that were housed at the UCLA Sepulveda Veterans Administration Non-human Primate Laboratory. These vervet monkeys had no prior exposure to human toys and had not been socialized by other members of the troop as to what toys would be "appropriate" for them to play with based on their gender; thus, if gender differences in toy preferences were found in these primates, they must be driven primarily by biological processes rather than socialization.

Hypothesis

If sex differences in toy preference are socially determined, no differences in toy preferences will be observed in male and female vervet monkeys.

Methods and Results

Alexander and Hines observed 44 male and 44 female vervet monkeys that ranged in age from 2 to 185 months interacting with human toys. These animals were members of 7 different troops, consisting of 17 to 28 animals, that lived in outdoor enclosures. After an introductory session where the monkeys were allowed to habituate to the presence of the experimenter, two or three trials of toy exposure were conducted for each monkey. During each trial the animal being observed was exposed sequentially, in random order, to one of six toys (a ball, police car, doll, pot, stuffed animal, or book) for five minutes. The first two toys in the above list were categorized as masculine, the third and fourth as feminine, and the fifth and sixth as neutral. The toys chosen for presentation to the monkeys were based on previous work by Hines (Berenbaum and Hines, 1992) and Maccoby and Jacklin (1974), who have demonstrated that in a wide age range of children boys are more interested in balls and police cars, whereas females are more interested in dolls and pots. To quantify their observations of toy preferences in the vervet monkeys, Alexander and Hines recorded the amount of time each animal spent interacting with each toy. What they found was striking. Like humans, male and female vervet monkeys preferred to interact with toys in a gender-typical manner. Males spent more time playing with both balls and cars, whereas females spent more time playing with both dolls and pots. No differences were found in the amount of time spent with the toys categorized as neutral (see Figure 2).

FIGURE 1. **Vervet monkeys playing with "male" or "female" toys.**
These photographs are from Alexander and Hines's (2002) original paper. They show a female vervet monkey examining a doll (A) and a male vervet monkey pushing a car (B). *Source: Reprinted from Figure 2, Alexander, G. M. and Hines M., (2002). Sex differences in response to children's toys in non-human primates (ceropithecus aethiops sabaeus). Evolution and Human Behavior, 23, 467–479, © 2002, with permission from Elsevier.*

(A)   (B)

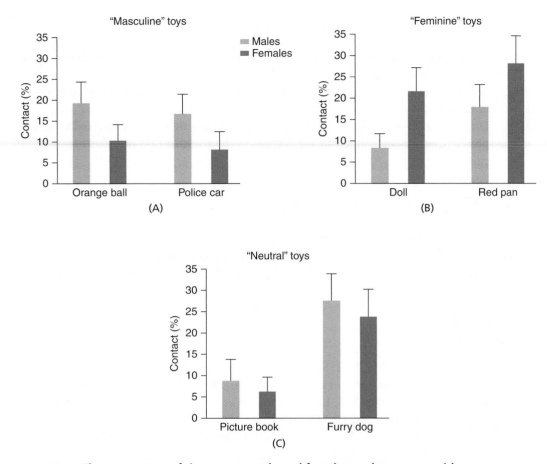

FIGURE 2. The percentage of time vervet male and female monkeys spent with masculine or feminine toys.

Source: Reprinted from Alexander, G. M. and Hines M., (2002). Sex differences in response to children's toys in non-human primates (ceropithecus aethiops sabaeus). Evolution and Human Behavior, 23, 467–479, © 2002, with permission from Elsevier.

Conclusions

Two things are remarkable about this study: (1) with over two decades of previous research on gender differences in toy preferences and play behaviour, no one had thought to look for possible differences in non-human primates; and (2) vervet monkeys, which have no socially or culturally determined expectations of which gender should play with which types of toys, are just like us! These animals had never been exposed to human toys; they certainly did not know the purpose of a car, pot, or book, and yet they still exhibited significant differences in the toys they preferred to play with based on their biological sex.

Future Directions

Since the publication of this initial study, others have confirmed similar patterns of behaviour in Rhesus monkeys. Further work has also been done in humans showing that gender differences in play behaviour and toy preferences correlate with the level of androgens a fetus is exposed to in utero. So what remains? At this point, the areas of the central nervous system (CNS) that are important for these, and many other, gender differences in behaviour are not well understood. With the help of some of our non-human primate friends and the current techniques for imaging the activity of the CNS, however, we hope to be able to answer this question soon.

Critical Thinking Questions

1. What is the biological term for the masculinization of the brain by hormones produced by the fetal testes?
2. Why were non-human primates used to study gender differences in toy preferences in human juveniles?
3. Did Alexander and Hines (2002) support the theory that gender differences in toy preferences are determined by differences in the socialization of offspring by their caregivers?

Further Research Question

Assuming that human males and females are influenced by hormonal exposure early in development, what other types of experiments can you think of that would allow you to study whether exposure to androgens during fetal development influences the development of gender differences in behaviour?

References

Alexander GM, Hines M. 2002. Sex differences in response to children's toys in nonhuman primates (*Ceropithecus aethiops sabaeus*). *Evol. Hum. Behav.* 23:467–479.

Berenbaum SA, Hines M. 1992. Early androgens are related to childhood sex-typed toy preferences. *Psychol. Sci.* 3:203–206.

Hassett JM, Siebert ER, Wallen K. 2008. Sex differences in rhesus monkey toy preferences parallel those of children. *Horm. and Behav.* 54:359–364.

Hines M. 2004. *Brain gender.* London: Oxford UP.

Maccoby EE, Jacklin CN. 1974. *The psychology of sex differences.* Stanford UP.

Gene Programming:
How Many Genes Does It Take to Program a Seed?

Mark Belmonte
University of Manitoba

Introduction

Seed plants dominate existing flora, representing about 85 percent of plant species found on Earth. Originating ~380 million years ago, the seed represents a major ecological and evolutionary advance in the survival and adaptation of the plant kingdom. From a global perspective, the bulk of calories consumed by the human population are derived from seeds, either directly or indirectly by eating animals that themselves ate seeds. Thus, as Earth's population continues to grow, scientists are faced with the challenge of improving seed quality and yield to meet our growing demands. We can achieve this goal by exploiting plant species with sequenced genomes. Through genetic tailoring of these genomes, we can specify the presence or absence of particular genes to help us understand exactly *how* a seed is made, genetically speaking. As a Brassicaceae and a close relative to canola, *Arabidopsis thaliana* is an excellent model system because it was the first sequenced plant.

> ### KEY CONCEPTS
> ■ During development, the seed relies on the sum of its parts.
> ■ The presence of mRNAs from many genes can be determined by using microarrays

PHOTO A. Pot of *Arabidopsis thaliana* grown in a controlled growth chamber.
Arabidopsis thaliana is one of the most commonly studied plant species. In addition to its sequenced genome, its small size and rapid development are ideal for experimentation.
Source: Lab of Dr. Mark Belmonte, University of Manitoba. Photographs taken by Mark Belmonte.

In addition, the vast body of literature surrounding this plant allows us to investigate developmental processes related to improving seed quality. Together with analytical procedures, a wide array of tools for the genetic and molecular dissection of this tiny model seed is now available and has allowed for major advances in the understanding of each of the three seed regions: the embryo, endosperm, and seed coat.

To understand the genes required to program a seed, we must first understand how a seed is made. In angiosperms, such as arabidopsis, seed development can be divided into two phases: morphogenesis and maturation. Seed development is triggered by a double fertilization event that leads to the formation of the three major regions of the seed. The haploid egg cell and the diploid central cell of the female gametophyte each fuse with one pollen cell to form the zygote and the endosperm, respectively. The zygote then undergoes a series of cell divisions, followed by differentiation events, resulting in the formation of an **embryo**. During the **morphogenesis phase** the embryo's body plan is established. The embryo is attached to surrounding tissues by a structure called the suspensor, which supports the embryo during early phases of development (see Figure 1, A–C).

Following morphogenesis is the onset of the **maturation phase** when the embryo begins to accumulate such storage reserves as starch, lipids, and proteins (see Figure 1, D–E). The accumulation of these reserves help the seed survive extended periods of dormancy until the environmental conditions are appropriate for seed germination. The second fertilization event within the central cell results in the formation of the triploid **endosperm**. This unique region of the seed includes the central cell, which undergoes a series of nuclear divisions in the absence of **cytokinesis** (the absence of cell wall formation). In arabidopsis, endosperm cellularization occurs in a wave-like fashion at the heart stage of development. In oilseeds, such as arabidopsis, the endosperm is a transient tissue where, at maturity, only the outermost layer of cells remains within the seed. The third major region of the seed, the **seed coat**, is derived from the integuments of the ovule and is of maternal origin. The seed coat plays an essential role in a number of processes, such as regulation of seed size, seed nourishment, and maintenance of seed dormancy.

During development, the seed relies on the sum of its parts. Mutations in certain genes, affecting any one of the three main regions of the seed early in development, can have profound effects on **seed viability** and may lead to **seed abortion**. To understand the genes required to program seed development, we must understand the genes underlying

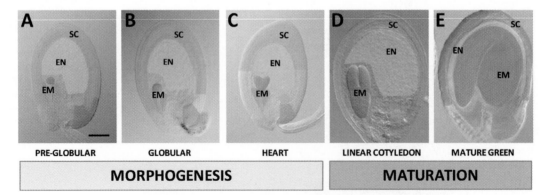

FIGURE 1. Seed development in *Arabidopsis thaliana*.
The seed undergoes the process of morphogenesis during the pre-globular (A), globular (B), and heart (C) stages of development. Accumulation of storage reserves at the linear cotyledon (D) and mature green (E) stages marks the maturation phase. Seeds at each representative stage can be further broken down into seed regions. The embryo (EM) is coloured in green, the endosperm in orange and pink (EN), and the seed coat in blue and purple (SC).
Source: Lab of Dr. Mark Belmonte, University of Manitoba. Photograph taken by Mark Belmonte.

every cell, tissue, and organ, and, more importantly, how and when these genes are expressed before, during, and after arabidopsis seed formation.

Research Question:
How many genes does it take to program a seed?

In a large collaborative effort, a team of researchers, including myself, set out to determine how gene activity is coordinated during seed development. One of the underlying mechanisms of seed development is caused by the activity of transcription factors, which bind to specific DNA sequences. These transcription factors are proteins that act as "on/off" switches, guiding the expression of genes at specific times and in different cells. Genetic studies using arabidopsis have uncovered several transcription factors essential for the regulation of seed development and show region-specific activity (Braybrook and Harada, 2008). Changes in the activity of transcription factors at specific times of seed development may play an important role in the differentiation and function of each seed region.

Hypothesis:
Gene activity correlates with changes in seed development where large numbers of genes are required to program both morphogenesis and maturation phases of the seed life cycle.

Methods and Results

To identify the genes active within the arabidopsis genome, Le et al. (2010) used **microarray technology** to profile mRNAs (messenger RNA carries gene information) that are shared or specific to particular stages of the seed life cycle. A microarray contains sequences of DNA fixed to a glass slide in an orderly arrangement and is used to survey the expression of many genes at a time. Since the sequences on a single microarray can number in the thousands, some microarrays can survey almost the entire genome and tell us which genes (and therefore which proteins) are being expressed. Microarrays are also called **GeneChips**. Sets of genes from the seed were compared with other parts of the plant before (unfertilized ovule) and after (seedling) seed formation. Of the ~28 000 genes found on the arabidopsis whole genome microarray, data identified at least 16 000 mRNAs required to program arabidopsis seed development from the earliest stages of fertilization to the onset of seed dormancy. The number of detected mRNAs dramatically decreased during seed maturation, however, and may be a result of mRNA turnover in preparation for the onset of seed dormancy. Further, the number of mRNAs detected in the seed relies on **gene annotation** (which describes the predicted or known function of a gene), to the limitations in detecting rare messages in specific or individual cells of the seed, or to the incompleteness of the microarray (which lacks approximately 20 percent of known arabidopsis genes) (Redman, 2004).

If the seed undergoes such dramatic changes in development, why are large numbers of mRNAs detected through the seed life cycle? To answer this question, researchers investigated the levels of mRNAs that accumulate over time and noted that the vast majority of mRNAs were quantitatively regulated, meaning they accumulate at different levels and at different times of development. The spatiotemporal accumulation of mRNAs specific to the seed reflects the biological processes that occur uniquely within seeds during the plant life cycle. For example, seeds accumulate large quantities of such storage reserves as starch, lipids, and proteins at late stages, in preparation for seed dormancy.

How are biological processes regulated within the seed? The activity of transcription factors is one of the underlying mechanisms regulating seed development. Arabidopsis DNA encodes for transcription factors by using a small set of mRNAs identified to be specific to the seed. mRNAs specific to the seed were determined by comparing microarrays from the seed with vegetative microarrays from the root, stem, and leaf. Interestingly, similar numbers of mRNAs were found in both seed and vegetative microarrays. Some of these transcription factors were determined to be seed-specific, such as the *LEAFY COTYLEDON* genes, and are known regulators of both morphogenesis and maturation phases of the seed life cycle. The researchers also identified additional regulators, which accumulate primarily within the globular to cotyledon period of seed development and correlate with major development events in the seed; however, the functions and roles of these regulatory genes have yet to be determined.

Conclusions

Taken together, these results tell us that (1) seed development is a dynamic part of the plant's life cycle and requires the coordinated development of seed regions, (2) large numbers of mRNAs are detected at all stages of seed development and are comparable to those from vegetative tissues, and (3) a small number of transcription factors may be regulating biological processes responsible for normal seed development.

Future Directions

A large collaborative group of researchers, including myself, is currently involved in a groundbreaking study characterizing the mRNAs in nearly every cell, tissue, and organ of the arabidopsis seed by using laser capture microdissection and GeneChip technologies. These experiments are showcasing the diversity and dynamics of mRNA populations in each part of the seed in both space and time (see the Gene Networks in Seed Development website), and are being carried out in collaboration with John Harada at the University of California, Davis, and Bob Goldberg at the University of California, Los Angeles. If we can understand the genetic processes underlying seed development, we can make bigger, better, and more nutritious seeds, and improve supply to meet the demand of Earth's population.

Critical Thinking Questions

1. Briefly describe the major phases of arabidopsis seed development.
2. Why does the number of mRNAs found within the seed decrease toward and during the seed maturation phase?
3. What are some possible roles of transcription factors in seed development?

Further Research Question

Why have so few seed-specific transcription factors been detected to date?

References

Braybrook S, Harada JJ. 2008. LECs go crazy in seed development. *Trends Plant Sci.* 12:624–630.

Gene Networks in Seed Development [Internet]. [cited 2010 Apr 9]. Available from: http://seedgenenetwork.net

Goldberg RB, de Paiva G, Yadegari R. 1994. Plant embryogenesis: zygote to seed. *Sci.* 266:605–614.

Le BH, Bui AQ, Wagmaister JA, Cheng C, Henry KF, Pelletier J, Kwong L, Belmonte MF, Kirkbride RC, Horvath S, et al. 2010 Jan. Identification of seed-specific transcription factors from a global analysis of gene activity during the *Arabidopsis* life cycle. PNAS 107: 8063–8070.

Redman JC, Haas BJ, Tanimoto G, Town CD. 2004. Development and evaluation of an *Arabidopsis* whole genome Affymetrix probe array. *Plant J.* 38:545–561.

Genomes Large and Small:
The Evolution of Genome Size in Eukaryotes

T. Ryan Gregory
University of Guelph

Introduction

We often hear DNA described as "the blueprint of life," especially in the popular media; however, this analogy can be very misleading. For one, real blueprints and the buildings that they represent share a one-to-one correspondence of all components. That is, each wall drawn on the blueprint corresponds to a real wall in the building, each door to a real door, and so on. With DNA, there is no such relationship; there is no specific region of your **chromosomes** that corresponds exactly and exclusively to your nose, for example.

A better (but still imperfect) analogy to describe the role of the **genome** would be a recipe. A recipe is a series of instructions that, if followed, will result in a particular outcome, such as a cake or a loaf of bread. But, unlike a blueprint, there is no direct correspondence between any one word in the recipe and any particular crumb in the cake. Also, the recipe includes more than just information about the ingredients, it incorporates the process of baking. Similarly, a genome includes information about the particular ingredients (proteins) that are used to make a product (a nose), but this must also involve a process (development) in order to obtain the specified result.

Now, you may be tempted to assume that the more complex the product, the longer the recipe would need to be. Certainly, a recipe for oatmeal would be much shorter than one for a wedding cake. On a very general level, this is true of genomes as well. Bacteria, which are relatively simple and consist of a single cell, tend to have very small genomes, whereas complex, multicellular animals generally have genomes that are much larger; however, when we examine patterns of **genome size** diversity across eukaryotes (i.e., differences in the total amount of DNA in the nuclei of different species), we see that this analogy quickly reaches the limit of its usefulness.

Genome Size Diversity and the C-Value Paradox

In the late 1940s, before the structure of DNA had been elucidated and even before it was established that DNA was the molecule responsible for genetic inheritance, researchers noted that the quantity of DNA tended to be constant in the cells of individual organisms and among individuals within a species. This led to the term **C-value** (*c* for *constant*), which referred to the amount of DNA in a gamete nucleus of a given species.

KEY CONCEPTS

- Genomes are far more complex than blueprints or collections of genes.
- Most of the DNA in animal and plant genomes consists of noncoding sequences of various types, especially transposable elements.
- The amount of DNA has important impacts on cell- and organism-level traits, leading to a complex interaction of evolutionary processes at multiple scales.

FIGURE 1. **The enormous
diversity in genome sizes,
based on data from about
10 000 species**
There is no link between
organism complexity and
genome size. Note that the
data are presented in
megabases (Mb) on a
logarithmic scale.
*Source: Figure by TR Gregory,
2010.*

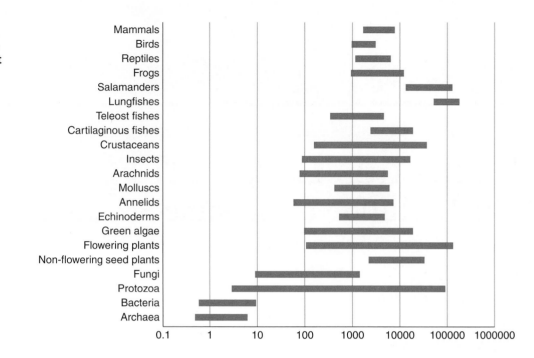

DNA constancy was taken as evidence that DNA, rather than proteins (which vary greatly in amount from cell to cell), was the hereditary material.

Within only a few years, however, it became clear that the situation was far more complicated than had been expected. When researchers began measuring the genome sizes of different species of animals and plants, they found that there is no relationship between complexity and amount of DNA per genome. For example, your genome is 10 times as large as the genome of a pufferfish, but only one-tenth as large as the genome of a newt (Gregory, 2005). Even an onion has five times more DNA in its cells than you do.

Such observations as these presented a real conundrum. On the one hand, DNA amount was thought to be constant because it is the stuff of which **genes** are made; but, on the other hand, genome size is unrelated to the expected number of genes. For more than 20 years, this remained a major puzzle in genetics; it even became known as the **C-value paradox** in the early 1970s.

Paradox Solved but Puzzles Remain

With genome size estimates now available for more than 10 000 species of animals and plants, the disconnect between DNA content and organism complexity is even clearer today (Gregory et al., 2007); however, this is no longer considered paradoxical because we now know that most DNA in a typical eukaryotic genome is not genes. Instead, the majority consists of various sorts of **non-coding DNA**. In other words, there is no reason to expect a large genome to contain more genes than a small one because the difference is based on variability in the amount of non-coding DNA. In humans, protein-coding **exons** make up less than 2 percent of the genome; the other 98 percent is non-coding.

The discovery of non-coding DNA solved the C-value paradox, but it also raised a series of new questions that are still being actively investigated (Gregory, 2001). For example, from where does all this non-coding DNA come? How is it gained and lost in genomes? Does it have any functions that do not involve coding for proteins? If it is not functional, does that mean it has no effects on the organism at all? And finally, why do some groups have very streamlined genomes while those of other groups are positively bloated?

What's in a Genome?

Thanks to the rise of rapid DNA sequencing technology, it is now possible to obtain a nearly complete sequence of DNA from a chosen genome. Because of this, we can now quantify the different types of non-coding DNA that occur in a genome, and we can compare this with other genomes that are larger or smaller. In addition to about 25 000 protein-coding genes, each copy of your genome includes the following (IHGSC, 2001):

- Non-coding **introns** interrupting the protein-exons within gene regions
- More than 20 000 **pseudogenes**, duplicates of protein-coding genes that have lost their coding function through mutation
- Simple repeated sequences, such as **microsatellites**, that form through errors of replication in which small numbers of bases are accidentally copied more than once. Many microsatellites are concentrated in **centromeres** and **telomeres** and thereby play important roles in chromosome structure and replication.
- More than 1 000 000 copies of a sequence called *Alu*, and 500 000 copies of another called *LINE-1*. These are examples of **transposable elements**, DNA sequences that are able to spread in the genome through their own means of replication. Overall, transposable elements constitute almost half your genome, making them about 30 times more abundant than your protein-coding sequences.

Based on this information, we can see that explaining diversity in genome size must incorporate information on the evolution of several different types of DNA sequences.

Impacts of Genome Size Diversity

Does it matter if an organism's cells contain 10 times more DNA than another's? Perhaps not in terms of the number of genes; but, nonetheless, there are important consequences of such a discrepancy in DNA amount. Most notably, more DNA generally means larger, more slowly dividing cells. Depending on the biological traits of the group in question, this can lead to impacts on body size (because bodies are made of cells), metabolic rate (because larger cells are less efficient for gas exchange), and developmental rate (because slower cell division means slower tissue growth). Thus, another major aspect of genome size research is the exploration of patterns linking DNA amount to physical, physiological, developmental, and ecological traits.

Here are just a few examples (Gregory, 2005; Bennett and Leitch, 2005): (1) In vertebrates, groups with high metabolic rates tend to have small genomes. Those that fly (i.e., birds and bats) have especially compact genomes. The largest bird genomes tend to be found in flightless species, whereas the smallest occur in hummingbirds.

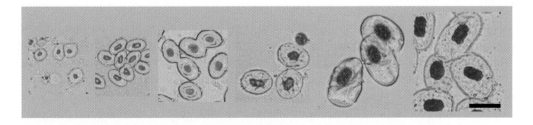

FIGURE 2. The strong relationship between genome size and cell size
These are photomicrographs of red blood cells from a variety of vertebrates, all taken at the same magnification (scale bar equals 20 μm). From left to right: Siamese fighting fish (*Betta splendens*, 630 Mb), chicken (*Gallus domesticus*, 1200 Mb), African clawed toad (*Xenopus laevis*, 3080 Mb), leopard frog (*Rana pipiens*, 6550 Mb), yellow-spotted salamander (*Ambystoma maculatum*, 29 300 Mb), red-spotted newt (*Notophthalmus viridescens*, 39 100 Mb).
Source: Image by TR Gregory, 2010.

(2) Among both amphibians and insects, groups that undergo metamorphosis during their development have smaller genomes than those that lack complete metamorphosis. Salamanders that do not metamorphose have some of the largest genomes among animals. (3) Plants that complete their life cycle in one year (annuals) have smaller genomes than plants that require more than one year (perennials).

Processes at Multiple Scales

Within the genome, transposable elements are capable of increasing in number through independent replication. In fact, those that are most efficient at increasing in number and avoiding deletion by the host genome will become the most abundant. This can lead to an enlargement of the genome, and indeed transposable elements make up the largest fraction of our own genome; however, total DNA amount affects cell-level properties including size and division rate. This, in turn, can have important consequences for the organism in terms of body size, metabolism, and development. The net result can be a conflict between pressures acting within the genome to increase its size, and pressures acting on organisms to limit the spread of non-coding DNA. The net constraints on genome size may be much stronger in some groups than in others. For example, the evolution of flight in birds, which requires very high metabolic rates, may have led to a reduction in genome size as smaller and more efficient cells evolved (Andrews et al., 2009). By contrast, the loss of metamorphosis in some aquatic salamanders may have removed a previous developmental constraint and allowed genome sizes to increase dramatically. To be sure, a bird with a salamander-sized genome would be at a major disadvantage, if it could survive at all.

Of course, this represents only a part of the story. As it turns out, there are occasions in which transposable elements that began as parasites of the genome now serve important functions. In vertebrates, for example, our adaptive immune system is able to create a tremendous variety of antibodies by cutting, rearranging, and rejoining a relatively small number of immunoglobulin genes, not unlike changing the order of railway cars in a train. This requires an ability to cut and splice specific pieces of DNA, something at which transposable elements excel. Intriguingly, it appears that some of the genes involved in our immune system were derived from former transposable elements (Kapitonov and Jurka, 2005). There is an increasing number of examples in which transposable elements appear to have taken on important functions; however, other transposable elements remain damaging mutagens that can insert into genes and cause disease (Belancio et al., 2009). Most, at least in our own genome, appear to be inactive "molecular fossils" that have lost their ability to transpose, although they still contribute to total genome size.

Conclusions

It can be tempting to describe the genome in simple terms, for example, as a blueprint or a book of genes. In reality, genome evolution is far more complicated and interesting than such a characterization would imply. To begin with, only a small fraction of most animal genomes comprise protein-coding genes. The most common sequences are transposable elements: sequences that behave, at least initially, as virus-like parasites. As a result of such processes as transposable element spread, genome sizes can vary greatly; however, the total amount of DNA has important implications for cell size and cell division, which in turn can affect the properties of organisms. In many cases, genome size is linked to organism-level traits, leading to a clearly non-random pattern of genome size diversity. After decades of research, we are beginning to understand how genomes evolve, what kinds of sequences they contain, and why they differ so dramatically in size, but a great deal remains to be discovered.

Critical Thinking Questions

1. Recent analysis of fossil cell sizes has suggested that theropod dinosaurs had smaller genomes than other dinosaurs. What is the significance of this finding with regard to bird genome sizes?
2. Frogs living in deserts have some of the smallest genomes among terrestrial vertebrates. Why might this be?
3. What are some possible explanations for why bacteria generally have very little non-coding DNA in their genomes?

Further Research Question

Visit the Animal Genome Size Database (http://www.genomesize.com) and the Cell Size Database (http://www.genomesize.com/cellsize). How do cell sizes compare with genome sizes in vertebrates? What do you notice about mammal red blood cell sizes as compared with other vertebrates? Why might this be?

References

Andrews CB, Mackenzie SA, Gregory TR. 2009. Genome size and wing parameters in passerine birds. *Proc. R. Soc. London Ser. B.* 276:55–61.

Belancio VP, Deininger PL, Roy-Engel AM. 2009. LINE dancing in the human genome: transposable elements and disease. *Genome Med.* 1:97. doi:10.1186/gm97.

Bennett MD, Leitch IJ. 2005. Genome size evolution in plants. In: Gregory TR, editor. *The evolution of the genome.* San Diego: Elsevier. p. 89–162.

Gregory TR. 2001. Coincidence, coevolution, or causation? DNA content, cell size, and the C-value enigma. *Biol. Rev.* 76:65–101.

Gregory TR. 2005. Genome size evolution in animals. In: Gregory TR, editor. *The evolution of the genome.* San Diego: Elsevier. p. 3–87.

Gregory TR, Nicol JA, Tamm H, Kullman B, Kullman K, Leitch IJ, Murray BG, Kapraun DF, Greilhuber J, Bennett MD. 2007. Eukaryotic genome size databases. *Nucleic Acids Res.* 35(Suppl. 1):D332–D338.

[IHGSC] International Human Genome Sequencing Consortium. 2001. Initial sequencing and analysis of the human genome. *Nature.* 409:860–921.

Kapitonov VV, Jurka J. 2005. RAG1 core and V(D)J recombination signal sequences were derived from *Transib* transposons. *PLoS Biol.* 3:e181. doi:10.1371/journal.pbio.0030181.

The Grad Student Life:
Thinking outside the Textbook

Logan Banadyga
University of Alberta

Introduction

Admit it, there is some part of you—big or small—that likes science. You are, after all, reading a biology textbook right now, and that means you're probably enrolled in an introductory-level biology course at your university or college. All the information and answers you need to ace this course are contained right here, in the few hundred pages of this book. But is that it? Can all the biological world really be contained within a single volume?

Some of you will finish this course and move on to something else, never to cross paths with the sciences again. Others of you will finish satisfied and content with what you have learned. But a few of you won't be satisfied. You'll close the textbook on this class, and you'll be left wanting more, wondering how these things were discovered in the first place. This textbook, although dense with facts and information, scratches only the surface of what there is to know about our world. For every answer it provided, you thought of 10 new questions. You're fascinated by knowledge and the discovery of it. You simply want to know more. If this sounds like you, well, you just might make the perfect graduate student.

> ### KEY CONCEPTS
> - Graduate students have a thirst for knowledge.
> - Graduate students are hard-working and focused.
> - Graduate studies is but a step in the pursuit of knowledge.

In the Pursuit of Knowledge

We graduate students exist outside the world of textbooks. The information contained in textbooks provides the base from which we reach out to explore the unknown. We are motivated by a powerful curiosity that compels us to examine and conceive hypotheses

PHOTO A. A pile of knowledge.
On your road to becoming a graduate student, you'll step outside the world of text-books and into a world filled with unanswered questions.
Source: © INSADCO Photography/ Alamy/Getstock.com.

based on what we know, and then to test those hypotheses. All with the goal of pushing back the darkness of ignorance and increasing, even slightly, the light of knowledge. The work of graduate students has improved our quality of life and expanded the horizons of human potential. Future graduate students will do the same, working from the base built by those before them.

Before you are ready to begin thinking outside the textbook, you must master what's already in it. Ahead of you, you face at least four years of what can be a gruelling quest for a BSc degree. Load up on biology courses, and work hard to do well at them. Figure out which aspect of biology—from microbiology to ecology—most interests you, and focus on it. Once you've pinpointed your area of interest, focus some more. If you like microbiology, for example, think about focusing on virology or bacteriology or parasitology. When you've defined your interests, seek out professors whose research fascinates you and talk to them. Work for them over the summer, or commit to a research project during the school year. As a graduate student in biology, your time will be spent doing research in the lab or the field, so you had better figure out if you like it. With experience and an idea of what interests you, you will be well prepared for life in the field or at the lab bench.

Life at the Bench

As a graduate student in biology, I live science. And science is hard work. The majority of my time is spent at a workbench in a research lab performing experiments designed to test the predictions of my hypotheses. Most science graduate students generate their hypotheses based on an overall project that they took on when they first began their graduate work. You can think of these projects as unified stories filled with various characters. Your job as a graduate student is to perform the experiments that will tell you the details of those characters, how each of them relates to the other, and how they all fit into the bigger picture of biology as a whole. It sounds fun, right? Each day you have the potential to uncover some new piece of information that no one else has ever discovered, and for a while you (and probably your supervisor) will be the only people in the world who know it. Discovering that new fact, that little piece of information that didn't exist until you came along, is intoxicating. As a graduate student, you'll experience that feeling all the time—but it won't always come easily. Your tenure as a

PHOTO B. **Inquiring minds want to know.**
Graduate students are curious, hard-working individuals looking for answers.
Source: Logan Banadyga.

graduate student will be filled with both peaks and valleys. The victory of a successful experiment will always be tempered by the failed experiments that came before it. However, a good graduate student will always persevere with hard work, critical thinking, a bit of humour, and the occasional well-deserved break.

Letting the World Know

Whatever project you take on as a graduate student, no matter how exciting or groundbreaking it may be, it won't mean anything unless you tell other people. The progression of science, and your scientific career, depends on getting your work published in the form of scientific papers in peer-reviewed journals. Assembling your data, writing up your results, and submitting your work to the scrutiny of others in your field is a daunting but necessary part of graduate school. The effort expended will be substantial, but the payoff will be worth it: your name forever linked to the knowledge you produced. Besides publishing your work, you'll also be expected to present it, perhaps as a poster or an oral presentation, to your colleagues around campus and the world. Being a graduate student has definite perks, and jetting off to international conferences in sometimes tropical locales is one of them.

Organize and Socialize

Now that you've capped off a week of 15-hour days in the lab, perfected the introduction to your next paper, and submitted your abstract for that conference in Hawaii, it's party time, right? Not quite. You still have to study for your midterms (yes, graduate students do take classes!). You have a pile of exams to mark for that undergraduate course you're helping to teach. You're presenting your research at a departmental seminar next week. And you still have to finish the background reading for that paper you're writing. Grad students are busy. Organization, a decent work ethic, and a healthy social life are the keys to minimizing stress and not becoming that pasty-faced, wild-haired lab geek about which your friends tease you.

But don't forget that none of this—the experiments, the studying, the stress—occurs in a vacuum. As a graduate student you will be a small component of a bigger lab in a much bigger department filled with other labs and other grad students. The

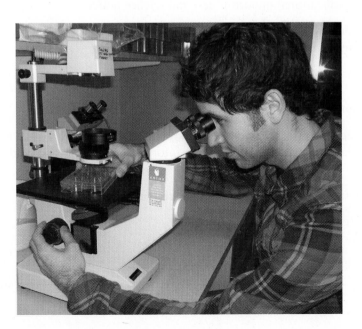

PHOTO C. **Working hard or hardly working?**
Graduate studies can be filled with long hours and late nights in the name of research.
Source: Logan Banadyga.

lab will be run by a professor who is there to provide guidance and mentorship. Just remember that as much as you depend on your supervisor, he or she depends on you and the good research that you do. Your lab might also be populated with other graduate students, research associates, or technicians, all of whom will be there to support you as much as you are there to support them. Although you may feel alone when you find yourself staring through a microscope in a dimly lit room or finishing off that pesky experiment in the middle of the night, as a graduate student you will always be part of a team.

Conclusions

Graduate studies are only a small step in the pursuit of knowledge. Whether you end up with an MSc or a PhD, a graduate degree will prepare you to think critically and imaginatively. You'll develop the tenacity to work through tough problems, and you'll cultivate an informed appreciation for the world around you. After graduate studies, you may decide to take your newly acquired (and highly transferable) skills and apply them elsewhere, or you may continue down the path of research science, apprenticing in new labs and studying new things. Eventually, you may even become a professor yourself, with graduate students of your own to mentor. By that time your research may have found its way into future editions of this textbook, only to inspire new students to ask questions of their own. And in the world of science, the questions are everything.

Critical Thinking Questions

1. What is your motivation for being at university? Why might you consider graduate studies?
2. The world of science is vast and complex. How might you determine the scientific subject that interests you most? How will you find a lab in which to work?
3. What is the difference between an MSc and a PhD?

Resources

American Association for the Advancement of Science: http://www.aaas.org
Science news, educational opportunities, and science policy

Canadian Institutes of Health Research: http://www.cihr-irsc.gc.ca/e/193.html
A national funding agency for health sciences

Natural Sciences and Engineering Research Council of Canada: http://www.nserc-crsng.gc.ca/
A national funding agency for a variety of sciences

NatureJobs.com: http://www.nature.com/naturejobs/news/postdocs-students/index.html
Job and scholarship resource, useful career information for post-docs and students

NewScientist.com: http://www.newscientist.com
Easily understandable science news and job resources

PHD.org: http://jobs.phds.org
A resource for finding jobs in the sciences

ScienceDaily.com: http://www.sciencedaily.com
A science news aggregator, great for catching up on a variety of different scientific topics

Human Adaptation to High Altitude Hypoxia:
Getting High

Trevor A. Day
Mount Royal University

Introduction

In the eighteenth and nineteenth centuries, early balloon aeronauts in France were unknowingly defining a whole new field of research: high altitude physiology. Many of these adventurers accidentally discovered some of the more dangerous risks associated with high altitude ascent, such as blindness, paralysis, and unconsciousness. These symptoms are caused by a reduced oxygen content in the air as one ascends in altitude, called **hypoxia**. The most famous and tragic of these flights was in 1875 when French balloonists Gaston Tissandier, Joseph Croce-Spinelli, and Theodore Sivel ascended in their balloon *Zenith* to more than 8600 m. Unfortunately, once the balloon finally returned to Earth, both Croce-Spinelli and Sivel were dead. Although Tissandier lived to publish

---

KEY CONCEPTS

- Our cells require oxygen to undergo cellular respiration to make energy.
- The amount of oxygen in the atmosphere decreases with increasing altitude.
- There are mechanisms for the human body to adapt to hypoxic (low-oxygen) conditions.

PHOTO A. Catastrophe of the balloon *Zenith*.
This engraving depicts an event that occurred in France, on April 15, 1875, when three men, Gaston Tissandier, Joseph Croce-Spinelli, and Theodore Sivel, travelled in a balloon to a height of more than 8600 m. Croce-Spinelli and Sivel died during the trip, but Tissandier survived.
Source: Apic/Hulton Archive/Getty Images.

his stories of balloon ascents, the experience left him permanently deaf. Interestingly, the maximum altitude they reached in their balloon is only a little lower than the height of world's highest peak, Mount Everest.

Mountain Adventures

Known locally as Chomolungma in Tibet and Sagarmatha in Nepal, Mount Everest (named after British surveyor Sir George Everest) is located in the Himalayan mountain range in Asia. It stands at 8848 m above sea level, approximately the cruising altitude of many modern commercial airplanes. Sir Edmund Hillary and Sherpa Tenzing Norgay used supplementary oxygen to make the first successful ascent of Everest on May 29, 1953 (see Photo B). Since then, there have been more than 4000 successful summit attempts by more than 2700 individual climbers. Reinhold Messner and Peter Habeler achieved the first successful ascent of Everest without extra oxygen on May 8, 1978, shocking the medical community by doing what was then thought impossible. Despite these successes, more than 200 climbers have died on the mountain from extreme weather, climbing accidents, and complications related to the severe hypoxia. The amount of oxygen in the air at the peak of Everest is approximately 30 percent of that at sea level. This level of hypoxia would be deadly to any human who had not undergone a process of slow physiological adaptation to this extreme environment.

Atmospheric Pressure and High Altitude Hypoxia

Much like a fluid, the atmosphere is a mixture of various gases that are under the influence of gravity. When we stand at sea level, we are at the bottom of an ocean of gases. The density of the atmosphere is the highest at sea level because those gases are most compressed by the gases above, in the same way that the pressure exerted by water increases the deeper you dive. The total atmospheric pressure at sea level is equivalent to 760 millimetres of mercury (mmHg), which decreases incrementally with higher altitudes because there is less gas above pressing down on us (see Figure 1). The atmosphere thins as you ascend.

The total pressure exerted by the atmosphere at any altitude is the sum of the pressures exerted by each individual gas. The major gases that make up the total mixture of the atmosphere are nitrogen (N_2, 78 percent) and oxygen (O_2, 21 percent). There are

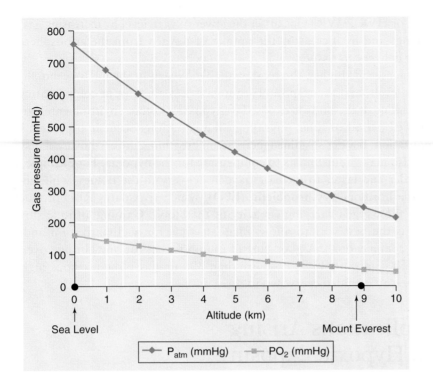

FIGURE 1. **The relationship between altitude and relative gas pressures.**
This graph illustrates the relationship between altitude (on the *x*-axis in kilometres) and relative gas pressures (on the *y*-axis in mmHg). P_{atm} (represented by the red diamonds) refers to the total atmospheric pressure, and PO_2 (represented by the orange squares) refers to the oxygen pressures. Note that the PO_2 is 21 percent of the total atmosphere at any altitude. Sea level is depicted at 0 km, and the peak of Mount Everest is depicted at approximately 8850 m.
Source: Based on raw data in West JB, Schoene RB and Milledge JS. High Altitude Medicine and Physiology 4th ed. Hodder Arnold/Oxford University Press. 2007, p. 19.

also small amounts of other gases, including argon (Ar, 0.9 percent) and carbon dioxide (CO_2, 0.04 percent), as well as variable amounts of water vapour (H_2O). The percentage of these gases is relatively constant independent of the altitude within the troposphere (i.e., the lowest 20 km of the atmosphere); however, the total atmospheric pressure drops as you ascend because the pressure exerted by each individual gas declines. Most important to high altitude climbers, the amount of oxygen in the air decreases the higher they climb. Because oxygen makes up 21 percent of the total pressure of the 760 mmHg at sea level, the amount of oxygen available is 160 mmHg. By comparison, on the summit of Everest, where the total atmospheric pressure is only ~250 mmHg, 21 percent of that is a mere 53 mmHg, approximately 32 percent of that at sea level.

Adaptations of the Human Body to High Altitude Hypoxia

Because of the abundance of oxygen in the air (21 percent), we do not have any difficulty obtaining oxygen from the atmosphere at sea level. In fact, most of us could fully oxygenate our blood even if we took only one breath every minute. Breathing exchanges gases between the atmosphere and the blood in the lungs, extracting oxygen from the atmosphere and eliminating CO_2. Most of the oxygen is carried in the blood by red blood cells (**RBCs**). RBCs contain a protein called **hemoglobin**, which binds reversibly with oxygen so that the oxygen can be transported from the lungs to metabolically active tissue. In the tissue, it is used in cellular respiration to make energy, and CO_2 is formed as a waste product. On average the RBCs make up approximately 45 percent of our blood volume, the rest of the blood being blood plasma and a small number of white blood cells. The ratio of RBCs to total blood volume is termed **hematocrit**. Each RBC can carry up to one billion oxygen molecules, and our arterial hemoglobin is approximately 98 to 99 percent saturated with oxygen at sea level. At high altitude, however, atmospheric oxygen levels are reduced and blood oxygen levels begin to fall. This triggers oxygen sensors in the major arteries to send a signal to the brain to stimulate an increase in breathing rate and depth (this is called **hypoxic ventilatory** response, or **HVR**). HVR helps offset the lower oxygen level by increasing gas exchange in the lungs and by increasing the uptake of oxygen from the atmosphere into the blood for delivery to tissues.

As one ascends higher, the total available oxygen in the air is eventually reduced to critical levels, and the respiratory system is less effective at compensating through the HVR alone. If the body is exposed to hypoxia or other environmental stressors for an extended period of time, physiological adaptations occur in a process known as **acclimatization**. Besides sustained increases in breathing, the cardiovascular system and kidneys also make adjustments to compensate for the hypoxia. For example, the heart beats harder and faster to increase oxygen delivery to the tissues, while the kidneys release the hormone **erythropoietin (EPO)**, which stimulates RBC production and enhances the oxygen-carrying capacity of the blood. Gaining altitude slowly when climbing is the best way to allow adequate time for acclimatization and to avoid potential complications. A good rule of thumb is that for any altitude over 3000 m, each night's camp should be no more than 300 m above the previous night's camp, with a rest day included every two to three days.

Complications Arising from Hypoxic Exposure

Acute mountain sickness (AMS) results from acute exposure to altitudes higher than 3000 m. Symptoms can include headache, nausea, loss of appetite, vomiting, dehydration, fatigue, lethargy, visual and cognitive impairment, loss of coordination, and difficulty sleeping. As one acclimatizes, these symptoms usually disappear within four to five days. If ascent continues without adequate acclimatization, particularly over 5000 m, the symptoms can worsen and life-threatening conditions may result. These conditions include high altitude pulmonary edema (**HAPE**) and high altitude cerebral edema (**HACE**), which may lead to unconsciousness and death. Over 8000 m (known as the **death zone**), the oxygen is so low that any previous acclimatization is insufficient to allow a climber to stay that high for sustained periods of time. Climbers travelling in the death zone are interested only in reaching a summit goal and then descending to a safe altitude as quickly as possible.

Using supplementary oxygen (from a small tank) can help prevent AMS; however, its use is cumbersome and hinders natural acclimatization. Accordingly, supplementary oxygen is normally restricted to very high altitudes where acclimatization is no longer effective or when subjects are already sick. Also, a number of pharmacological options prevent or treat symptoms as they arise. Common drugs include (1) acetazolamide (e.g., Diamox), a respiratory stimulant that helps the climber acclimatize faster, and (2) dex-amethasone (e.g., Decadron), a synthetic steroid that reduces the life-threatening swelling associated with HAPE and HACE. Of course, in the most severe cases the best treatment is actually the simplest: descend!

Potential Benefits Resulting from Hypoxic Exposure

Beyond high altitude climbing, our knowledge of physiological responses to hypoxia may have benefits for athletic performance. Since hypoxic exposure stimulates the production of RBCs, hematocrit and oxygen-carrying capacity also increase. These principles have been exploited by professional athletes for decades through a number of illegal methods. **Blood doping** is a process by which athletes donate and store their own RBCs until needed. Prior to an event, the stored RBCs are returned to them,

PHOTO C. **Federico Ezquerra in the mountains.** This image shows Ezquerra, a Spanish cyclist, climbing the mountains in the French Alps during the 1934 Tour de France.
Source: © Collection Spaarnestad Photo, Netherlands.

increasing hematocrit directly. Another method involves injecting a synthetic version of the hormone EPO into the body, which artificially triggers a long-lasting increase in hematocrit.

A more natural (and legal) method of increasing hematocrit is to expose the athlete to hypoxia and trigger acclimatization responses. Athletes can sleep and train at high altitude, or they can be exposed to simulated high altitude conditions by sleeping in hypoxic tents or chambers. These methods can be highly advantageous to some, but not all athletes derive the same benefits. The discomfort of sleeping in a tent and reduced sleep quality caused by the hypoxia can adversely affect the athletes' training and outweigh the benefits.

Conclusions

It is difficult to predict who will fare well at high altitude. Interestingly, the ability to acclimatize is partly determined by genetics and is largely independent of a subject's age and fitness. Coincidentally, the peak of Mount Everest likely represents the highest possible altitude to which we can be exposed following acclimatization and still survive. If Everest were any higher, or if humans were any less able to adapt to the sustained severe hypoxia of the almost 9000 m–high peak, it would remain insurmountable by terrestrial means, leaving this altitude to the migrating birds and the commercial aircraft that fly over it. However, because the summit is just within the limits of human achievement, it continues to inspire the dreams of adventurers and to fascinate us all with its stories of human drama.

PHOTO D. **Mount Everest.** This photograph shows the south face of Mount Everest at sunset.
Source: © Thomas E. Dietz.

Critical Thinking Questions

1. What are the symptoms of acute mountain sickness? How are they treated?
2. How does the body acclimatize to exposure to high altitude hypoxia?
3. How can professional athletes benefit from hypoxic exposures?

Further Research Question

How do commercial airplanes, the cruising altitude of which are approximately as high as Mount Everest, avoid the disastrous outcome of the 1875 ride of the *Zenith* balloon and allow passengers and crew to ride in comfort without distress? How might your answer here relate to another possible treatment for acute mountain sickness sufferers when climbing at high altitude?

References

Krakauer J. 1999. *Into thin air: a personal account of the Mt. Everest disaster.* Toronto (ON): Anchor Canada.

Silverthorn DU. 2010. *Human physiology: an integrated approach.* 5th ed. Toronto (ON): Pearson.

West JB, Schoene RB, Milledge JS. 2007. High altitude medicine and physiology. 4th ed. London (UK): Hodder Arnold.

Identifying Proteins Involved in Plant Cell Wall Modification:
How Forward Genetics Can Be Used to Study Biology

George Haughn
University of British Columbia

Introduction

Have you ever made jam or watched someone else do it? If you have, then you know that the berries initially form a liquid as they cook, but as the liquid cools, it becomes gelatinous. The substance that turns berry juice into a thick spread is called **pectin**. Pectin is a complex carbohydrate that is an important component of plant cell walls. Plant cells make pectin and secrete it to the wall, where it acts as an adhesive, keeping cells glued together. When plants need to shed organs, such as when trees lose their leaves or floral organs are dropped (abscission), or to loosen tissue during fruit ripening, the pectin between the cells must be dissolved with pectin-degrading enzymes. In addition to its role as an adhesive, pectin forms a hydrophilic (absorbs water) barrier or filter between the plant cell and the external environment. Because of its importance, scientists would like to know more about the cellular proteins that are involved in pectin synthesis and modification. However, progress in this area has been slow, in part because pectin is a large, complex, and heterogeneous molecule that can vary with cell types.

Because all proteins are encoded by genes, one approach to identifying and studying proteins involved in pectin formation and deposition is to use genetics. Mutants with defective pectin will typically have mutations in genes that encode proteins needed for pectin synthesis or modification. Mapping the mutations to a specific position on a chromosome allows scientists to isolate the mutated gene (**positional cloning**) and identify the protein that it encodes. Further, the specific defect observed in the mutant provides information concerning what the protein does in the plant. But how can scientists find pectin mutants in the first place? Although many strategies exist, one way is to exploit the seed coat because in some plant species, like the model organism for plant genetics, *Arabidopsis thaliana*, the seed coat epidermal cells make large amounts of pectin (**mucilage**) that extrudes from the seed when it is exposed to water (see Photo A).

Research Question
Can seed coat mucilage extrusion be used as a phenotype to identify mutants defective in genes needed for pectin biology?

Mutants unable to extrude mucilage can be easily identified by screening seeds produced by plants from a mutagenized population. When such a screen was carried out by researchers in my laboratory at the University of British Columbia, several

---

KEY CONCEPTS

- Mutants can be used to identify genes that encode the proteins involved in various biological processes.
- A mutant phenotype provides information concerning when, where, and how proteins function in an organism.
- Pectins are important components in plant cell walls.

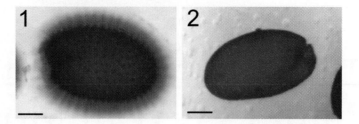

PHOTO A. Normal and mutant arabidopsis seeds following exposure to water.
A1. Ruthenium red, a dye that stains pectin, allows the seed coat mucilage, that extrudes when seeds are placed in water, to be easily observed. A2. Mutants producing seeds with defects in mucilage extrusion, such as this Mum2 seed, can be identified by using ruthenium red staining. The scale bars in A1 and A2 represent 100 μm.
Source: Dean et al., 2007. The Arabidopsis MUM2 Gene Encodes a, β-Galactosidase Required for the Production of Seed Coat Mucilage with Correct Hydration Properties. Plant Cell 19: 4007–4021. Fig. 1 A and B © 2007 American Society of Plant Biologists.

mucilage-deficient mutants were identified. Failure to extrude mucilage can occur (1) because the mutant does not make enough pectin in the seed coat or (2) because the pectin produced is abnormal and does not swell when exposed to water. One mucilage extrusion mutant, called mucilage modified 2 (Mum2 in Photo A2), has seeds with a normal amount of mucilage, suggesting that the Mum2 mutant has mucilage with a modified structure. The *MUM2* gene was cloned by position and sequenced, and the protein it encodes was deduced. MUM2 protein was found to have similarity to β-galactosidases, enzymes that remove galactose sugar molecules from complex polysaccharides, such as pectin. In addition, the MUM2 protein was predicted to have a signal sequence (a sequence of amino acids that directs the movement of a protein), suggesting that it is secreted from the cell.

Hypothesis

The MUM2 protein is an enzyme that is made and secreted from the seed coat epidermal cells, where it modifies the structure of pectin to allow it to expand on exposure to water.

Methods and Results

Four testable predictions arise from the hypothesis. First, MUM2 protein should be present in the seed coat and, if it is, its mRNA is likely to be detectable in seed coat epidermal cells. To test this prediction, the amount of MUM2 mRNA was measured at different times during seed coat development by using a technique called quantitative reverse transcriptase polymerase chain reaction. It was found that MUM2 mRNA was detectable in the seed coat and reached its highest level at the precise time when mucilage was being produced.

Second, if MUM2 protein is a β-galactosidase enzyme, it should be able to remove galactose molecules from carbohydrates in vitro (independent of the cell). To isolate purified MUM2 protein, a **recombinant** *MUM2* gene was engineered that could be expressed in yeast and easily purified from a mixture of yeast cellular proteins. A recombinant gene combines parts of different genes from two or more sources. In this case, the new *MUM2* recombinant gene included three parts: (1) transcriptional regulatory sequences from yeast, (2) the protein-coding region from the *MUM2* gene, and (3) an extension to the MUM2 coding region. The translation of the extension to the coding regions results in a small number of amino acids (**epitope**) that can be recognized by a commercially available antibody. The antibody is used to recognize and purify the recombinant MUM2 protein from all other proteins in yeast. This recombinant *MUM2* gene was transformed into yeast. Large numbers of yeast cells were grown, the

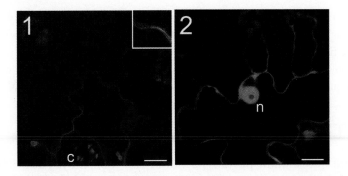

PHOTO B. The MUM4-GFP fusion protein is secreted from the cell, while GFP alone is not.
B1. GFP fluorescence is associated with only the cell boundaries of tobacco mesophyll cells containing the *MUM2-GFP* fusion gene, although some autofluorescence is observed in chloroplasts (c). The fluorescence is located outside the cell membrane, stained red with a dye (see the inset photo).
B2. In cells containing the *GFP* gene alone, GFP fluorescence is found throughout the cytoplasm, including the region surrounding the nucleus (n). The scale bars in both B1 and B2 represent 30 μm.
Source: Dean et al., 2007. The Arabidopsis MUM2 Gene Encodes a, β-Galactosidase Required for the Production of Seed Coat Mucilage with Correct Hydration Properties. Plant Cell 19: 4007–4021. Fig. 5 A and B © 2007 American Society of Plant Biologists.

cells were broken open, and the MUM2 protein purified. When MUM2 protein was mixed with a carbohydrate containing galactose, MUM2 was able to remove the galactose, just like other known β-galactosidases.

Third, if MUM2 is required for the removal of galactose from the pectin of mucilage, then the mucilage extracted from Mum2 mutant seeds (those that lack functional MUM2 protein) should have more galactose than the mucilage of normal (wild-type) seeds. Mucilage from both wild-type and normal seeds was extracted and degraded into single sugar molecules, and the amount of each sugar was determined by high-performance liquid chromatography. As predicted, Mum2 mutant mucilage contained a higher percentage of galactose than the mucilage of normal seeds.

Fourth, if the MUM2 protein is actually secreted from the cell, it should be detectable outside the cell membrane. To test this prediction, a recombinant gene was made by fusing the MUM2 coding region with that of a green fluorescent protein (GFP). The GFP is a small protein, derived from jellyfish, that fluoresces when exposed to blue light. The recombinant *MUM2-GFP* gene, when translated, produces a fusion protein. Its location in the cell can be followed by using a fluorescence microscope. When the *MUM2-GFP* gene was introduced into tobacco, the MUM2-GFP protein was found to be located outside the cell in the cell wall, whereas GFP alone was found in the cytoplasm (see Photo B). These data confirmed that the MUM2 protein contains signals that result in its secretion from the cell.

Conclusions

The evidence supports the major predictions of the hypothesis. The *MUM2* gene is transcribed in the seed coat and encodes a β-galactosidase enzyme. The enzyme is secreted outside the cell, where it removes galactose molecules from mucilage, thus altering the mucilage's properties and allowing it to be extruded from the cell.

Future Directions

An important question remains concerning the function of MUM2: How does the removal of the galactose molecules change the mucilage pectin properties to allow it to be extruded from the seed coat? To answer this question, the precise structure of mucilage pectin in both normal and mutant seeds needs to be determined. The question is an important one because it is likely that extrusion is dependent on the biophysical properties of pectin or its interactions with other types of carbohydrates. Knowing the answer may allow the horticultural industry to manipulate pectin's adhesive properties and prevent abscission of floral organs, and it may allow the food industry to manipulate the softening of ripening fruit and to create new types of pectin for use as gelling agents.

Critical Thinking Questions

1. What kind of a mutant phenotype would you look for if you wanted to find a plant with a mutation in a gene encoding an enzyme that dissolves pectin during abscission?
2. When making MUM2 protein, why was the plant *MUM2* gene introduced into yeast and not into a plant?
3. Why was it necessary to test in vitro that the MUM2 protein functions as a β-galactosidase when its predicted protein sequence already indicated that MUM4 was very similar in sequence to such enzymes?

Further Research Question

Pectin is an important component of all primary plant cell walls. Where in the cell is it made and how does it get outside the cell?

References

Dean, GH, Zheng H, Tewari J, Huang J, Young DS, Hwang YT, Western TL, Carpita NC, McCann MC, Mansfield SD, et al. 2007. The arabidopsis *MUM2* gene encodes a [[iotatonos]]-galactosidase required for the production of seed coat mucilage with correct hydration properties. *Plant Cell.* 19:4007–4021.

Haughn G, Chaudhury A. 2005. Genetic analysis of seed coat development in arabidopsis. *Trends Plant Sci.* 10:472–477.

Sila DN, Van Buggenhout S, Duvetter T, Fraeye I, De Roeck, Van Loey A, Hendricks M. 2009. Pectins in processed fruits and vegetables: part II—structure–function relationships. *Compre. Rev. Food Sci. Food Saf.* 8:86–104.

Invertebrates in Medicine:
Maggots, Leeches, and Hookworms

Sharon L. Gillies
University of the Fraser Valley

Introduction

Does the thought of a parasitic worm attached to your intestines fill you with dread? What about the thought of having a bunch of maggots eating away at you? Is the idea of coming out of a pond with leeches firmly attached to your big toe repugnant to you? How would you feel if you lost that toe in an accident and your doctors used leeches when they reattached it?

Maggots

In 1935, William Robinson conducted a survey of the use of sterile blowfly **maggots** (the larval stage of *Lucilia sericata*, phylum Arthropoda) in surgery and the treatment of infections in the United States and Canada. The results showed that 91.2 percent of surgeons had favourable opinions of maggot therapy. Maggot therapy was common during World War I and for a period afterwards. After the discovery of antibiotics, maggot therapy virtually disappeared.

Maggot therapy has recently re-emerged because of the benefits it offers: **debridement** (eating dead flesh), disinfection, and stimulation of wound healing. Maggots have been used extensively to remove dead tissues and clean a variety of wounds. Such chronic wounds as pressure ulcers and diabetic foot ulcers are difficult to treat and often do not heal well, if at all. Even in cases of amputation, doctors have successfully used maggots to save limbs. Maggot therapy is also inexpensive compared with conventional treatment. Despite these benefits, patients—and even some physicians—cannot always accept the thought of having maggots eating their flesh. The acceptability of maggot therapy has increased with the invention of such systems as the **Biobag** (a pouch that holds the maggots and keeps them out of sight). This reduces the squeamishness of some patients; although others may never be able to accept their use.

Maggot therapy has also increased recently because of the rise in antibiotic-resistant bacteria, such as methicillin-resistant *Staphylococcus aureus*. Maggots eliminate bacteria from a wound by eating them and producing antibacterial secretions. The use of maggots to treat wounds containing multiresistant bacteria is an active area of current research, as is the antibacterial activity of maggot secretions.

KEY CONCEPTS

- Invertebrates have a variety of medicinal uses.
- Parasitism is a symbiotic relationship in which the parasite benefits and the host is harmed in the process.
- Disruptions in immune system function can elicit or exacerbate disease.

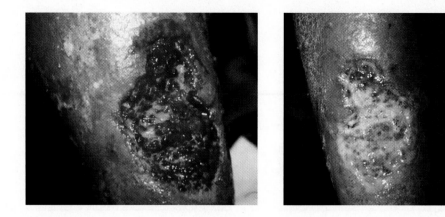

PHOTO A.
The photo on the left shows a leg ulcer prior to maggot therapy. The photo on the right shows the leg ulcer 48 hours after maggot therapy.
Source: Jones M. 2009. An overview of maggot therapy used on chronic wounds in the community. Br. J. Community Nurs. *14:16–20, p. S18. Used with permission of MA Healthcare.*

Leeches

Leeches are members of the phylum **Annelida** (segmented worms). A leech feeds by attaching to a host with its suckers and by injecting an anaesthetic into the host's skin before slicing into it with its three jaws. It can feed for 20 to 40 minutes and can increase its body weight by 10 times before dropping off of the host. A leech keeps the host's blood from coagulating by secreting hirudin, a natural anticoagulant. It also produces chemicals to dilate vessels and increase blood flow. Unwary swimmers who go into leech-filled waterways can expect their wounds to continue bleeding for 9 to 10 hours after removing their unwelcome dinner guests.

Before they fell out of favour, leeches were used in the past as a traditional medical treatment. Modern medicine is now using the medicinal leech (*Hirudo medicinalis* and related species) once again. Since the mid-1980s, doctors have used medicinal leeches to relieve severe postsurgical venous congestion after finger, toe, ear, and scalp reattachment. Because microvascular surgery is much more successful in reconnecting arteries than veins, dangerous levels of venous blood can collect in reattached body parts. The ability of leeches to increase blood flow and prevent clotting has permitted the reattachment of skin flaps and ears that otherwise would have been unsuccessful.

The use of medicinal leech therapy has improved the success of these types of surgery by more than 60 percent; however, the problem with using leeches is the presence of bacteria in their guts. In particular, *Aeromonas* (gram-negative bacteria) can reduce this success rate to 30 percent. *Aeromonas* live symbiotically within the guts of leeches; here, they produce the enzymes necessary to digest vertebrate blood. The chance of post-operative infection increases without the use of antibiotics during leech therapy.

PHOTO B.
The leeches in this photo are increasing the blood flow in a damaged toe. They are preventing the buildup of venous blood.
Source: Ira Block/National Geographic Stock

Researchers are looking at the ability of hirudin and its derivatives to prevent and dissolve clot formation in heart attack, stroke, and deep-vein clotting. The hirudin gene has been placed into yeast to produce lepirudin, a recombinant hirudin (r-hirudin). The recombinant hirudin lacks a sulphate group on its 63rd amino acid, tyrosine, but is only slightly less effective than natural hirudin. Lepirudin was the first direct thrombin inhibitor approved for use on humans for the treatment of **heparin-induced thrombocytopenia complicated by thrombosis** (patients produce antibodies against heparin, and the antibodies then bind to platelets causing blood clots, which lowers their platelet count). Another recombinant hirudin, desirudin, was approved for **thrombosis prophylaxis** (prevent blood clots) after major orthopedic surgery.

Zonghang Zhao and colleagues from University of Calgary and Harbin Medical University in China are looking at other uses of r-hirudin. They found that r-hirudin decreased **edema** (swelling) after **intracerebral hemorrhage** (bleeding within the brain) in rats. R-hirudin blocked the effects of thrombin and helped reduce edema by altering **aquaporins** (channel proteins for water) found in the plasma membrane of **astrocytes** (glial cells in the brain). Maurice Moloney, also from the University of Calgary, is attempting to place the gene for hirudin into a plant in order to cheaply produce large amounts of the drug.

Hookworms

Intestinal worms infect over 1 billion people worldwide. Parasitic intestinal worms can be members of the phylums **Platyhelminthes** (flat worms), **Nematoda** (round worms), or **Annelida** (segmented worms). Many of these parasites can be fatal; others are not.

Parasitic nematode infection by hookworms is common in undeveloped countries, with almost 800 million people currently afflicted. Hookworms are a major cause of chronic anaemia and stunted growth in children worldwide. The two hookworm species that commonly infect humans are *Ancylostoma duodenale* and *Necator americanus*. Infection by hookworm larvae generally occurs through the skin. Once inside the body, they migrate to the lungs and up to the trachea where they are swallowed. Upon reaching the digestive tract, the hookworms attach to capillary beds in the small intestine and suck the blood of their host. Many programs are underway to eliminate hookworms around the world. As we see these parasite infections disappear, however, we are also seeing an increase in allergies.

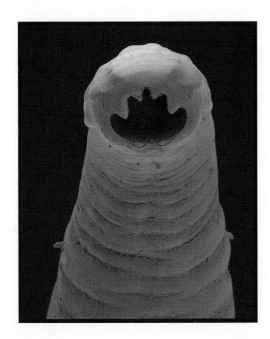

PHOTO C.
Close-up of a hookworm.
Source: David Scharf/Science Photo Library.

In Canada and other developed countries, incidence of allergic diseases, such as asthma, has increased in the past few decades. Asthma appears to be a disease of urban residents and now affects between 6 and 20 percent of Canadians. The hygiene hypothesis proposes that the immune system requires contact with "germs" to properly develop. Children from extremely clean environments may be more susceptible to allergies because their immune systems did not learn to differentiate between harmless antigens, such as pollen, and infectious organisms. Have we become too clean for our own health?

Many studies have shown that infection by some intestinal worms reduces a child's likelihood of developing asthma and other allergies. A recent analysis of published studies concluded that the nematode parasite *Ascaris lumbricoides* increases the odds of asthma, but hookworm infection is associated with a strong reduction in asthma and wheezing. Hookworms may alter their host's immune system, reducing its activity. Individuals with overactive immune systems may suffer from allergies because the immune system mistakenly responds to harmless antigens in the environment.

New research is looking at the effect of intestinal parasites on such autoimmune diseases as inflammatory bowel disease, type 1 diabetes, multiple sclerosis, and autoimmune liver diseases. Researchers continue to investigate the relationship of exposure to micro-organisms and parasites and our immune system. The old-friends hypothesis has been proposed as a modified version of the hygiene hypothesis: we may have adapted to the suppression of our immune system that occurs when we are exposed to parasites that have co-evolved with us. This suppression may keep our immune systems from reacting to our own antigens, causing autoimmune diseases, or to harmless antigens in the environment, such as pollen grains, causing allergies.

Researchers John Webster and Genhui Chen from Simon Fraser University (SFU) discovered several compounds with antibiotic properties from nematodes. Together with SFU chemist Jason Li, they are actively involved with Welichem Biotech Inc. They are testing compounds that target autoimmune and inflammatory diseases, such as Crohn's. Two of their compounds, WBI-1001 and WBI-1062, inhibit the production of inflammatory molecules and suppress T cells. One day we may be able to attain the benefits of immune system suppression by using specific compounds produced by nematodes without having to be infected by them.

Conclusions

As creepy and crawly as they may be, the invertebrates mentioned in this essay are now a part of the modern medical team. The use of leeches and maggots may save limbs and lives. Hookworms may help reduce the incidence of allergies as well as autoimmune and inflammatory diseases. The biggest hurdle to using these animals in medicine is that we find them gross. This yuck-factor means that even when faced with losing a limb, some people may not agree to having these useful critters wriggling on or inside them.

Critical Thinking Questions

1. Why is maggot therapy once again becoming a valuable medical tool?
2. What are some of the advantages and disadvantages of leech therapy?
3. Why might some biologists allow their children to get dirty and even to eat dirt?

Further Research Question

What are the current and potential medical uses of chitin from crab and shrimp?

References

Adams SL. 1988. the medicinal leech. a page from the annelids of internal medicine. *Ann. Inter. Med.* 109:399–405.

*Alves NM, Mano JF. 2008. Chitosan derivatives obtained by chemical modifications for biomedical and environmental applications. *Int. J. Biol. Macromol.* 43:401–414.

Björkstén B. 2008. Environmental influences on the development of the immune system: consequences for disease outcome. Nestlé Nutritional Workshop Series: Pediatric Program 61:243–254.

Cooper PJ. 2004. Intestinal worms and human allergy. *Parasite Immunol.* 26:455–467.

Elliott DE, Summers RW, Weinstock JV. 2005. Helminths and the modulation of mucosal inflammation. *Curr. Opin. Gastroenterology.* 21:51–58.

Gupta A. 2008. a review of the use of maggots in wound therapy. *Ann. Plas. Surg.* 60: 224–227.

Harnett W, Harnett MM. 2008. Parasitic nematode modulation of allergic disease. *Curr. Allergy Asthma Rep.* 8: 1529–7322.

Harnett W, Harnett MM. 2008. Therapeutic immunomodulators from nematode parasites. *Expert Rev. Mol. Med.* 10:18.

Lunn PG, Northrop-Clewes CA. 1993. The impact of gastrointestinal parasites on protein-energy malnutrition in man. *Proc. Nutr. Soc.* 52:101–111.

Parnes A, Lagan M. 2007. Larval therapy in wound management: a review. *Int. J. Clin. Prac.* 61:488–493.

Reddy A, Fried B. 2009. An update on the use of helminths to treat Crohnís and other autoimmune diseases. *Parasitol. Res.* 104:217–221.

Robinson W. 1935. Progress of maggot therapy in the United States and Canada in the treatment of suppurative diseases. *Am. J. Surg.* 29:67–71.

*Sahoo D, Sahoo S, Mohanty P, Sasmal S, Nayak PL. 2009. Chitosan: a new versatile bio-polymer for various applications. *Des. Monomers Polym.* 12:377–404.

Sherman RA, Shapiro CE, Yang RM. 2007. Maggot therapy for problematic wounds: uncommon and off-label applications. *Adv. Skin Wound Care.* 20:602–610.

Sun Z, Zhao Z, Zhao S, Sheng Y, Zhao Z, Gao C, Li J, Liu X. 2009. Recombinant hirudin treatment modulates aquaporin-4 and aquaporin-9 expression after intracerebral hemorrhage in vivo. *Mol. Biol. Rep.* 36:1119–1127.

Whitaker IS, Kamya C, Azzopardi EA, Graf J, Kon M, Lineaweaver WC. 2009. Preventing infective complications following leech therapy: is practice keeping pace with current research? *Microsurgery* 29:619–25.

*Yantis MA, O'Toole KN, Ring P. 2009. Leech therapy. *Am. J. Nurs.* 109:36–42.

Japanese Knotweed:
Invasion of the Clones?

Sharon L. Gillies
University of the Fraser Valley

Introduction

Have you ever seen headlines like this one? "Watch for flying carp" from the *Toronto Sun*, May 24, 2009. Because of amazing photos of Asian carp flying through the air and YouTube videos of people fishing being struck by fish in their boats, this highly visible invasive species is hard to miss. Other introduced species are not so noticeable, and some invasive plants have beautiful flowers that we admire. High-profile or almost invisible, introduced species are a major threat to biodiversity. Many introduced species do not succeed in new environments. Others, however, are highly successful, and without predators or diseases, they can spread rapidly and disrupt natural communities.

Since the introduction of Japanese knotweed (*Fallopia japonica*) to North America about a century ago, it has gone from being a prize-winning horticulture plant to being labelled one of the world's top 10 invasive species. In England, Japanese knotweed is sterile and is considered a single, large female **clone**. In terms of biomass, it is the largest individual female on Earth. With each new plant genetically identical to its mother, it spreads by **fragmentation** (small pieces breaking off and starting new plants). Evidence indicates that in other parts of Europe and North America, in the absence of male partners of their own species, female Japanese knotweed plants are mating with males from other species. Female Japanese knotweed plants are being fertilized by pollen from giant knotweed (*Fallopia sachalinensis*), as well as a few other *Fallopia* species. The fertile hybrid Bohemian knotweed (*Fallopia xbohemica*) is the product of the cross between Japanese knotweed and giant knotweed, and has become quite common (see Photos A, B, and C).

KEY CONCEPTS

- Comparing genome sequences provides clues to evolution and development.
- Speciation can take place with or without geographic separation.
- Human activities threaten Earth's biodiversity.

PHOTO A. Japanese knotweed.
Source: © Jason Smalley/Nature Picture Library.

PHOTO B. **Giant knotweed.**
Source: © John T. Fowler.

PHOTO C. **Bohemian knotweed.**
Source: King County Noxious Weed Control Program, Seattle, Washington.

Should we consider the hybrid *F. xbohemica* to be the same species as *F. japonica*, or should we consider it a new species? This is a difficult question to answer. The concept of species is crucial to the classification system in biology; but, the literature contains different definitions of species. The biological species concept, which is based on all members within a species potentially being able to interbreed but being reproductively isolated from other species, is the most frequently used. An alternative model is the genetic species concept, where species is defined as being genetically isolated (different genes and/or chromosomes) from another species but not reproductively isolated.

A new species can evolve very quickly in plants through **polyploidy,** an increase in the normal set of chromosomes. Humans are diploid (*2n*), with two complete sets of chromosomes. Polyploid organisms can be triploid (*3n*), tetraploid (*4n*), pentaploid (*5n*), etc. Although rare, some animals, such as some goldfish and rats, are polyploids. In plants, however, this is much more common and has played an important role in plant evolution. Many agricultural crops, such as apples, bananas, and wheat, are polyploid plants.

A special case of polyploidy called **allopolyploidy** occurs when two different species interbreed and produce fertile hybrid offspring. Japanese knotweed is octoploid (88 chromosomes); giant knotweed is tetraploid (44 chromosomes); and many researchers have found varying numbers of chromosomes in the hybrids, with the most common being hexaploid (66 chromosomes). Is the hybrid *F. xbohemica* a new species—an example of **sympatric speciation** (the development of a new species occurring without geographic isolation from the parent species)? Are we witnessing ongoing speciation within genus *Fallopia* as hybrids interbreed with each other?

A **pioneer species** (a species capable of growing in disturbed and exposed environments) that colonizes volcanoes in Japan, Japanese knotweed is a shrub with extensive underground rhizomes. Whereas it can tolerate a variety of soil conditions, it prefers full or partial sun and moist soils. Combined with its aggressive growth habit, the plant has the ability to out-compete native flora. Japanese knotweed is now present in eight Canadian provinces. In British Columbia, it can sometimes even be seen out-competing another highly invasive plant, Armenian blackberry (*Rubus armeniacus*).

Antoine Lecerf from the University of British Columbia has shown that Japanese knotweed has a negative impact on stream ecology because it alters invertebrate populations and lowers stream nutrient levels. Research in the Pacific Northwest by Lauren Urgenson indicates that Japanese knotweed also has a negative impact on riparian forests (i.e., forests near waterways or lakes): it displaces native species and reduces the nutrient quality of litter inputs, thereby possibly causing long-term changes in the structure and functioning of riparian forests and the adjacent aquatic habitats.

The control or elimination of these invasive plants is difficult. Mechanical methods often must be repeated for years to be effective. Herbicides are not always effective because of the persistence of underground rhizomes. Current research is focused on developing or finding a biological control agent—a highly specific parasite, a disease, or a herbivore—that will attack or eat *F. japonica* but leave related native plants untouched. But will such a highly specific biological control agent be equally effective against hybrids? In order to predict the effectiveness of a biological control, we must know with what species and/or hybrids are present in an area.

Research Question

How do we determine if the plants invading British Columbia are Japanese knotweed clones, giant knotweed, or hybrid Bohemian knotweed?

I became interested in researching Japanese knotweed while teaching a biology course on native plants and animals of British Columbia. During field trips in 2006, my class observed an unfamiliar shrub at mid-elevation on Seymour Mountain and at low elevation riparian areas of the Fraser Valley. I later identified the plant as Japanese knotweed. I am now collaborating with Rob Bourchier, a research scientist from Agriculture and Agri-Food Canada in Lethbridge, Alberta, to determine the identity of the knotweed populations in Abbotsford, British Columbia, and to discover if they represent more than one species.

Hypothesis

Invasive knotweeds in the Abbotsford area of British Columbia are a mix of Japanese knotweed, giant knotweed, and hybrid Bohemian knotweed.

Methods and Results

Morphological characteristics were compared: trichome size (the size of small hair-like outgrowths on veins on the underside of leaves), leaf shape, and leaf size. Figure 1 shows the different morphological characteristics helpful in identifying knotweeds. Japanese knotweed leaves tend to be small with no leaf-base indent and have either no obvious trichomes or a small bump; hybrids are intermediate in size, have a small base indent, and have trichomes made of one to four cells; giant knotweeds have large leaves with large leaf-base indents and have large trichomes composed of many cells.

It can be difficult to separate hybrids from the two-parent species using a single morphological trait because they can appear more like one parent or the other. Rhizome pieces were grown and fresh white roots were used to do chromosome counts. Our results were similar to those of other researchers: *F. japonica* plants had 88 chromosomes and *F. sachalinensis* plants had 44. Most of the hybrid *F. xbohemica* plants had 66, but researchers have found the ploidy levels in hybrids can vary from tetraploid to octoploid. A comparison of morphological characteristics and chromosome counts (see Table 1) indicated that sites in Abbotsford had Japanese knotweed and giant knotweed, but most sites appeared to have hybrid Bohemian knotweed.

There was a strong relationship between leaf length and leaf-base indent as a good morphological indicator of species and hybrids (see Figure 2). Growing fresh roots to

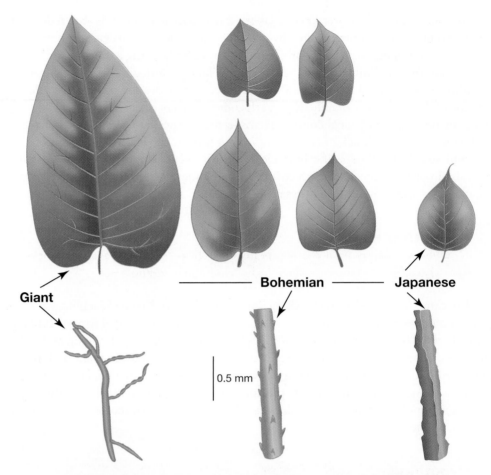

FIGURE 1. Morphology of invasive knotweed species in British Columbia.
Giant knotweed leaves are large (20–40 cm long); Japanese knotweed leaves are small (3–10 cm long); and hybrid Bohemian knotweed leaves are intermediate (5–30 cm long). Trichomes are large with many cells on the veins on the underside of giant knotweed leaves; they are not visible or are only small bumps on Japanese knotweed leaves; and they are intermediate in size on hybrid Bohemian knotweed leaves.
Source: Based on Wilson, L.M. 2007. Key to Identification of Invasive Knotweeds in British Columbia. B.C. Ministry of Forests & Range, Forest Practices Branch, Kamloops, B.C. Adapted with permission.

TABLE 1. Relationship between Trichome Characteristics and Average Leaf Length and Chromosome Number

Trichome Characteristics	Average Leaf Length (cm)	Chromosome Number	
No obvious trichomes or single small bump	14.56 ± 5.58 (SD)	88	*F. japonica* Japanese knotweed
Trichome composed of one to four cells	23.88 ± 6.18 (SD)	44, 66*	*F. xbohemica* Bohemian knotweed
Trichome composed of more than four cells	42.3 ± 7.6 (SD)	44	*F. sachalinensis* Giant knotweed

*Most frequent chromosome number
Source: S. Gillies, 2010.

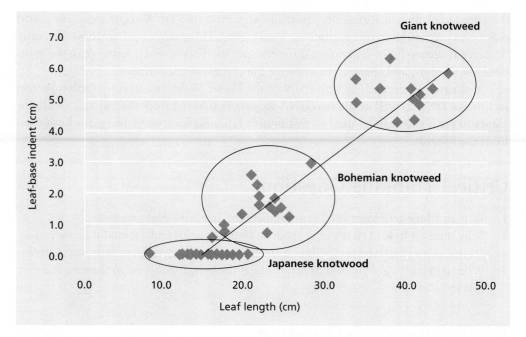

FIGURE 2. Relationship between leaf length and leaf-base indent of Japanese knotweed from Abbotsford sites.
The morphological characteristics of leaf length versus leaf base form three clusters that approximately relate to Japanese knotweed, giant knotweed, and hybrid Bohemian knotweed.
Source: S. Gillies, 2010.

determine chromosome number is time-consuming and can be done to confirm identification, but for most field studies using morphological criteria is suitable.

Conclusions

Invasive knotweed in the Abbotsford area of British Columbia are a mix of Japanese knotweed, giant knotweed, and hybrid Bohemian knotweed. Hybrid knotweed in other areas of North America are producing viable seed. Sexual reproduction results in genetic variation in the offspring. No longer clones, hybrid knotweeds have the potential to further adapt to environmental conditions and increase their competitive advantage. With the predominance of hybrids in the Abbotsford area, it is likely that sexual reproduction is also taking place here and plants are dispersing by both fragmentation and seeds. What may have started as an invasion of Japanese knotweed clones has now become complicated by the creation of a new sexually reproducing invader hybrid, but is it a new species?

Future Directions

The International Barcode of Life project began in Canada. At the Canadian Centre for DNA Barcoding (CCDB), the University of Guelph members Mehrad Hajibabaei and Sujeevan Ratnasingham have been actively involved in developing the barcode of life for plants. The goal is to use short DNA sequences from a standardized and agreed-upon position in the genome as a molecular diagnostic for species-level identification. The barcode of life is the practical application of genomic analysis and the comparison of many species. It will eventually provide biologists with a standard method that is reasonably quick and cheap for confirming the identification of a species. In August 2009, the barcode of life consortium temporarily approved two DNA sequences—*rbcL* and *matK*—as required barcode regions for land plants. These sequences are, however, only 72 percent successful in separating different species. This is much lower than the standard for animals, and research to improve the success rate continues.

A research project at the University of the Fraser Valley is currently testing several sections of DNA as well as the two DNA sequences selected from the barcode of life for plants to see if they can be used to distinguish Japanese knotweed and giant knotweed from the hybrids.

Critical Thinking Questions

1. Why can Japanese knotweed out-compete many native plant species?
2. Why might a hybrid that can reproduce both sexually and asexually be more successful as an invasive species than a sterile plant that reproduces only asexually?
3. What criteria would you use to determine if the hybrid *Fallopia xbohemica* is a new species?

Further Research Question

How will the barcode of life help biologists in their research?

References

Baker RJ, Bradley RD. 2006. Speciation in mammals and the genetic species concept. *J. Mammal.* 87:643–662.

*DNA barcoding: A new tool for identifying biological specimens and managing species diversity [Internet]. [cited 2010 Apr 12]. Available from: http://www.barcoding.si.edu/PDF/CBOL-ABS%20Brochure%20-%20FINAL.pdf

De Queiroz K. 2007. Species concepts and species delimitation. *Syst. Biol.* 56: 879–886.

Forman J, Kesseli RV. 2003. Sexual reproduction in the invasive species *Fallopia japonica* (Polygonaceae) *Am. J. Botany.* 90:586–592.

Grimsby JL, Tsirelson D, Gammon MA, Kesseki R. 2007. Genetic diversity and clonal vs. sexual reproduction in *Fallopia* spp. (Polygonaceae). *Am. J. Botany.* 94:957–964.

Hollingsworth ML, Bailey JP. 2000. Evidence for massive clonal growth in the invasive weed Fallopia japonica (Japanese Knotweed). *Bot. J. Linn. Soc.* 133:463–472.

Hollingsworth ML, Bailey JP, Hollingsworth PM, Ferris C. 1999. Chloroplast DNA variation and hybridization between invasive populations of Japanese knotweed and giant knotweed (Fallopia, Polygonaceae). *Bot. J. Linn. Soc.* 129:139–154.

Hollingsworth PM, Forrest LL, Spouge JL, Hajibabaei M, Ratnasingham S, et al. 2009. DNA barcode for land plants. *Proc. Nat. Acad. Sci.* 106:12794–12797.

Lecerf A, Patfield D, Boiché A, Riipinen MP, Chauvet E, Dobson M. 2007. Stream ecosystems respond to riparian invasion by Japanese knotweed (*Fallopia japonica*). *Can. J. Fish. Aquat. Sci.* 64:1273–1283.

*Pereira F, Carneiro J, Amorim A. 2008. Identification of species with dna-based technology: current progress and challenges. *Recent Pat. DNA Gene Sequences* 2:187–200.

Urgenson LS. 2006. The ecological consequences of knotweed invasion into riparian forests [master's thesis]. University of Washington.

Wilson LM. 2007. Key to identification of invasive knotweeds in British Columbia. B.C. Ministry of Forests & Range, Forest Practices Branch, Kamloops, B.C.

Maintenance of Genome Stability:
Why Breaking Up Is Hard to Do

Ebba U. Kurz
University of Calgary

Introduction

You've heard it, I've heard it, everyone has heard it: there is no such thing as a safe tan. Yet many people, particularly after a long, cold winter, can't resist the lure of a sunny beach or a weekend basking on the dock at the cottage. What few realize, however, is that ultraviolet rays in bright sunlight cause damage at more than 100 000 sites in the DNA of *each* exposed cell every hour! In fact, the DNA in our cells faces a barrage of insults every day from both **endogenous** (from within the body) and **exogenous** (from outside the body) sources. How does all this damage occur, and what happens to our DNA? How do our cells cope with the enormous task of repairing this damage? And what are the consequences when our cells fail to fix their damaged DNA?

KEY CONCEPTS

- Sunlight causes DNA mutations (DNA damage).
- We have multiple pathways for DNA repair.
- Repair mechanisms can be exploited for therapy.

Types of DNA Damage

Our DNA, with about 3 billion base pairs distributed on 46 chromosomes in every cell, encodes the blueprint for all cellular structures and functions. With each cell division, this DNA must be faithfully copied and equally distributed into daughter cells. Failure to do so carefully and precisely can lead to the accumulation of mutations in our DNA, cell aging, and, ultimately, the development of diseases, such as cancer. Each cell in the human body endures tens of thousands of daily insults to its DNA. Much of this DNA damage occurs spontaneously from endogenous sources, a consequence of our DNA reacting with oxygen and water in the cell, or is caused by errors made when DNA is copied before cell division. For example, at body temperature (37°C), each cell in the body loses approximately 18 000 adenine (A) and guanine (G) bases per day through the breakage of the chemical bond connecting these bases to the DNA backbone. Paradoxically, oxygen, although essential for life, is converted to **reactive oxygen species** (including hydrogen peroxide, H_2O_2; superoxide anion radical, $O_2^{\cdot-}$; and the hydroxyl radical, $\cdot OH$) as by-products of cell metabolism. These species can attack DNA at numerous sites, causing more than 70 types of damage, including breaks in the DNA backbone. Of all the types of DNA damage our cells endure, **double-stranded breaks**, which occur when opposite strands of DNA in close proximity are broken, are the most lethal: a single unrepaired double-stranded DNA break can lead to cell death.

In addition to the spontaneous DNA damage arising within our bodies, our lifestyles and day-to-day experiences can also take a heavy toll on our DNA. Naturally occurring

PHOTO A. **Sunlight streams through tree branches.**
Sunlight is composed of many wavelengths, including ultraviolet radiation, which can damage DNA, particularly with prolonged or repeated exposure.
Source: Courtesy of Ebba Kurz.

radiation found in Earth's crust and emanating from space, airline travel, X-rays, consumption of charred and cured meats, and tobacco smoke can add to the level of damage our DNA sustains. However, among the most pervasive sources of damage is the lasting impact that prolonged and repeated exposure to sunlight (**ultraviolet radiation**) can have on our genome (see Photo A).

The sun emits ultraviolet (UV) light that is commonly divided into three segments, based on the wavelength of light: UVA, UVB, and UVC. The most dangerous light, UVC, is absorbed by the ozone layer, while UVA and UVB reach Earth's surface. Together, these two types of radiation can induce an astonishing 100 000 lesions in each exposed cell every hour. The most frequent lesions caused by exposure to UV light are **pyrimidine dimers**, which are formed when two adjacent thymine (T) or cytosine (C) bases on the same DNA strand chemically bond to each other rather than their complementary base on the opposite DNA strand (see Figure 1). This leads to a localized bending of the DNA backbone, which, if not repaired, can prevent DNA replication and RNA transcription or can lead to DNA mutation. Exposure to UVA light also triggers an increase in the production of reactive oxygen species, which can lead to breaks in the DNA backbone. Scientists have determined that this DNA damage occurs within 1 picosecond (10^{-12} seconds) of UV exposure.

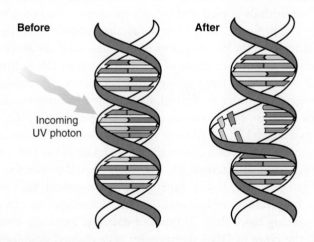

FIGURE 1. UV-induced pyrimidine dimers distort the shape of DNA.
Pyrimidine dimers formed in DNA following the exposure of cells to UV radiation can cause bulging of the DNA backbone. This distorted shape, if unrepaired, prevents DNA replication and RNA transcription or can lead to the introduction of DNA mutations.
Source: NASA Earth Observatory/Illustration by David Herring, available from http://earthobservatory.nasa.gov/Features/UVB/

Detection and Repair of DNA Damage

DNA is critical to life itself; but given how fragile it appears to be and how severe the consequences of mutation or damage can be, why would nature evolve such precarious genetic material? In fact, no matter how serious a mutation may be for an individual, without mutation there can be no evolution. DNA mutation and repair can be viewed as two aspects of the evolutionary process that have been selected for over time, creating the potential for change in populations versus promoting the survival of individuals to reproductive age.

Perhaps in response to this, more than 200 human genes are known to be involved in intricate and overlapping networks responsible for the detection and repair of DNA damage. Some common spontaneous forms of DNA damage can be reversed almost immediately through the action of a single repair enzyme, but many forms of DNA damage trigger a cascade of events that involves multiple proteins and many steps. The DNA damage response initially involves the DNA damage sensor proteins, the first responders that survey the genome and sound the alarm when damage is encountered. The DNA damage sensors initiate signalling pathways that trigger subsequent events, often by using protein **phosphorylation,** a common and reversible modification that alters protein function. These events may include halting the cell growth cycle to ensure that the cell does not replicate its damaged DNA or undergo mitosis with broken DNA strands, or modifying the nuclear packaging of DNA to give the repair proteins access to the damage site. The signalling pathways, each specific for the type of DNA damage detected, also trigger activation of the appropriate DNA-repair machinery. By using multiple proteins, the cell typically removes the damaged portion of DNA and some of its surrounding bases, resynthesizes the missing DNA by using the unaffected DNA strand as a template, and reseals the repaired strand.

Although these multiple repair pathways are very efficient at maintaining the stability of our genome, they are not infallible. At times, the damage encountered may be too extensive. When this occurs, the DNA damage sensors signal the cell to undergo **apoptosis** (also known as programmed cell death) or enter **cellular senescence** (permanent cessation of cell growth), which can lead to aging (see Figure 2). More troubling is that some cells fail to repair the damage or inaccurately repair their damaged DNA. These errors can lead to mutations or chromosomal breaks, both of which increase the risk of cancer.

The Consequences of Inadequate Repair

The critical nature of DNA-repair mechanisms is evident in individuals in whom one of the genes involved in DNA damage detection or repair is mutated or missing. In almost all cases, the syndromes caused by these rare genetic mutations are characterized by accelerated aging or a significantly increased risk for cancer. For example, people with **xeroderma pigmentosum,** an inherited defect in the protein pathway used in the repair of UV-induced DNA damage, are 2000 times as likely to get skin cancer as the average person. Although some limited overlap between repair pathways occurs, the loss of even a single repair protein has profound consequences.

Exploiting DNA Damage and Repair Networks for Cancer Therapy

Most traditional cancer chemotherapeutics exert their cell-killing effects by damaging DNA to such an extent that cellular repair systems are overwhelmed. Unfortunately, these chemotherapeutics are not specifically targeted to cancer cells, leaving patients to endure significant side effects, including nausea and vomiting, hair loss, fertility problems, and low blood cell counts. Newer approaches to treatment, however, are taking

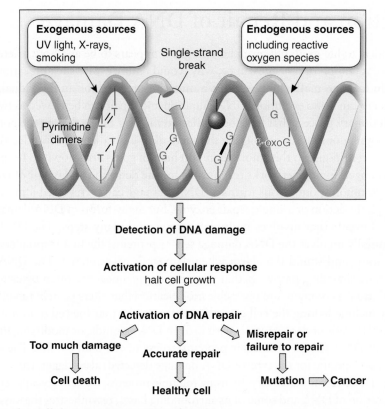

FIGURE 2. The cellular response to DNA damage.
DNA damage can arise from endogenous sources (such as reactive oxygen species) or exogenous agents (including UV radiation). DNA damage is recognized by a series of DNA damage sensors that activate signal transduction cascades that can lead to a halt of the cell growth cycle. DNA-repair proteins are subsequently activated. In general, one of three outcomes occurs: (1) if the damage is accurately repaired, the cell remains healthy; (2) if the damage is too great, the cell dies; or (3) if the cell fails to repair the damage properly, DNA mutation may occur, which increases the risk of cancer.

Source: Adapted from Hoeijmakers JHJ. 2009. DNA Damage, Aging, and Cancer. New England Journal of Medicine 361(15):1475–1485, October 8, 2009, Figure 1, p. 1476. Copyright © 2009 Massachusetts Medical Society. All rights reserved.

advantage of the fact that many tumour types have accumulated defects in their DNA-repair pathways, which are part of what contributes to their genomic instability and the development of the cancer. After years of laboratory and clinical research, it has now been shown that tumours lacking one of the critical proteins for repairing double-stranded DNA breaks are particularly sensitive to inhibitors of a second DNA-repair pathway. Intriguingly, these inhibitors are relatively non-toxic to normal cells of the body, but they cause the tumour cells to die. Clinical trials are currently underway to test these inhibitors in people with repair-deficient tumours.

Conclusions

Although our cells are very efficient at recognizing and repairing their damaged DNA, the methods are not always foolproof. It is clear that accumulated DNA damage plays a significant role in aging and in the development of cancers. However, we must recognize that cancer is a relatively rare disease in the young and becomes more prevalent only after decades of accumulated damage. Nevertheless, this timeline can be accelerated by prolonged or repeated exposure to DNA-damaging chemicals (such as those found in cigarette smoke) or other environmental sources (such as sunlight). The caution that there is no such thing as a safe tan is something that everyone should heed. It is hoped that research will continue to advance our understanding of how cells detect and repair DNA damage, which will identify ways to prevent the accumulation of mutations or to exploit them to improve cancer therapies.

Critical Thinking Questions

1. Why is sunlight so damaging to our DNA?
2. Why have we evolved more than 200 proteins that are involved in DNA damage detection and repair?
3. Why are some tumour cells particularly susceptible to inhibitors of DNA-repair pathways?

Further Research Question

How does cigarette smoke cause DNA damage?

References

Friedberg EC. 2003. DNA damage and repair. *Nat.* 421:436–440.

Friedberg EC, Walker GC, Siede W, Wood RD, Schultz RA, Ellenberger TE, eds. 2006. *DNA repair and mutagenesis.* 2nd ed. Washington (DC): ASM Press.

*Hoeijmakers, JHJ. 2009. DNA damage, aging and cancer. *New Engl. J. Med.* 361: 1475–1485.

*Jackson SP, Bartek J. 2009. The DNA-damage response in human biology and disease. *Nat.* 461:1071–1078.

Schreier, WJ, Schrader TE, Koller FO, Gilch P, Crespo-Hernández CE, Swaminathan VN, Carell T, Zinth W, Kohle B. 2007. Thymine dimerization in DNA is an ultrafast photoreaction. *Sci.* 315:625–629.

Maternal Stress:
Is My Mother Harming or Helping Me?

Oliver P. Love
University of Windsor

Introduction

KEY CONCEPTS

- Stress hormones are a mechanism of communication between the mother and her offspring.
- The fitness of the mother differentially influences the short-term and long-term effects on her reproductive success.

You're overworked, under stress, and you're pregnant, again. Every human mother knows that producing and raising just one offspring can be difficult enough, even at the best of times. Now imagine you are a female bird raising multiple young while facing the environmental stressors of finding enough food, trying to avoid predators, and having to reproduce in a harsh or unpredictable world. If a mechanism could evolve that fine-tunes the match between a mother's ability to raise her young and the demand that offspring place on her, both parties may end up benefiting in the long run. **Glucocorticoids** (stress hormones) passed from mother to offspring via the egg may be just such a mechanism.

Glucocorticoids, such as corticosterone in birds, reptiles, and amphibians, are steroid hormones released by the adrenal gland that are primarily known for their role in helping individuals respond and adjust to stressful events. They increase in the bloodstream following exposure to acute or chronic stressors, such as a lack of food, attacks from predators, and even human disturbance. These hormones help individuals manage stressful events by maintaining homeostasis through the synthesis of glucose from proteins and fats. Because of their strong link with energetic balance, individuals who are in poor condition often have chronically high glucocorticoid levels in the blood, and these hormones can therefore provide researchers with a physiological snapshot of the general quality of an individual.

We have known for some time that lower-quality mothers with correspondingly high levels of glucocorticoids in the blood expose offspring to these hormones via the placenta in mammals and via the yolk in some birds, reptiles, and fish. However, we have only recently begun to appreciate that prenatal exposure to maternal stress hormones has a number of **phenotypic** (expressed) developmental effects in vertebrate offspring, including smaller size at birth or hatching, and lower post-birth/hatch growth rates. These apparently negative effects seem to represent an immediate cost to offspring, and long-term costs to mothers, since small size at birth and slow growth rates in animals can often put offspring at increased risk of mortality. But what if being smaller and less demanding was actually a benefit if a low-quality mother was raising you? In that case, these developmental adjustments could be adaptive mechanisms that *match* the demand of the growing offspring with the mother's ability to raise them.

Examining both the longer-term costs and the benefits to offspring and mothers can help researchers to better understand this perplexing phenomenon. For example, perhaps mothers or their offspring receive benefits (i.e., improved future reproductive success and survival prospects) from having a better match between mother and offspring early in life. These benefits could outweigh the risks that small size can have on survival early in development. Researchers can test whether a low-quality mother (because of environmental stress) that exposes her offspring to an honest signal of her quality (prenatal stress hormones) does better in the long run than a similar mother that does not inform her offspring of her reduced ability to raise them. To investigate this, researchers can examine the immediate effects of exposure to maternal stress on offspring. They can compare the immediate effects with the long-term effects on maternal success and survival to understand the evolutionary reasons that mothers may have been selected to allow this to occur. In essence, mothers may be informing their offspring of their own rearing capabilities and, by extension, how good or bad the immediate environment will be for offspring once they are born. These insights allow us to better understand the costs and benefits of maternal stress, whether offspring should "listen" to a stressed mother, and even how they should developmentally respond.

Research Question
Do prenatal, stress-induced changes in offspring phenotype help to match low-quality (i.e., poor condition) mothers to offspring demand?

Hypothesis
Mothers in poor condition exposing offspring to a hormonal signal (prenatal stress hormones) of their quality will have higher reproductive success and survival compared with similar mothers of poor condition raising unstressed offspring.

Methods and Results

Experiments were conducted in free-living European starlings (*Sturnus vulgaris*; see Photo A) breeding in a nest-box population in Vancouver, British Columbia.

Male starlings are larger when they hatch, grow quicker, and are larger as adults than females. This makes male starlings more energetically costly for low-quality mothers to raise. Moreover, since male size is important for competitive access to mates, small males are an evolutionary cost for low-quality mothers as these males may never reproduce. In our previous studies, we found two important things: (1) mothers in poor condition (low quality) had higher plasma (blood) levels of the glucocorticoid corticosterone

PHOTO A.
European starling (*Sturnus vulgaris*).
Source: Mark Robinson, Williton, UK/Wikipedia: European Starling, http://en.wikipedia.org/wiki/European_Starling, accessed 27 February 2010.

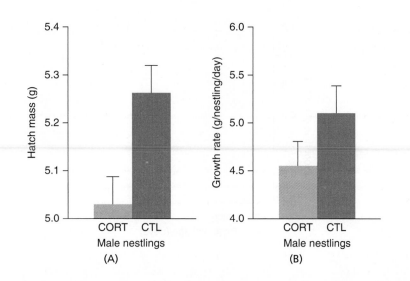

FIGURE 1. **Stressed males were lighter at hatching and grew more slowly than their unstressed counterparts.**
A. Males exposed to corticosterone (CORT) were smaller on hatching than their control (CTL) counterparts, who had received only the oil control injection.
B. Males who were exposed to CORT grew more slowly than the controls after hatching.
Source: Love, O.P., Chin, E.H., Katherine E. Wynne-Edwards and Williams, T. D. 2005. Stress hormones: a link between maternal condition and sex-biased reproductive investment. American Naturalist 166(6): 751–766. Figures from pp. 759 & 760.

(CORT) than mothers in good condition (high quality), and (2) mothers deposited corticosterone into eggs via the yolk in proportion to the levels in their blood. To understand whether exposure to prenatal corticosterone matches the demand of the offspring to the mother's ability to rear them required the integration of two different experiments. First, to understand whether offspring were developmentally sensitive to the mother's stress, we injected freshly laid eggs with corticosterone dissolved in sesame oil (to produce stressed offspring) and compared these with unstressed control (CTL) eggs injected with oil only (to produce unstressed offspring). Second, to understand whether low-quality mothers benefited from these stress-induced changes in offspring phenotype, we then gave these two sets of offspring to mothers that had been experimentally manipulated to make them low-quality mothers. For this experiment, "lower-quality mothers" are birds that have been subjected to a flight-feather-clipping treatment, which reduced the number of feeding trips that mothers made to the nest, thereby reducing maternal quality from the offspring's point of view. By following all the experimental mothers across multiple breeding attempts and years, we tracked long-term reproductive success and survival.

Stressed male offspring were smaller and grew more slowly than their unstressed counterparts, whereas females of both treatments hatched at similar sizes and grew at similar rates (see Figure 1 and Photo B).

More of the stressed males died during post-hatching development than unstressed males because of their smaller initial size and lower growth rates, further reducing the overall demand on mothers raising stressed nestlings (Figure 2).

PHOTO B.
Nestling European starlings.
Source: Courtesy of Dr. Christina Semeniuk.

FIGURE 2. **A greater pro-portion of stressed male nestlings died during postnatal development compared with their unstressed counterparts.**
Source: Adapted from: Love, O.P. and Williams, T.D. 2008. The adaptive value of stress-induced phenotypes in the wild: sex allocation, cost of reproduction and maternal fitness. American Naturalist 172: E135–E149, p. E141.

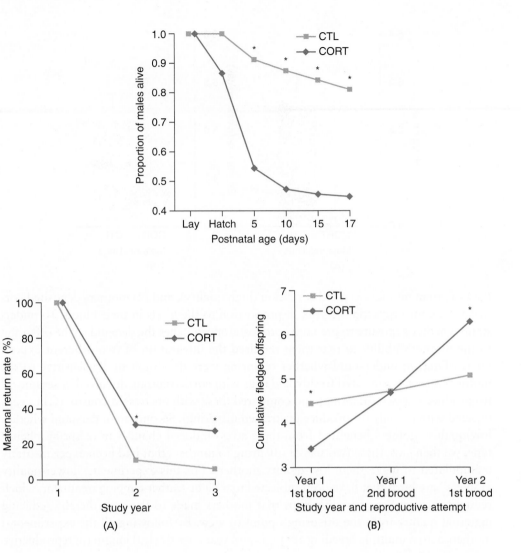

FIGURE 3. **Low-quality mothers with stressed offspring fared better overall.**
Low-quality mothers raising stressed offspring had lower rates of mortality (A) and higher reproductive success leading to higher overall fitness (B) compared with similar mothers raising unstressed offspring.
Source: Adapted from: Love, O.P. and Williams, T.D. 2008. The adaptive value of stress-induced phenotypes in the wild: sex allocation, cost of reproduction and maternal fitness. American Naturalist 172: E135–E149, p. E143.

When we compared the long-term effects of low-quality mothers raising stressed off-spring to low-quality mothers raising unstressed offspring, some interesting results were revealed. Mothers who raised offspring who were matched to their rearing ability (low-quality mother and stressed offspring) (1) returned to lay their second clutches in the same year in better condition, (2) raised more and higher-quality offspring that year and the following year, and (3) survived better through the next two years as compared with mismatched mothers and offspring (low-quality mother and unstressed offspring). Over-all, then, low-quality mothers raising stressed offspring initially had **lower reproductive success** (lost more offspring in the first brood). In the long run, however, they had **higher overall fitness** (the combination of reproductive success and survival) compared with similar mothers whose quality was mismatched to their offspring (see Figure 3).

Conclusions

Although prenatal exposure to maternal stress is often thought of as a negative circum-stance that mothers cannot avoid, starling mothers that are already in poor condition appear to be able to fine-tune the match between their rearing ability and their off-spring's demand by exposing those offspring to stress hormones. As such, the apparently negative short-term effects on offspring (reduced male size and growth) provide us with a hormonal mechanism to explain the evolutionary reasons that mothers might expose offspring to an honest signal of their quality.

Future Directions

As of yet, we have only long-term information on potential benefits for mothers. More work needs to be carried out that examines longer-term costs and benefits for offspring, especially males, to better understand why males risk initial survival prospects by hatching at smaller sizes and growing more slowly to be better matched to their mothers.

Critical Thinking Questions

1. What traits in males make them the more proximately (energetically) and ultimately (evolutionarily) costly sex for a low-quality mother?
2. What are the benefits and costs for a low-quality mother if she exposes her offspring to maternal stress and if she shields them from it?
3. If exposing offspring to maternal stress benefits low-quality mothers, would you expect to find low-quality female starlings that do not employ this strategy? Why?

Further Research Question

Would you expect all species to benefit from this type of hormonal matching mechanism?

References

Breuner C. 2008. Maternal stress, glucocorticoids and the maternal/fetal match hypothesis. *Hormones Behav.* 54:485–487.

Love OP, Chin EH, Wynne-Edwards KE, Williams TD. 2005. Stress hormones: a link between maternal condition and sex-biased reproductive investment. *Am. Natural.* 166:751–766.

Love OP, Williams TD. 2008. The adaptive value of stress-induced phenotypes in the wild: sex allocation, cost of reproduction and maternal fitness. *Am. Natural.* 172:E135–E149.

A Matter of Life and Death:
Viruses Inhibit Cell Suicide

Logan Banadyga and Michele Barry
University of Alberta

Introduction

You can feel it: that familiar, annoying itch at the back of your throat. It started as a tickle, barely noticeable, but hour by hour the grating, sandpapery pain is becoming more and more persistent. Now your nose is running, and you're stuffed up. Soon you'll feel tired, you might begin to cough, and you'll crave nothing more than some chicken soup and the warmth of your bed. This isn't the first time you've been felled by a common cold virus, and it won't be the last. In a couple of days you'll feel better, no worse for wear. After all, the common cold is not a matter of life and death.

Or is it? Amid the harsh microcosm of the human body, your cells face constant assault from viral intruders of all types. Viruses, at about a thousandth the size of the average cell in your body, are **obligate intracellular parasites**. They must infiltrate your cells, duplicate themselves by commandeering your own biochemical machinery, and then escape to find their way into a new host to begin the cycle anew. Whether they end up making you very sick or not, viruses often leave a path of dead and damaged cells in their wake. At every step along this path, however, your body's immune system fights back. Your innate immune response generates a torrent of cytokines that push your immune system into overdrive, the plasma cells of your humoral immune response produce antibodies that can bind to the circulating virus and remove it, and your cell-mediated immune response unleashes cytotoxic T cells that destroy virus-infected cells. But before your body has time to mount any of these offences, the first thing that an infected cell will do is try to kill itself.

> **KEY CONCEPTS**
>
> - Apoptosis is a form of programmed cell death.
> - Viruses are obligate intracellular parasites that require living hosts.
> - Viruses encode proteins to inhibit apoptosis.

Cellular Suicide

It may seem counterintuitive, but an infected cell wants to die and the virus wants to keep that cell alive. Within each cell of your body—and, indeed, within each cell of every multicellular creature on Earth—is a set of specific genetic instructions that tell the cell exactly when and how to commit suicide. This process, known as **apoptosis**, is a form of programmed cell death that has evolved to protect the life of the organism at the expense of the life of a single cell in that organism. For example, apoptosis helps prevent serious disease by eliminating damaged cells before they can become cancerous. The reason you don't have webbed feet is thanks to apoptosis removing the skin cells that once tethered your fetal toes together (see Photo A). And your body's ability to survive viral infections, including the common cold, depends in part on the rapid and organized suicide of infected cells.

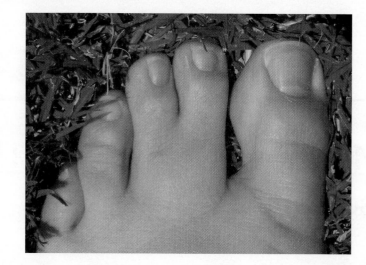

Without a living, metabolically active cell to hijack, a virus is nothing more than an inert sac of chemicals. The sacrifice of a few infected cells therefore denies viruses their chance at reproduction and, as a result, protects the rest of your cells from further infection.

The death of an infected cell by apoptosis is a tightly choreographed response involving a bewilderingly complex network of cellular **proteins** and **enzymes**. A viral infection can trigger any number of hundreds of different cellular signalling pathways that all lead to apoptosis. Almost all these pathways, however, converge at the **mitochondria**. Normally thought of as the powerhouses of the cell, not only do mitochondria provide energy for life, but they also control the effectors of death. The inter-membrane space of mitochondria sequesters a pool of **cytochrome c**, a component of the electron transport chain that, when released into the cytoplasm, commits the cell to death. The release of cytochrome c is controlled by the **Bcl-2 family** of mitochondrial proteins. Certain members of this family, such as Bcl-2 and Bcl-X_L, inhibit cytochrome c release, whereas others, such as **Bak** and **Bax**, promote it. Once released into the cytoplasm, cytochrome c triggers a signalling cascade that leads to the activation of **caspases**. Caspases are a group of enzymes known as **proteases** that, when activated, cleave (break down) numerous cellular proteins and, in effect, dismantle the apoptotic cell. Systematically, the nucleus will fragment as the cell's genomic DNA is chopped up, the entire cell will detach from its surroundings as it shrinks, and, finally, the cell will disintegrate into small blebs (see Photo B) of membrane to be phagocytosed and digested by nearby macrophages. Apoptosis, in a neat and tidy manner, completely removes an infected cell in less than 60 minutes.

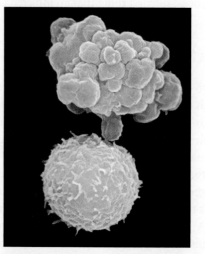

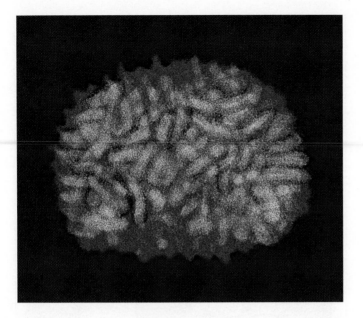

PHOTO C. The complex poxvirus.
Poxviruses are large, complex viruses that contain large dsDNA genomes and replicate in the cytoplasm of infected cells. Their large genomes allow poxviruses to encode numerous proteins that interfere with the host immune system.
Source: Science VU/Visuals Unlimited, Inc.

Viruses Want You Alive

Apoptosis is a death sentence for both the cell and the virus attempting to replicate within it. Thus, preserving the life of the infected cell is a top priority for all viruses. **Poxviruses,** in particular, are renowned for their ability to manipulate the cells they infect (see Photo C). Members of this virus family infect animals ranging from chickens and penguins to rabbits and deer; however, the most infamous and deadly poxvirus is variola virus, the causative agent of smallpox. Relatively speaking, poxviruses are giants among viruses, and their large, double-stranded DNA (dsDNA) genomes encode numerous proteins that interfere with aspects of the host's immune system, including apoptosis. In fact, poxviruses have evolved ways to inhibit almost every aspect of the complex signalling pathways that regulate cell death.

Upon poxvirus infection, the innate immune system is activated and cytokines are released. So-called death receptors, such as the tumour necrosis factor alpha (TNF) receptor on the surface of the cell, bind these cytokines and trigger an intracellular chain reaction that can lead to apoptosis. Some poxviruses, such as variola virus, produce soluble (or "free") cytokine receptors that are secreted from the infected cell and sop up the pro-death cytokines before they have a chance to bind the cellular, membrane-bound receptors and activate the apoptotic cascade. Other poxviruses, such as cowpox, which actually infects rodents, produce proteins that function after the release of cytochrome c to deactivate caspases and prevent their dismantling of the cell.

Perhaps the most effective method for inhibiting cell suicide, however, is the direct inhibition of cytochrome c release from the mitochondria. The release of cytochrome c is ultimately controlled by two members of the Bcl-2 family of proteins, Bak and Bax. Following virus infection, Bak and Bax become activated and aggregate to form pore-like structures in the outer mitochondrial membrane. These pores are thought to be of a sufficient size for cytochrome c to escape and activate caspases. Both Bak and Bax are independently capable of facilitating the release of cytochrome c, and without at least one of these proteins, cytochrome c cannot escape the mitochondria and apoptosis cannot occur. Vaccinia virus, the prototypical poxvirus used in the past to immunize people against smallpox, encodes a protein, termed F1L, that inactivates Bak and Bax, to inhibit the release of cytochrome c and prevent apoptosis. By inhibiting Bak and Bax, F1L eliminates the two proteins most critical to the entire apoptotic cascade (see Figure 1). Surprisingly, F1L is not alone in its ability to inactivate Bak and Bax: several other poxviruses, and several viruses other than those belonging to the poxvirus family, encode

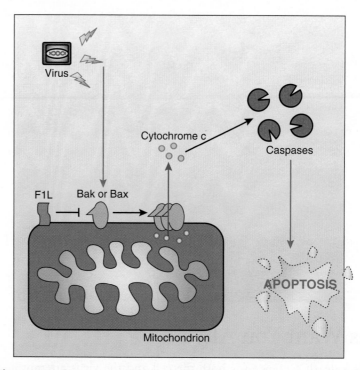

FIGURE 1. The apoptotic response to virus infection.
Virus infection produces numerous "danger" signals within the infected cell that can trigger apoptosis through numerous pathways. Almost all pathways converge on the mitochondria with the activation of Bak and Bax. Bak and Bax control the induction of apoptosis by regulating the release of cytochrome c from the mitochondria into the cytoplasm. Once activated, Bak and Bax aggregate to form pores that allow cytochrome c to escape. When released into the cytoplasm, cytochrome c activates a group of proteases known as caspases. Caspases cleave a variety of cellular proteins and apoptosis ensues. Viruses can inhibit apoptosis, however, by interfering with almost any step in the apoptotic cascade, and several viruses interfere with events at the mitochondria. The vaccinia virus protein F1L, for example, inhibits apoptosis by inactivating Bak and Bax, thereby preventing the release of cytochrome c.
Source: Logan Banadyga.

proteins that also interfere with Bak and Bax. What's more surprising is that many of these viral inhibitors of apoptosis appear to belong to the same cellular protein family as Bak and Bax. It appears as if viruses have adopted our own cellular death machinery and are using it against us—to keep us alive.

Conclusions

That a virus should want to keep our cells alive despite the best efforts of those cells to die is, at first, counterintuitive. But, for both the cells and the virus, it makes perfect sense. Apoptosis provides a way to limit viral infection by rapidly removing our own infected cells and the virus replicating inside of them. From the virus's point of view, this is a problem. Many viruses have, therefore, evolved mechanisms for overcoming apoptosis and forcing the infected cell to remain alive and capable of supporting viral replication. In the lab, we exploit the mechanisms that viruses use to inhibit cell suicide in an effort to better understand apoptosis itself and the diseases, such as cancer, that the dysregulation of apoptosis can cause. Although you may not think twice the next time you face off against a cold, for the virus and your cells, it will, as always, be a matter of life and death.

Critical Thinking Questions

1. Why must viruses inhibit apoptosis?
2. Many viruses encode more than one protein that functions to inhibit apoptosis. Why might a virus require multiple different proteins to inhibit apoptosis?
3. A vaccinia virus mutant that does not express F1L induces apoptosis in infected cells. What might be expected if that same mutant vaccinia virus were to infect a cell devoid of Bak? Of Bax? Of both Bak and Bax?

Further Research Question

Human cytomegalovirus encodes the protein vMIA (viral mitochondria-localized inhibitor of apoptosis) that, like vaccinia virus F1L, inhibits the release of cytochrome c. How does the inhibition of apoptosis by vMIA differ from that of F1L?

References

Poncet D, Larochette N, Pauleau AL, Boya P, Jalil AA, Cartron PF, Vallette F, Schnebelen C, Bartle LM, Skaletskaya A, et al. 2004. An anti-apoptotic viral protein that recruits Bax to mitochondria. *J. Biol. Chem.* 279:22605–22614.

Taylor JM, Quilty D, Banadyga L, Barry M. 2006. The vaccinia virus protein F1L interacts with Bim and inhibits activation of the pro-apoptotic protein Bax. *J. Biol. Chem.* 281:39728–39739.

A Most Pervasive Prion Disease:
Chronic Wasting Disease Continues to Spread and Shows No Signs of Slowing

Sandra Haney
PrioNet Canada

Michelle Wong
PrioNet Canada

Lyanne Foster
Alberta Prion Research Institute

Introduction

Chronic wasting disease (CWD) is a neurological disease found in deer, elk, and moose (collectively called **cervids**) and belongs to a family of diseases known as prion diseases. **Prions** are infectious pathogens that cause various neurodegenerative diseases. Prions are not bacterial, fungal, or viral; unlike bacteria or viruses, prions do not have DNA or RNA, and yet they are able to act as disease-causing agents. A prion begins as a harmless protein in its natural form (PrP^C), but by folding into an aberrant shape, the normal prion protein turns into a rogue agent ($PrPS^c$). All proteins can fold and misfold, but not all misfolded proteins cause disease. Prions are different from other misfolded proteins because they act as infectious agents and cause normal proteins to misfold into disease-causing forms.

Prion diseases are fatal and transmissible—from host to host within a single species and sometimes from one species to another—and are collectively called *transmissible spongiform encephalopathies* (TSEs). Prions cause neurodegenerative disease by aggregating and forming plaques, which disrupt the normal tissue structure of the brain. This disruption creates holes in the brain tissue, giving it a spongy appearance. Prions are the cause of TSEs in several other species, such as bovine spongiform encephalopathy in cattle; scrapie in sheep; and Creutzfeldt-Jakob disease, variant Creutzfeldt-Jakob disease, and kuru (documented primarily in tribes in Papua New Guinea) in humans. No simple diagnostic test, vaccine, or treatment is currently available for any prion disease.

Thousands of wild deer across North America are infected with CWD, mainly in the Canadian prairies (Saskatchewan and Alberta) and in the plains of the United States (South Dakota, Wyoming, and Colorado). Consequently, CWD is a disease of increasing concern for wildlife managers both in CWD-endemic areas and across North America. The recent discovery of CWD in a Saskatchewan deer not far from the Manitoba border underscores the need to better understand the disease's transmission. Animals infected with CWD exhibit various symptoms, such as head tremors, depression, drooling, difficulty swallowing, increased thirst, paralysis, pneumonia, separation from other

KEY CONCEPTS

- Chronic wasting disease is a prion disease that results in neurodegeneration.
- Prion proteins exist in a harmless form but can become infectious agents when they misfold.
- Prion diseases can be transmitted within and between species.
- Contamination of affected environments enhances the spread of prion diseases.

animals in the herd, loss of coordination, unusual behaviour, excessive urination, and chronic weight loss that inevitably leads to death. Obvious symptoms are apparent only a few weeks to several months before the animal dies.

Animals infected with CWD can transmit misfolded prion proteins to their surrounding environments through saliva and excretions, such as urine and feces. The prion proteins are also abundant in the carcasses of diseased animals and persist in the environment even after the bodies have decomposed. These factors contribute significantly to the complexities of CWD transmission in wild deer and to the options for control and destruction of CWD in the natural landscape.

The Spread of Infection

CWD was first seen in 1967 in mule deer at a wildlife research facility in northern Colorado, but the definitive origin of CWD is unknown. Because scrapie, a prion disease of sheep, was first recognized in the United States in the 1940s, it is possible that CWD derived from scrapie. It is also possible that CWD is a spontaneous TSE that arose in deer, developed biological features that promote transmission to other cervids, and subsequently gained entry into zoos and game farms.

In Canada, CWD was first recognized in a captive mule deer in the Toronto Zoo in the mid-1970s. The symptoms were not confirmed as CWD until 1981, after the entire herd had died. No evidence suggests that CWD is present in captive or free-ranging white-tailed deer and elk in Ontario. In 1996, a farmed elk in Saskatchewan tested positive for CWD. The Canadian government took strong action from 2000 to 2004 to eradicate CWD from its farmed elk populations in Saskatchewan: 42 farms containing approximately 18 000 animals (elk and white-tailed deer) were depopulated, costing the government about $40 million. These measures, however, failed to eradicate CWD from Canada, because the disease had already spread to wild deer populations before it was eliminated from farmed populations. Growing numbers of wild deer are being diagnosed with CWD at multiple locations, first in Saskatchewan and now in Alberta. CWD continues to spread.

Interspecies and Intraspecies Transmission

CWD is an efficiently transmitted prion disease among cervids and the only prion disease known to affect both farmed and free-ranging (wild) animals. Thus far, transmission of CWD has occurred among white-tailed deer (*Odocoileus virginianus*), mule deer (*Odocoileus hemionus*), Rocky Mountain elk (*Cervus elaphus nelsoni*), and moose (*Alces alces shirasi*). No affected moose have been detected in Canada, but two have been found in the United States. It is not yet known whether CWD affects caribou or reindeer (*Rangifer tarandus*); however, studies are being conducted by the Canadian Food Inspection Agency to determine the species' susceptibility. Other ruminant species, such as sheep and goats, are also being investigated.

Research has not shown that CWD transmits to humans, and scientists hope to discover that CWD is like scrapie, which is not transmissible to humans. A natural species barrier that reduces humans' susceptibility to CWD and other prion diseases has been demonstrated by in vitro studies; however, the species barrier with CWD is complicated. For example, in experimental models, the CWD prion from mule deer will infect other cervids and ferrets but not hamsters (see Figure 1). Conversely, CWD established in ferrets will transmit to hamsters (see Figure 2).

With the enormous number of CWD prions carried by wild cervids in North America and with the number of different species that may ingest these prions by feeding on carcasses, it is very hard to establish what (if any) species barriers exist, including a barrier for transmission to humans. Research using non-human primates as subjects to determine the likelihood of CWD transmission from cervids to humans is ongoing, but

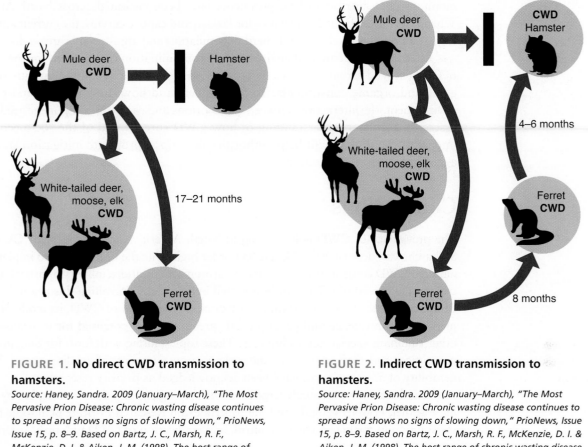

FIGURE 1. No direct CWD transmission to hamsters.
Source: Haney, Sandra. 2009 (January–March), "The Most Pervasive Prion Disease: Chronic wasting disease continues to spread and shows no signs of slowing down," PrioNews, Issue 15, p. 8–9. Based on Bartz, J. C., Marsh, R. F., McKenzie, D. I. & Aiken, J. M. (1998). The host range of chronic wasting disease is altered on passage in ferrets. Virology 251, 297–301.

FIGURE 2. Indirect CWD transmission to hamsters.
Source: Haney, Sandra. 2009 (January–March), "The Most Pervasive Prion Disease: Chronic wasting disease continues to spread and shows no signs of slowing down," PrioNews, Issue 15, p. 8–9. Based on Bartz, J. C., Marsh, R. F., McKenzie, D. I. & Aiken, J. M. (1998). The host range of chronic wasting disease is altered on passage in ferrets. Virology 251, 297–301.

results are not expected for years. These results will be used to establish a comprehensive risk assessment and to develop diagnostic tools for CWD.

Socio-economic Risks and Impacts on Vulnerable Populations

It is essential to determine the risk of transmission of CWD from animals to humans in vulnerable populations, such as hunters and Aboriginal peoples. Deer and moose are important sources of nutrition for many families and communities in both Alberta and Saskatchewan. Aboriginal community members (including non-hunting members) are at high risk of exposure through the practice of meat sharing within their communities. PrioNet Canada and the Alberta Prion Research Institute have joined forces to assess Aboriginal communities' sensitivity to CWD and to assess the implications the disease has for Aboriginal communities and for other stakeholders, such as hunters. It is important to educate vulnerable populations about CWD to manage the real and perceived socio-economic and cultural effects of this disease.

Managing the Spread of CWD

Several factors make it difficult to manage the spread of CWD in captive and free-ranging cervids. The limited ability to diagnose infection in live cervids, the long incubation period of the disease, the subtlety of early clinical signs, and the persistence of prions in the environment all impede the management of CWD. Extensive surveillance programs that monitor CWD distribution and prevalence have been instituted across North America. When CWD is confirmed in facilities for farmed and captive cervids, the current approach is quarantine, followed by whole herd depopulation and appropriate carcass disposal.

Effective management of environmental contamination is important for the control of CWD in wild cervids. Soil is a heterogeneous matrix that contains a mixture of inorganic and organic constituents. To fully understand how these prions persist in the environment, the interaction between CWD prions and each soil component needs to be assessed. A greater understanding of how CWD spreads and of the socio-economic impact of the disease will help authorities develop appropriate mitigation strategies against the spread of infection.

Conclusions

The prevalence of CWD is increasing in North America. The discovery of CWD in a Saskatchewan deer near the Manitoba border highlights the urgent need to implement a national CWD control strategy so that a harmonized, multidisciplinary approach to controlling the spread of CWD can be adopted in Canada. Controlling this prion disease is complicated because of uncertainties surrounding the origin of CWD, its mode of transmission, its prevalence and geographical spread, and the potential for transmission to other ruminant species and to humans. These topics, along with tools for diagnosis and prevention, and analysis to assess the socio-economic impacts of the disease and the vulnerability of at-risk groups, have been acknowledged as priority research areas.

This disease has potentially large economic, ecological, and human costs, but by working together, PrioNet Canada and the Alberta Prion Research Institute plan to be part of the solution in the management, control, and eradication of CWD in North America.

Critical Thinking Questions

1. What is chronic wasting disease (CWD)? What species are affected by this disease in Canada? Describe some symptoms of CWD.
2. What factors contribute to the complexities of CWD transmission in the wild?
3. Describe the worst transmission risk scenario for CWD and the socio-economic impact it would have on Canadian society.

Further Research Question

How are prion diseases (transmissible spongiform encephalopathies, or TSEs) different from other infectious diseases?

References

Haney S. 2009. The most pervasive prion disease: chronic wasting disease continues to spread and shows no signs of slowing down. *PrioNews*. 15:8–9.

Leighton F. 2008. Chronic wasting disease: the TSE of North American cervids. PrioNet Canada Board of Directors Presentation; Dec 12; Vancouver, BC.

PrioNet Canada. 2009. Chronic wasting disease risk management workshop summary. Third International Chronic Wasting Disease Symposium: CWD Advancing the Science and Developing the Tools; July 22–24; Park City, UT.

The Myriad Causes of Autism:
Structural Variation Is a Significant Contributor

Rick J. Scavetta

The Max Planck Institute for Evolutionary Biology

Introduction

Everyone in the world shares the same genes and yet every person is different. These differences occur because every gene has many small possible variations. It's the combination of genetic variation and environmental influences that makes each of us unique. The study of genetics is really the study of genetic variation, but variation in the genetic code can be detected only by comparing the same sequence in two or more individuals. For decades, this meant identifying either the small mutations (one to a few base pairs long) that cause disease and natural variation in phenotypes or very large chromosomal abnormalities (as occur in Down syndrome, for example). Changes in a single nucleotide are called single nucleotide polymorphisms (SNPs) and are widely studied partly because they can cause functional changes in genes.

The surprising amount of complex genetic variation between these two extremes of small mutations and large abnormalities has recently become strikingly apparent. Thanks largely to new technologies, intermediate-size genetic alterations (from 1000 to 1 million bases) can now be detected at the whole-genome level. These intermediate-size variations are collectively referred to as *structural variations*. Rather than being sequence changes, they are **inversions** (changes in the direction of DNA), **translocations** (movement to another chromosomal location), **deletion-insertion** (the loss or gain of part of a chromosome), and **increase-decrease in the copy number** (copy number variants, or CNVs) errors. In a CNV, a region of DNA of more than 1 Kb (1 kilobase or 1000 base pairs) has more or fewer copies when compared with a reference genome. The reference genome may be the genome sequence available in a public database or an internationally available biological sample. As long as all samples in an experiment are compared with the same reference, structural variation can be consistently detected. For example, if the reference genome has two copies of a segment (i.e., duplication) but other individuals in the population have one, three, or more copies, that segment is a CNV. Figure 1 depicts the distribution of CNV loci (positions) on a small region of the human genome.

The extent of natural variations encompassed by CNVs was unexpected and has forced geneticists in all fields of biology to change how they think about such things as genes and disease-causing mutations. For example, duplications and deletions of an entire gene would usually be considered disease causing, because the amount of gene product (i.e., protein) would be too high or too low. However, the observation that seemingly healthy individuals have such large numbers of copy number variations

KEY CONCEPTS

- Structural genetic variation occurs in healthy and autistic individuals.
- Copy number variations are abundant even in healthy individuals.

Nucleotide Position on Chromosome 16 at Cytogenic Band 16p11.2

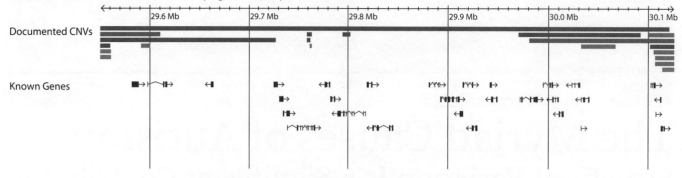

FIGURE 1. CNVs are remarkably abundant and complex.
On this region of chromosome 16 (16p11.2), several studies have detected overlapping CNV regions (increases, red bars; decreases, blue; or both, green) spanning 1 to several hundred Kb. These structural variations encompass several genes (purple) and the regulatory regions surrounding those genes. Only 0.57 Mb of the total 89 Mb of chromosome 16 are diagrammed here.
(Kb = kilobase, 1000 base pairs; Mb = megabase, 1 million base pairs).
Source: Image provided by Jeffrey MacDonald and Stephen Scherer, The Hospital for Sick Children.

changes our understanding of what *the* human genome actually is. We now know that far more genetic variation exists in the genome than previously expected and that many genes can be present in different copy numbers with apparently no harmful effects. Nonetheless, the discovery of such abundant structural variation is also significant in understanding disease; the mutation frequency of CNVs is much higher than that of SNPs, and those mutations may have more drastic consequences than changes to single nucleotides. These characteristics mean that CNVs could be the cause of many different diseases, because not every region of the genome can withstand duplications and deletions without consequence.

Autism is a neurodevelopmental disorder that has been linked to CNVs. It is characterized by impaired communication and reciprocal social interaction skills (e.g., making eye contact) combined with restricted repetitive behaviours. Autism spectrum disorder (ASD) includes a broader range of phenotypes, such as autism and the less severe Asperger's syndrome. In approximately two thirds of ASD cases (excluding Asperger's syndrome), people also exhibit developmental disabilities. Ten percent of cases are associated with other Mendelian disorders, such as Down syndrome and phenylketonuria. ASD is difficult to characterize because people have such a wide spectrum of phenotypes, even within a family. And although some diseases have straightforward heritable genetic links (if one family member has the disease, other family members have a greater chance of having it too), ASD has less heritability than scientists first predicted. These two findings suggest that the genetic origins of ASD are complex and involve many genes.

Research Question

What contribution does structural variation make to the development of ASD?

Autism has a large genetic component, which has focused attention on uncovering common genetic variants associated with the condition. A host of genes that play a role in the development of autism have been found in studies that survey many unrelated autistic individuals for common genetic variants not present in non-autistic control populations. Specific autism-causing genes have not been detected, however, which may be because of the **multifactorial** (contributions from several interacting genes) and heterogenic (many different genes resulting in the same condition) nature of the disease. Studies have also shown that cytogenic (i.e., large) abnormalities are frequently found in the chromosomes of people with autism. This result raised two questions: What is the architecture of structural variation in autistic people? Which genes are affected and how? To dissect this complex puzzle, scientists from across Canada, in collaboration with colleagues in Europe and the United States, undertook a detailed genetic analysis of structural variation in people with autism.

Hypothesis
Genomic structural variation contributes to the development of ASD.

Methods and Results

DNA extracted from blood samples of 427 unrelated ASD cases were analyzed by using **karyotyping** (photomicrograph of chromosomes from individuals) and **DNA microarrays**. Microarrays are commonly used to obtain genome-wide information from DNA or RNA. Small fragments of single-stranded DNA (a few dozen to hundreds of thousands of base pairs long) are attached in an array of little dots (microns in diameter) to a glass slide called a chip. The sample DNA is then labelled with a fluorescent marker and **hybridized** (bound together by using the natural hydrogen bonding between complementary DNA sequences) to the DNA on the chip. The biochemical conditions are optimized such that DNA will hybridize only where sequence matches occur. The chip is then read with a scanner, and the fluorescent signal at each spot is measured. Several chip models are available for detecting CNVs, and in this case, an array designed to detect 500 000 SNPs was used. At each dot on the chip, DNA carrying specific alleles bind to a different position in the dot, revealing information about the sequence for a specific SNP. In addition to using the fluorescent signal to get information about SNPs, the researchers determined whether regions of DNA were present at a higher copy number than normal. A region was called a CNV if more than one copy was present. This technique has the noted advantage of providing information on two forms of genetic variation: SNPs and CNVs.

The study included 500 samples from a control population. These samples were analyzed in the same way, and common CNVs from the two data sets were removed so that scientists could isolate the CNVs that were unique to the people with ASD. On all chromosomes (excepting Y), 277 CNV regions were found only in people with ASD, making these potentially disease causing loci.

Chip analysis was the first approach used to detect structural variation among the samples, but individual cases were later confirmed by other laboratory techniques, such as quantitative polymerase chain reaction (PCR) or karyotyping, in which stained chromosomes are visually examined to detect abnormalities from the typical staining pattern.

Conclusions

In 7 percent of individuals, *de novo* CNVs (i.e., not inherited from either parent) were present. However, in some instances, siblings without ASD and unrelated individuals had the same CNV and some siblings with ASD did not, a result of the heterogenic nature of autism (see Photo A).

The study also identified several possible ASD regions not previously considered as disease causing. Scientists have now identified some of the underlying genotypic differences, and the phenotypic effects of ASD are known, and so the remaining question is,

PHOTO A. An autistic girl and her unaffected sister.
The autistic girl on the left has a *de novo* duplication at locus 16p11.2, a region found to be associated with autism in this study. However, her sister (right) also has a duplication but is not autistic. *Source: Figure 3f from: Fernandez BA, et al. Phenotypic Spectrum Associated with De Novo and Inherited Deletions and Duplications at 16p11.2 in Individuals Ascertained for Diagnosis of Autism Spectrum Disorder. J. Med. Genet. 2009 Sep. 24. Used with permission.*

what do these genomic differences mean at the cellular level? The structural aberrations seemed to affect genes whose protein products appear in the synapses between neurons, or proteins that have previously been implicated in developmental disabilities. A higher copy number of a gene may result in more gene product being produced, which could have a negative impact on the cell's physiology. However, the biological relevance of any single CNV will need to be resolved with further experimentation. Finally, the researchers confirmed that some genes already known to be involved in ASD are also associated with CNV regions. This result confirms the involvement of those genes in ASD and highlights the complex nature of the genetic changes in those regions.

Future Directions

This study provided a framework on which future studies on the genetics of autism have expanded. The CNVs identified were deposited into a database of structural variation and some particularly interesting loci were chosen for further study. Follow-up experiments have focused on one such region, called 16p11.2, a CNV found in about 1 percent of people with ASD. As the phenotypic effects of each CNV are uncovered, scientists move ever closer to understanding the underlying causes of ASD and other CNV-related diseases.

Critical Thinking Questions

1. What is a microarray chip?
2. What kinds of genes were found in CNV regions of people with autism?
3. Why has it been so difficult to uncover the genetic basis of autism?

Further Research Question

The study described a CNV at 16p11.2 at about 1 percent frequency. What could be the causative gene in this CNV and are any other mental health disorders associated with this CNV?

References

Marshall CR, Noor A, Vincent JB, Lionel AC, Feuk L, Skaug J, Shago M, Moessner R, Pinto D, Ren Y, et al. 2008. Structural variation of chromosomes in autism spectrum disorder. *Am. J. Hum.* Genet. 82(2):477–488.

Redon R, Ishikawa S, Fitch KR, Feuk L, Perry GH, Andrews TD, Fiegler H, Shapero MH, Carson AR, Chen W, et al. 2006. Global variation in copy number in the human genome. *Nat.* 444(7118):444–454.

Neuropathic Pain:
Are You Too Sensitive?

Sarah Hewitt
Mount Royal University

Introduction

We're all familiar with the sudden shock we feel when we hurt ourselves, whether it is the discomfort of a paper cut or the teeth-gritting pain of a broken bone. But why do we have mechanisms to feel pain at all? It seems counterintuitive that pain is beneficial, but, in fact, pain warns us of actual or potential damage to tissue, allowing us to quickly respond to dangerous situations. Sensory neurons transmit touch and pain stimuli to the spinal cord; from there, the signals are sent to the sensory cortex in the brain. If these sensory pathways are damaged, not only do we lose a critical self-protection mechanism but the neurons can also become dysfunctional and a condition known as **neuropathic pain** can develop.

Neuropathic pain has no simple definition, and it is used as a catch-all term to describe a state of chronic pain that can arise when neurons have been damaged because of amputation, cancer, direct injury to the spinal cord or peripheral nerves, or pathologies related to diabetes or human immunodeficiency virus (HIV). Neuropathic pain is characterized by the development of **allodynia** of the sensory pathways. Allodynia is sensitization to a stimulus that would not normally be painful but now is, making even a light summer breeze or the softest touch of clothing against the skin seem excruciating.

Between 2 and 3 percent of Canadians experience neuropathic pain. It is a devastating condition that can reduce people's quality of life. Over-the-counter pain medications are largely ineffective in alleviating symptoms. Currently, researchers are trying to identify the underlying causes of neuropathic pain, with the hope that more effective treatments can be developed. Scientists from Laval and McGill Universities in Quebec have collaborated to investigate the cellular mechanisms through which neuronal hypersensitivity develops after injury.

KEY CONCEPTS

- Sensory neurons transmit pain information to the central nervous system.
- Damage to pain pathways can result in long-term pathological changes in neurons.

Research Question

How does injury lead to neuronal hypersensitivity and allodynia?

Surprisingly, the secret may lie not in the neurons at all but in a type of neuroimmune cell found throughout the central nervous system (CNS)—namely, microglial cells (see Photo A). **Microglia** are a type of glial cell. Glial cells are a family of non-neuronal cells in the CNS that modulate neuronal signalling and support and protect neurons. Specifically, microglia are immune cells that patrol the CNS and become activated in response to invading pathogens, stress, and damaged tissue. Once activated, they release

PHOTO A. **Microglia in the brain.**
Microglia are neuroimmune cells in the CNS. They extend and retract their processes, and they scour the CNS for invading pathogens or damaged tissue.
Source: Photo by Cheryl Sank, University of Calgary.

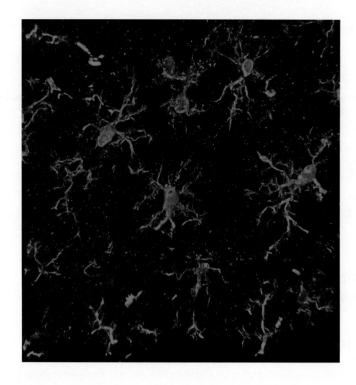

signalling molecules, including growth factors. One such growth factor is **brain-derived neurotrophic factor (BDNF)**. BDNF initiates multiple biochemical pathways, some of which alter the activity levels of neurons, making them fire more or less often. The release of BDNF may be an underlying cause of the changes that take place following injury to neurons.

Hypothesis

In response to neuronal damage, microglia release signalling molecules (BDNF) that increase the excitability of sensory neurons in the spinal cord and lead to allodynia.

Methods and Results

With rats as a model system, a team led by Yves De Koninck at Laval University used a combination of behavioural tests and electrical recordings from sensory neurons in the rat spinal cord to explore this hypothesis.

To assess the sensitivity of the touch pathways, the researchers measured the paw-withdrawal reflex. Following stimulation of the rat's paw, they measured how quickly the rat would pull its paw away and compared the withdrawal times before and after the spinal cord had been damaged. The spinal cord was damaged by placing a compression cuff around the cord to cause a crushing injury. If the rat withdrew its paw faster after injury, it likely meant that the sensitivity of the pathway had increased and that the rat perceived the stimulus as more uncomfortable, an example of allodynia. As expected, rats did display a faster withdrawal reflex (i.e., they pulled back faster) after spinal cord injury than before, which indicated that the sensory pathways had become hypersensitive.

Next, the researchers asked whether the application of either microglia or BDNF could lead to hypersensitivity when the spinal cord was intact. To assess this, activated microglia or BDNF were injected into the spinal cords of healthy rats, and again the withdrawal reflex was measured. Both manipulations initiated a more sensitive

TABLE 1. Summary of Experiments

Experiment	Spinal Cord	Microglia	BDNF Present	Neuronal Excitability	Paw Withdrawal Reflex
Control	No damage	Inactive	No	Normal	Normal
Activated microglia added	No damage	Active	Yes	Increased	Sensitized
BDNF added	No damage	Inactive	Yes	Increased	Sensitized
Spinal cord injury	Damaged	Active	Yes	Increased	Sensitized

paw withdrawal. Thus, the in vivo manipulations of direct injury, the injection of activated microglia, and the injection of BDNF all sensitized the system and elicited allodynia.

Was this sensitization the result of a change in the spinal cord neurons themselves or a change in the way the brain integrates sensory information? A technique called electrophysiology was used to answer this question. With this technique, researchers can make direct electrical recordings from spinal cord neurons and measure how excitable the neurons are. Exposing the spinal cord neurons to (1) activated microglia or (2) BDNF made the neurons more excitable. These effects were blocked when pharmacological inhibitors that prevent microglia from becoming activated or prevent BDNF from interacting with its membrane-bound receptor were used. These experiments demonstrated that it was the direct effect of BDNF released from activated microglia on spinal cord neurons that caused allodynia of the paw-withdrawal response and increased the excitability of the neurons. These experiments are summarized in Table 1.

Conclusions

The results from these experiments tell us that an injury to the spinal cord activates microglia, causing these cells to release the signalling molecule BDNF, which triggers the spinal cord neurons to become more excitable. The hypersensitivity of the sensory pathway may lead to the development of neuropathic pain symptoms, such as allodynia. This cellular pathway is summarized in Figure 1.

Future Directions

The future lies in identifying which steps in the cellular pathway are the most susceptible to clinical interventions that will be safe for people. Because the treatments available in Canada involve a long list of prescription medications, each with substantial side effects, the most promising course of action may be to prevent neuropathic pain before it develops. As more is discovered about the link between nerve damage and the development of hypersensitivity, more potential targets for medication may be found, helping people to effectively manage this painful condition.

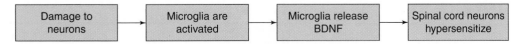

FIGURE 1. **Cellular pathway in the development of neuropathic pain.**

Critical Thinking Questions

1. Why is the ability to sense pain actually a good thing?
2. Why were microglia identified by the researchers as a potential target for a role in the development of neuropathic pain?
3. How did the researchers examine changes in the sensitivity of pain-sensing pathways?

Further Research Question

What are some of the current techniques used to address neuropathic pain in people?

References

*Coull JA, Beggs S, Boudreau D, Boivin D, Tsuda M, Inoue K, Gravel C, Salter MW, De Koninck Y. 2005. BDNF from microglia causes the shift in neuronal anion gradient underlying neuropathic pain. *Nat.* 438:1017–1021.

Coull JA, Boudreau D, Bachand K, Prescott SA, Nault F, Sik A, De Koninck P, De Koninck Y. 2003. Trans-synaptic shift in anion gradient in spinal lamina I neurons as a mechanism of neuropathic pain. *Nat.* 424:938–942.

*Gilron I, Watson CP, Cahill CM, Moulin DE. 2006. Neuropathic pain: a practical guide for the clinician. *Can. Med. Assoc. J.* 175:265–275.

Milligan ED, Watkins LR. 2009. Pathological and protective roles of glia in chronic pain. *Nat. Rev. Neurosci.* 10:23–36.

New Species Right Before Our Eyes:
How Birdfeeders Can Influence Speciation

Sarah Hewitt
Mount Royal University

Introduction

Few things define the Canadian fall like the iconic V formation of Canada geese as they fly south; it's a sure sign that winter is near. Their return en masse in the spring means that we'll soon have to watch out for goslings and nests near the ponds and rivers in our cities. Countless generations of geese have followed this migration pattern, and many species of birds throughout the world migrate. However, we now have evidence that human activities may be altering the migration patterns of some species, a change that could lay the groundwork for **speciation**, the development of entirely new species.

Central European blackcaps (*Sylvia atricapilla*; see Photo A) have their breeding grounds in south central Europe (mostly in Germany and Austria).

At one time this entire blackcap population would migrate together and spend the winters where it is warmer: in Portugal, Spain, and North Africa. Then, in the 1960s, birdwatchers in Britain reported seeing blackcaps in their gardens throughout the winter months. Since then, the numbers have soared, and more and more blackcaps are now making the British Isles their winter home. It seems that a split has occurred in the blackcap ranks: one part of the blackcap population heads northwest to England for their

KEY CONCEPTS
■ The evolution of species is an ongoing process.
■ Humans can affect speciation.
■ Sympatric speciation can occur rapidly.

PHOTO A.
European blackcap (*Sylvia atricapilla*).
Source: © FLPA/Alamy/Getstock.com

FIGURE 1. Map of black-cap migration routes.
Blackcaps breeding in Central Europe now have two distinct migration routes: northwest toward Britain (A) and southwest toward Portugal, Spain, and North Africa (B).

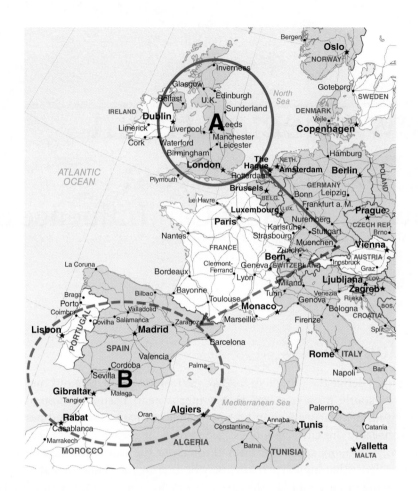

wintering grounds, and the other part travels the previously preferred southern route. This is no small change as a migration path to England takes these birds 1200 to 1800 km north of their traditional Mediterranean wintering sites (see Figure 1).

Approximately 10 percent of the blackcap population breeding in southern Germany now migrates northwest to Britain. This alternative migration pattern arose in only 30 generations and is a great example of evolution in action. Migratory behaviour is a partially inherited trait, meaning that parents pass down the propensity for migrating northwest or south to their offspring. But what drove this change in behaviour?

Recent findings point to human activity as the driving force for this change; all we did was feed the birds. Over a few decades, increasingly more people in Britain were setting out birdfeeders in their backyards, providing birds with food year-round. With an endless food supply and a warming climate, blackcaps started over wintering in Britain instead of heading south. After all, if the food is plentiful and the weather isn't too bad, why leave? After a handful of generations, however, this simple act has caused profound changes in the blackcap population. Scientists have studied these changes as mechanisms that likely underlie the formation of new species.

Research Question

What effect does the change in migratory route have on blackcaps?

Scientists across Europe and North America have tackled this question with some fascinating results. Researchers predict that the emergence of different migration patterns could lead to the evolution of the blackcap population into two separate species, a phenomenon known as **speciation**. Speciation can happen in two ways: a population is separated into two groups because of some geographical barrier (**allopatric speciation**) or a reproductive barrier emerges so that two groups who live in the same region no longer interbreed (**sympatric speciation**).

In 2005, scientists demonstrated that the different migration patterns have facilitated some reproductive isolation at the breeding grounds. When blackcaps arrive in southern Germany and Austria for the breeding season, the first thing they do is find a breeding territory and mate. Scientists have found that blackcaps who winter together are more than 2.5 times as likely to mate with each other as with blackcaps who winter elsewhere. Choosing a mate that is similar in some way (such as one who migrates to the same wintering grounds) is known as **positive assortative mating**. Assortative mating in this case is due simply to timing. In Britain, compared with southern regions, a more dramatic change occurs in the length of the day when spring arrives. This change in day length is what prompts migration and the birds in Britain leave for their breeding grounds earlier than do the southern blackcaps. The combination of leaving earlier and travelling a shorter distance means that the birds wintering in Britain arrive at the breeding grounds about two weeks earlier than their southern counterparts. The birds that arrive first find their mates right away, without waiting for latecomers. Reproductive isolation caused by the timing of breeding is an example of temporal isolation, and so the different migratory routes render each migratory group reproductively isolated from each other: a perfect recipe for sympatric speciation. Once reproductive isolation is established, the genotypes and phenotypes of the blackcaps are likely to diverge.

Hypothesis

The migratory divide within the blackcap population has led to reproductive isolation that is associated with genotypic and phenotypic divergence.

Methods and Results

To investigate this hypothesis, scientists captured blackcaps on their breeding grounds in Germany. First they had to resolve where each particular bird had spent the previous winter. To do this, scientists used a clever technique that is based on the type of water found in the bird's tissues (feathers). Rainwater in different regions contains different concentrations of certain hydrogen **isotopes**. Scientists found that the levels of a particular hydrogen isotope in the bird's tissues corresponded to the levels of that isotope in the rainwater of the region where the bird had overwintered. Birds that overwintered in Britain had hydrogen isotopes in their tissues typical of those found in British rainwater, and birds that overwintered in the Mediterranean had hydrogen isotopes in their tissues typical of the rainwater from that region.

With the wintering grounds established, the researchers then compared the genetic and phenotypic differences between the two groups of birds. For the genetic analysis, DNA was extracted from blood samples. Wing and beak shape and length were measured, and plumage colouration was analyzed for phenotypic comparisons.

The genetic data revealed that the blackcaps that migrate to Britain are genetically distinct from the rest of the blackcap population, even though they breed in the same geographic location. This means that the DNA is becoming more dissimilar between the two groups, and these changes cannot be attributed to anything other than their different migration routes. This genetic divergence indicates reproductive isolation, putting these blackcaps on the path toward sympatric speciation.

Researchers also found differences in the shape of the wings between the two groups. The shape of the wing provides different aerodynamic advantages. Pointier, more streamlined wings are good for long distance migration but are not as manoeuvrable as rounder wings. Wing pointedness is measured by the Holynski index. A lower number on the index means that the wing is less pointed (more rounded). Across many

FIGURE 2. **Wing pointed-
ness in relation to the
migratory distance of
different blackcap
populations.**
A population of sedentary
blackcaps that does not
migrate at all (A) are compared
with the northwest (short distance) migrants (B) and southwest (long distance) migrants
(C). As the migration distance
increases, so too does the
Holynski index number and
thus the pointedness of the
wings.
*Source: Adapted from: Figure 3 of
Rolshausen G, Segelbacher G,
Hobson KA, Schaefer HM. 2009.
Contemporary evolution of reproductive isolation and phenotypic
divergence in sympatry along a
migratory divide.* Current Biology
19: 2097–2101. © 2009, with permission from Elsevier.

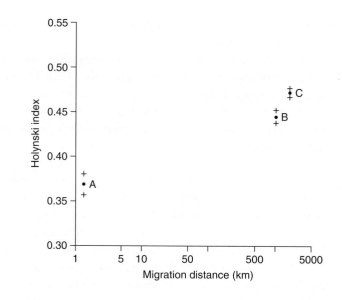

European bird species, shorter migration routes are associated with a lower Holynski index. Blackcaps migrating to Britain for the winter have a shorter distance to travel and need to manoeuvre around bird feeders once they arrive. Compared with the southwest-migrating birds, these blackcaps have less pointed, more rounded wings and thus a lower Holynski index (see Figure 2). Because the whole population used to have the same migration route, this difference in wing shape is likely a result of the different selective pressures associated with migration.

Not only are the wings different shapes but the beaks are also distinct. Birds have different beak shapes to exploit various food sources. The SW migrants tend to have broader bills, allowing them to grasp fruits, such as olives, that make up the majority of their Mediterranean diets. In contrast, the NW migrants have relatively narrower and longer beaks that allow them to probe seeds and fats from the bird feeders in Britain.

Finally, the plumage colours of the two groups were compared. NW migrants had feathers that were relatively browner compared with the greyer feathers of the SW migrants. These colour differences could result from differences in the timing of moulting or possibly from changes in melanin (colour pigment in feathers) production between the two groups. The researchers suggest that these differences in hues provide a way for birds to identify birds belonging to the same migratory group.

Conclusions

The simple desire to attract more birds to our gardens has enabled scientists to identify mechanisms that could lead to sympatric speciation. Providing a source of winter food meant the adoption of a new migratory pattern for the birds, which in turn led to their temporal reproductive isolation in the breeding season. In a mere handful of blackcap generations, genotypes and phenotypes have diverged to the point where a group of blackcaps could start down a new evolutionary path.

Future Directions

Evolution is often studied indirectly because it takes place over long time spans, much longer than the human lifespan. Examples such as this allow scientists to observe the mech-anisms that underlie evolutionary processes in action. They can watch as evolutionary forces, over generations, shape the future of a species. It isn't known if the selective pres-sures experienced by the two migratory groups will cause even further divergence, and only future research will give us this answer. Beyond the effects on the blackcaps, this work also shows the profound impact human behaviour can have on a species. Simply hanging a feeder in the backyard can cause ripples through a species' evolutionary future. For better or worse, all our actions affect the other species that share the planet with us.

Critical Thinking Questions

1. When the birds were caught at their breeding grounds in the spring, how did the scientists determine where particular birds spent the winter?
2. What findings have lead to the prediction that blackcaps are experiencing sympatric speciation as opposed to allopatric speciation?
3. If migratory orientation is controlled by one or a few genes, what might you predict about the migration route of the offspring from a northwest migrant and a southwest migrant?

Further Research Question

A previous study (Bearhop et al., 2005) discovered that blackcaps that spent the winter in Britain also produced more offspring at the breeding grounds. Why might this be?

References

*Bearhop S, Fiedler W, Furness RW, Votier SC, Waldron S, Newton J, Bowen GJ, Berthold P, Farnsworth K. 2005. Assortative mating as a mechanism for rapid evolution of a migratory divide. *Science*. 310:502–504.

Berthold P, Helbig AJ, Mohr G, Querner U. 1992. Rapid microevolution of migratory behaviour in a wild bird species. *Nature*. 360:668–669.

*Rolshausen G, Segelbacher G, Hobson KA, Schaefer HM. 2009. Contemporary evolution of reproductive isolation and phenotypic divergence in sympatry along a migratory divide. *Curr. Biol.* 19:2097–2101.

Phytoremediation:
Plants to the Rescue

Sharon L. Gillies
University of the Fraser Valley

Introduction

Soil contamination is a major problem in Canada, and not just around mining operations and oil fields, the locations we might expect. In fact, we all may be living closer to one of the many contaminated sites in Canada than we think (see Figure 1). The gas station at the end of our street may have petroleum hydrocarbons leaking from its storage tanks into the soil. Our backyards may have old oil tanks buried in them, left over from when oil was used in home heating systems. Industrial accidents can result in chemical or heavy metals contamination. Even radioactive compounds and PCBs have been found in Canadian soil. These toxic materials can cause cancer and other diseases. Removing tons of soil and treating it is costly, and these actions have their own detrimental effects on the environment. Fortunately, Canada is a world leader in the field of **phytoremediation** (using plants to clean up contaminated soil). It doesn't get any greener than that.

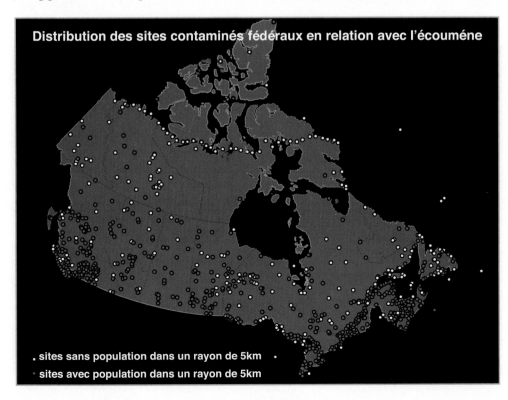

FIGURE 1. Distribution of federal contaminated sites across Canada, 2003–2004. This map shows federally owned contaminated locations. Red dots indicate sites within 0.5 km of populated areas, and white dots indicate that sites are not within 0.5 km of populated regions. (This map is available only in French.).
Source: Reproduced with the permission of the Minister of Public Works and Government Services Canada, 2010.

Phytoremediation and Heavy Metal Contaminants

Researchers have discovered many plants useful in rehabilitating contaminated sites. Plants can remove, destroy, or sequester (isolate) toxic compounds found in soils. They can take up and concentrate metals into their tissues (**phytoextraction**), or release volatile compounds, such as arsenic and mercury, into the atmosphere by **phytovolatilization**. For example, some plants remove toxic methyl mercury from the soil and convert it into the less toxic elemental mercury before releasing it.

About 450 plants have been identified as **hyperaccumlators** (take up and store large quantities) of metals (Shah and Nongkynrih, 2007). A single gene may be responsible for differences between Cu and Zn hyperaccumulators and non-hyperaccumulators (Shah and Nongkynrih, 2007). *Alyssum murale* is an example of an Ni hyperaccumulator. *Alyssum murale* can take up both Ni and Co through its roots and translocate it to shoot tissues. Using X-ray tomography, it is apparent that *A. murale* compartmentalizes Ni in epidermal cells, but Co remains in the extracellular space and cells near leaf tips and margins (see Photo A).

Hyperaccumulators can concentrate up to 100 times the amount of toxic compounds than non-accumulators. In fact, hyperaccumulator plants have been used for **phytomining** (using plants to mine metals). Imagine growing alfalfa (*Medicago sativa*) or canola (*Brassica juncea*) on gold mine tailings (waste left from mining operations) and being able to harvest a kilogram of gold from each contaminated hectare (Anderson and Meech, 2002). Research by John Meech from the University of British Columbia and Chris Anderson from Massey University in New Zealand has shown this may be possible.

Metals such as Fe, Cu, Co, and Zn are **micronutrients** (essential to the growth and survival of plants in minute amounts). In large amounts, these metals are toxic. Other non-essential heavy metals are often toxic to both plants and animals. How do hyperaccumulating plants survive high concentrations of heavy metals? Some may use **chelators** (bind the metal with another compound), such as the amino acid histidine and the tripeptide glutathione, to reduce their toxicity. Others may **sequester** (isolate) the toxins in their central vacuole or have biochemical pathways to convert the metal into a non-toxic form.

PHOTO A. Distribution of Co and Ni in *Alyssum murale* leaves.
Well-watered *A. murale* leaves were imaged using X-ray tomography, Co (red) and Ni (green). The top photos show the distribution of metal in the leaf tip; the middle photos are the middle-leaf regions; and the bottom photos show the metal distribution in relation to the leaf cell structure. Images were acquired with synchrotron-based differential absorption-edge computed-microtomography, which uses X-rays to create cross-sectional images of a three-dimensional object).
Source: Photo adapted from Chaney RL, Angle JS, Broadhurst CL, Peters CA, Tappero RV, Sparks DL. 2007. Improved understanding of hyperaccumulation yields commercial phytoextraction and phytomining technologies. J. Environ. Qual. 36:1429–1443, Figure 2, p. 1437.

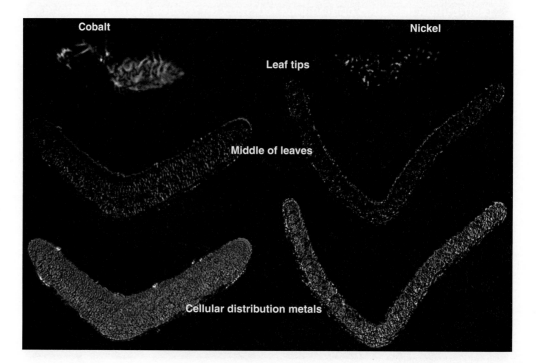

Cobalt Nickel

Leaf tips

Middle of leaves

Cellular distribution metals

Phytoremediation and Organic Contaminants

Such organic compounds as pesticides, PCBs, petroleum hydrocarbons, and trinitrotoluene (TNT) are also soil contaminants. Some soil bacteria can metabolize many of these compounds, but the process is very slow. Certain plants have been identified as being capable of stimulating the bacterial degradation of organic molecules in the soil. Grasses, corn, wheat, soybean, peas, and beans have extensive and fibrous root networks that promote an active **rhizosphere**. The rhizosphere is the region influenced by plant roots and the associated micro-organisms. The more activity in the rhizosphere, the more contaminants will be broken down and removed. Many sites are contaminated by persistent, toxic explosives left from military testing or manufacturing. Neil Bruce from York University has been investigating the role of plants and bacteria in the breakdown and removal of these contaminants. Research by Bruce and his colleagues has found that plants are capable of degrading novel organic compounds, such as TNT; researchers in Bruce's lab have proposed a biochemical pathway (see Figure 2) (Gandia-Herrero, 2008). He is currently working on developing a remediation strategy for soil contaminated by explosives.

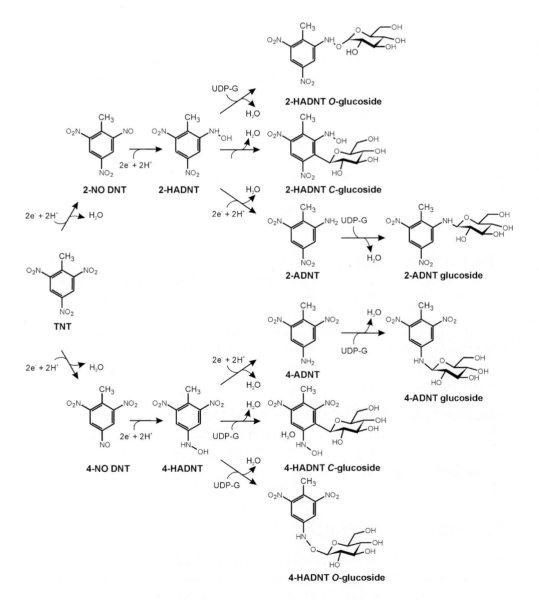

FIGURE 2. Proposed glucsylation pathway of 2,4,6-trinitrotoluene (TNT) in arabidopsis.
Source: Gandia-Herrero F, Lorenz A, Larson TR, Graham IA, Bowles DJ, Rylott EL, Bruce NC (2008) Detoxification of the explosive 2,4,6-trinitrotoluene in Arabidopsis-discovery of bifunctional O- and C-glucosyltransferases. The Plant Journal 56:963–974. Figure 8, p. 971. Used with permission.

The Role of Bacteria in Improving Phytoremediation

One of the problems with phytoremediation is that many hyperaccumulating plants tend to be small and slow-growing. The ability to remove and accumulate contaminants from the soil is dependent on plant growth. Plants may become stressed and slow their growth in response to the toxicity of these compounds. Bernard Glick and colleagues from the University of Waterloo have been conducting research on bacteria that promote plant growth and how this plant–bacteria interaction may enhance phytoremediation in soil contaminated by petroleum hydrocarbons and heavy metals. Glick states:

> Plant growth–promoting bacteria are soil bacteria that are involved in a beneficial association with plants. These bacteria use a variety of mechanisms (from helping the plant to acquire needed nutrients to modulating the levels of plant hormones, which affects plant growth and development, to preventing pathogenic agents from inhibiting plant growth) to facilitate the positive impacts they have on plant growth. Among the major mechanisms used by plant growth–promoting bacteria is the presence and functioning of the enzyme 1-aminocyclopropane-1-carboxylate (ACC) deaminase, which cleaves the compound ACC, the immediate precursor of the plant stress hormone ethylene in all higher plants, and synthesizing the plant hormone indoleacetic acid (IAA). Plant growth–promoting bacterial strains that both contain ACC deaminase and produce IAA provide a wide range of different plant species with a significant level of protection from the damage caused by various environmental stresses, including drought, flooding, a variety of pathogenic agents, temperature extremes, high levels of salt, and the presence of heavy metals and organic environmental contaminants.

Plants treated with plant growth–promoting bacteria that protect the plant against these stresses are much more efficient at the phytoremediation (i.e., breakdown and removal) of metals and organic environmental contaminants than are plants that don't have these bacteria. In this way, the plants and the bacteria act as partners in a mutually beneficial relationship that results in more efficient environmental clean up (2010 email to the author; unreferenced).

Research Question
When high levels of toxic compounds are in the soil, plants grow slowly and this limits the utility of using phytoremediation. How can plant growth be improved?

Plants grown on contaminated sites, even hyperaccumulators, experience stress. As a result they can be slow growing and small. This is a problem when using phytoremediation, because the amount of contaminant removed or degraded is proportional to size of the plants.

Hypothesis
Plant growth–promoting rhizobacteria (PGPR) will enhance the phytoremediation ability of plants that are used to treat petroleum hydrocarbon contaminated soil (Gurska, 2009).

Methods and Results

For three years, Gurska et. al. conducted field tests at an oil refinery in Ontario where petroleum sludge had been regularly spread on the soil and tilled over for 20 years. At the start of the study, soil was tilled to provide aeration and increase photo-oxidation

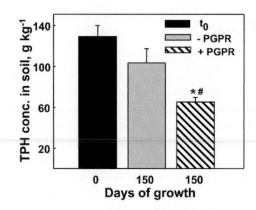

FIGURE 3. Effect of annual rye grass and plant growth–promoting rhizobacteria on hydrocarbon waste.
Decease in total petroleum hydrocarbon (TPH) concentration after 150 days, using annual ryegrass in year one. Treatments were as follows: T_0 had no plants; -PGRP had annual ryegrass seeds planted; and +PGRP had annual ryegrass seeds coated with plant growth–promoting rhizobacteria, *Pseudomonas*. There was a significant decrease in TPH concentration in the plots with +PGRP.
Source: Reprinted with permission from Gurska J, Wang, W, Gerhardt KE, Khalid AM, Isherwood DM, Huang X, Glick BR, and Greenberg BM. 2009. Three year field test of a plant growth promoting rhizobacteria enhanced phytoremediation system at a land farm for treatment of hydrocarbon waste. Environmental Science and Technology 43(12): 4472–4479. Figure 3A, page 4476. © 2009, American Chemical Society.

(solar-induced breakdown) of organic compounds. In year one, annual ryegrass was planted both with and without PGRP. Both of the ryegrass plots were compared with control plots with no plants. In years two and three, in different plots of contaminated ground, ryegrass, barley, and tall fescue were planted with and without PGRP.

In year one, plants without PGRP were significantly smaller, had less total **biomass** (living matter in an area), and were shorter than plants treated with PGRP. There was no significant difference in the concentration of petroleum hydrocarbons between the soil of non-PGRP plants and soil that had no plants at all. This is likely because of the fact that few non-PGRP plants survived; those present were small and did not grow well. Soil from sites with plants treated with the addition of PGRP, however, had significantly less petroleum hydrocarbons in the soil (see Figure 3). Results were similar in years two and three, although the total amount of petroleum hydrocarbons removed by plants with PGRP was less than in year one.

Conclusions

Using a PGRP-enhanced phytoremediation system was more effective than using phytoremediation alone in removing petroleum hydrocarbons from soil. Phytoremediation is less expensive than chemical or mechanical decontamination, but can be a slow process because the toxicity of the contaminants reduces plant growth. Plants alone are not always successful in removing persistent hydrocarbons from soils, and ongoing research is looking to develop fast and effective phytoremediation systems using PGRP. Plant growth is enhanced with the addition of PGRP because the bacteria produce the plant hormone IAA and the enzyme ACC deaminase, which lowers ethylene levels in the plants. There is also some evidence that the addition of symbiotic mycorrhizal fungi (fungi that live symbiotically with plant roots) as well as PGRP can reduce the stress experienced by plants used for metal phytoremdiation, and also increase their growth (Gamalero, 2009).

Future Directions

Future strategies may include breeding programs to enlarge plant root mass to increase the rhizosphere. It may be possible to genetically engineer plants to increase the production of chelators and other mechanisms for detoxifying or sequestering toxins. Researchers are also looking at genetically modifying rhizosphere micro-organisms to increase their metabolism of hydrocarbons and plant growth–promoting activity (Gerhardt, 2009). The ability of plants to remove contaminants from soil makes them an important ally in the clean-up of major industrial contamination sites, those in our neighbourhoods and even our own backyards.

Critical Thinking Questions

1. Why might a small amount of lead be toxic to a plant but a similar amount of iron is not? Would the concentration of these metals in soils affect human health?
2. Why do some plants have biochemical pathways that can detoxify compounds, such as TNT, they have never before encountered? What are some of the potential problems involved in using genetically altered plants and microbes for phytoremediation projects?
3. What are some of the disadvantages of using phytoremediation?

Further Research Question

How does the interaction between plant roots and rhizobacteria increase the breakdown of contaminants (see Gerhardt et. al.)?

References

Anderson C. Meech JA. 2002, Sept. Growing gold: using metal-accumulating plants to produce gold [Internet]. Centre for Environmental Research in Minerals, Metals, and Materials. [cited 2010, Apr 12]. Available from: http://www.mining.ubc.ca/cerm3/growing metals.html

Gamalero E, Lingua G, Berta G, Glick BR. 2009. Beneficial role of plant growth promoting bacteria and arbuscual mycorrhizal fungi on plant responses to heavy metal stress. *Can. J. Microbiol.* 55:501–514.

Gandia-Herrero F, Lorenz A, Larson TR, Graham IA, Bowles DJ, Rylott EL, Bruce NC. 2008. Detoxification of the explosive 2,4,6-trinitrotoluene in Arabidopsis: discovery of bifunctional O- and C-glucosyltransferases. *Plant J.* 56: 963–974.

*Gerhardt KR, Huang X, Glick BR, Greenberg BM. 2009. Phytoremediation and rhizomediation of organic soil contaminants: potential and challenges. *Plant Sci.* 176:20–30.

*Glick BR. 2003. Phytoremediation: synergistic use of plants and bacteria to clean up the environment. *Biotechnol. Adv.* 21: 383–393.

Gurska J, Wang, W, Gerhardt KE, Khalid AM, Isherwood DM, Huang X, Glick BR, Greenberg BM. 2009. Three year field test of a plant growth promoting rhizobacteria enhanced phytoremediation system at a land farm for treatment of hydrocarbon waste. *Environ. Sci. Technol.* 43:4472–4479.

*Shah K, Nongkynrih JM. 2007. Metal hyperaccumulation and bioremediation. *Biol. Plantarum* 51: 618–634.

The Process of Science:
Brain Food

Jay Ingram
Discovery Channel

Introduction

Half a century ago a group of researchers made the jaw-dropping announcement that they had been able to transfer memories from one organism to another by allowing them to eat each other. The organisms in question were tiny flatworms called planaria. Scientists believed that they had shown that memories are stored as chemicals and that these could be transferred from one worm to another, simply by allowing an untrained worm to eat the chopped-up remains of an expert one that had been trained in a particular task. If memories were indeed coded in chemicals, then you could dream of learning a new language or memorizing the lines of a play—or the sequence of the Krebs cycle—just by taking a pill; something that would no doubt create huge lineups in pharmacies. You can imagine the kind of stir this claim caused in the scientific community.

It was sensational science while it lasted; it ended not with a dramatic experiment demonstrating that memories couldn't be transferred (the way things are supposed to happen in science) but with the scientific establishment simply turning away to pursue other research. The majority doubted that worms could learn by eating other worms, and most couldn't be bothered backing up those doubts with experiments. They may have been turned off by the personality of the scientist involved; it is almost certain that the episode will always be cloaked in uncertainty.

Memories in a Molecule

In the 1950s, American psychologist James McConnell and his colleague Robert Thompson had apparently done with tiny flatworms what Pavlov had done with dogs: they established a conditioned response. Pavlov's dogs salivated at the sound of a bell; McConnell's flatworms scrunched up at the flash of a light. The dogs were conditioned to perform that unusual act by having food presented together with the sound. The flatworms first experienced the light together with an electric shock, and eventually the light alone was enough to trigger a defensive posture.

That was fascinating enough, given that the planarian brain isn't much more than a cluster of neurons (see Figure 1). But much more spectacular experiments were on the way. A few years later, McConnell took advantage of a strange planarian ability: if one is sliced in half, the head end will regenerate a tail, and the tail will grow a

FIGURE 1. Planarian's central nervous system.
A. Ventral view of the planarian's central nervous system stained with the neuron-specific PH04 gene.
B. Schematic drawing of its ganglia.
Source: Reprinted from Aoki R, Wake H, Sasaki H, and Agata K. 2009. Recording and spectrum analysis of the planarian electroencephalogram. Neuroscience 159(2) : 908–914, © 2009 with permission from Elsevier. Modified from Agata et al. (1998) with permission from the Zoological Society of Japan.

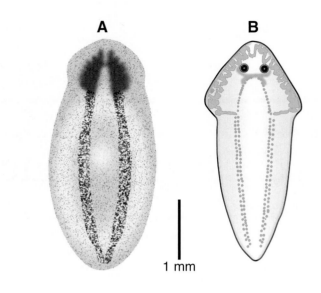

head, producing two intact worms. In fact, depending on its size, a worm can be cut into dozens of pieces that will regenerate new worms (see Photo A).

McConnell then wondered what would happen if a worm was taught to react to the light and then *that* worm was cut in half. Do the worms that regenerate still remember the light and the shock? Yes, they do. McConnell trained a set of worms, and then chopped them in half and allowed them four weeks to regenerate. At the same time, other worms were cut in half without being conditioned first, and a third group was conditioned, then allowed simply to rest for four weeks.

The worms regenerated from the head end reached the status of "fully trained" much sooner than they had when they were originally trained, meaning that the memory had been preserved. That made sense given that the head end contained the brain. But the worms regenerated from the *tails* also appeared to have retained the memory, in some cases even better than the heads.

PHOTO A. Planarians have remarkable regeneration abilities.
A. Planarian after six initial cuts.
B. Over time, seven individual planarians developed.
Source: Courtesy of Kiyokazu Agata, Department of Biophysics Graduate School of Science, Kyoto University.

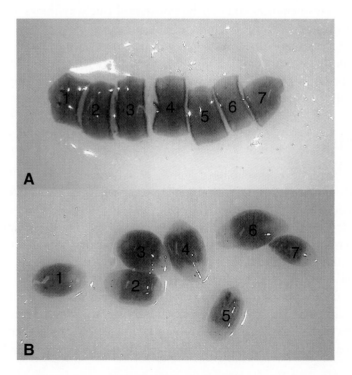

What could possibly allow the tail end of a trained worm to remember? Perhaps it was a memory molecule that wasn't restricted to the brain. But the idea that a memory could migrate freely around in the worm's body was too much for McConnell's fellow psychologists. Doubt and opposition began to grow, although much of it remained unpublished, even unspoken.

But McConnell wasn't finished. He and his colleagues embarked on the most controversial experiment yet: training worms, chopping them up, and feeding them to hungry untrained worms. The amazing result was that cannibal worms performed significantly better on test runs after they had eaten trained worms, although this instant learning decreased over the following few days. McConnell admitted in one of the first publications of these data that "we are most definitely out on a limb of some kind."

Two kinds of opposition arose to McConnell's work: formal and informal; the informal type was just as damaging to his work and his reputation. For one thing, many scientists simply didn't believe McConnell's results, because they didn't think they *could* be true. A perfect example was a meeting McConnell had in the late 1950s with invertebrate expert Libbie Hyman of the American Museum of Natural History. When told that regenerated heads and tails retained their conditioning, Hyman said, "I'm very sorry, but I just can't believe that."

It wasn't the idea that planaria could learn that was hard to swallow but the idea that memories seemed to be neat molecular packages that could be moved from one animal to another. Already people held strong opinions that memories involved some form of rewiring in the brain, which wasn't something you could feed your neighbour.

However, holding an opinion is one thing; in the court of science evidence is primary, and that means replication. Controversial experiments should be repeated in an open-minded way by other scientists in other labs: either the results hold or they don't—at least, that's the way it's supposed to go.

It's really hard to know exactly how many people were able to replicate these experiments and how many weren't, at least partly because of the tendency for other groups to fiddle with the original experiments. However, as you read the scientific literature of the 1960s, you can't avoid the uneasy feeling that whether the evidence against McConnell's work was clear-cut or not, the tide was turning against him.

The first published discrepancies appeared in 1964. A California group tried to replicate the cannibalism experiments and found that worms that had eaten trained worms did better all right, but so did worms that dined on worms exposed only to light or even worms just handled by the experimenters. There seemed to be no sensible explanation of these results, but at the very least they called into question the reliability of McConnell's results.

In the same year, a different team reported it had failed to replicate McConnell's results, and the particularly damaging aspect of these experiments was not the results, or even the conclusion the team drew (a relatively mild "learning was not yet proven"), but who did them. One of the two-man team was Melvin Calvin, a Nobel laureate in chemistry. Once a laureate contradicts experimental results publicly, those experiments are in trouble.

A second refutation was published in 1966. Although it was actually an attempt to extend McConnell's experiments to rats, it dealt a heavy blow to all memory transfer research. It was signed by 23 researchers from seven different institutions, all of whom failed to find any evidence of the chemical transfer of memories.

When I asked researchers what it was that brought down McConnell's work, several remembered—sometimes vaguely—this letter in *Science*. (Some of these were the same people who told me they couldn't remember what happened because they had never believed it in the first place). Yet even the *Science* letter concludes with a plea for continued work in this area: "We feel it would be unfortunate if these negative findings were to be taken as a signal for abandoning the pursuit of a result of enormous potential significance... . Failure to reproduce results is not, after all, unusual in the early phase of research when all relevant variables are as yet unspecified."

Despite these noble words, the letter writers could hardly have been surprised that their letter was seen as a critical blow against memory transfer research. Certainly their remark about "all relevant variables" was appropriate to the planaria research. At one point an estimated 70 variables could have influenced the experimental results, including the size of the worms, the colour of the light, the nature of the electric shock, the time of day, the phase of the moon, you name it. Planaria weren't easy to work with, and McConnell and his co-workers found that practice with the worms, and learning to recognize when they were ready to learn, was an important part of the procedure. But that meant certain people were better at the experiments than others, and situations like that always raise suspicions.

The bottom line is that by the early 1970s, the planaria work had been abandoned, even though some researchers who lumped all the experiments together and analyzed them came up with more positive results than negative. That's science for you—it's not just about the data.

Future Research

Could there even *be* a future for McConnell's work, abandoned so long ago? The surprising answer is yes—maybe. Some scientists are looking to the emerging field of RNAi, or *interference RNA*, for a possible explanation of learning by cannibalism. RNAi is a double-stranded RNA molecule that, once inside a cell, can interfere with the production of specific proteins by degrading the messenger RNA coding for them. How might it connect to McConnell's work? First, he argued at the time that the mystery molecule being passed among his planaria was RNA. Second, RNAi can work even if it's just injected into the body cavity of a target organism (remember cannibalism!), and third, it can actually change the range of protein molecules a cell makes and therefore the cell's function. However, what remains a puzzle is how shutting down genes in cells (presumably neurons) facilitates learning. But it is intriguing, and, curiously, it appears that some laboratories are having trouble replicating RNAi transfer experiments. Sound familiar?

Critical Thinking Questions

1. If you were designing an experiment on planarian behaviour, what variables would you need to control each time you performed the experiment?
2. If an experiment cannot be easily replicated, should the results be discredited?
3. How might interference RNA (RNAi) function in the transmission of memory from one planarian to another that eats it?

Further Research Question

What is meant by "peer review" with respect to scientific findings? Why is the peer review process important?

References

*Abbott SM, Wong GK. 2008. The conditioning and memory retention of planaria (*Dugesia tigrina*) for directional preferences. Bios. [Internet]. Dec [cited 2010 Apr 18];79(4):160–170. Available from: http://www.jstor.org/stable/25433841

Aoki R, Wake H, Sasaki H, Agata K. 2009. Recording and spectrum analysis of the planarian electroencephalogram. *Neurosci.* 159:908–914.

Block RA, McConnell JV. 1967. Classically conditioned discrimination in the planarian *Dugesia dorotocephala. Nature* 215:1465–1456.

McConnell JV. 1962. Memory transfer through cannibalism in planarium. *J. Neuropsychiat.* 3:542–548.

McConnell JV, Cornwell PR, Clay M. 1960. An apparatus for conditioning planaria. *Am. J. Psychol.* 73:618–622.

*Smalheiser NR, Manev H, Costa E. 2001. RNAi and brain function: was McConnell on the right track? *Trends in Neurosci.* 24:216–218.

Thompson R, McConnell JV. 1955. Classical conditioning in planarian *Dugesia dorotocephala. J. Comp. Physiol. Psychol.* 48:65–68.

Radioisotopic Imaging:
Taking a Picture in Order to See Clearly

Nathan Ackroyd
Mount Royal University

Introduction

KEY CONCEPTS

- The use of unstable isotopes provides one method of diagnostic imaging.
- Diagnostic imaging provides information unavailable through other methods.

Thanks to years of observations and experiments, we know a lot about blood flow, such as ideal blood pressure ranges, where blood flows from, where it is supposed to flow to, and what makes it flow. Science has given us in-depth knowledge of how a typical human heart works. Not long ago, I personally experienced the science behind this investigation. After taking a prescribed medicine to help reduce recently diagnosed high blood pressure, I developed chest pains. Because this was not the expected reaction, my doctor wanted to know more about how my blood flows. The general science developed in the field might not tell me in detail how my own blood flows because my heart may or may not match the typical profile. How can we learn about individual differences in blood flow? **Diagnostic imaging** may provide us with the most accurate and complete assessment. A number of imaging techniques, such as magnetic resonance imaging (MRI), computed tomography (CT), and ultrasound, are available. To get a better picture of what was going on in my heart, my doctor ordered a thallium stress test, a type of **nuclear imaging**, which generates images from the decay of unstable isotopes within the body.

General Diagnostic Imaging: MRI and CT

All types of imaging typically involve two steps. First, the patients are injected with an **imaging agent**. Next, the patients lie in a detector that measures how radiation from the electromagnetic spectrum passes through their bodies. For MRI (magnetic resonance imaging) and CT (computed tomography), which are both non-nuclear imaging techniques, the imaging agent is used to darken the dark spots or lighten the light spots of the image. It is often called a **contrast agent**. MRI then looks for how low-energy radio-frequency waves are absorbed by different body tissues. CT looks at how various body tissues scatter higher-energy X-rays. Nuclear imaging combines these two steps by using an imaging agent that is the *source* of the waves that are detected (so the waves are coming out of the patient's body instead of passing through it).

How Nuclear Imaging Works

In nuclear imaging, the imaging agent is radioactive. Every isotope of an element has the same number of protons in its nucleus. Not every isotope has the same number of neutrons. Some have too many neutrons to form a stable nucleus, and some have too few.

These unstable atoms, or **radioisotopes**, decay by releasing energy, which is often accompanied by subatomic particles. The resulting nucleus has a more stable ratio of protons to neutrons. The energy emitted by decaying nuclei inside the body can be detected and turned into an image by a radiologist with a body scanner. To get a good picture of my blood flow, a technician gave me an injection of a trace amount of thallium-201, an unstable isotope that decays with a half-life of about three days. The thallium goes where my blood takes it, and the image generated by detecting the decay of the unstable nuclei becomes a picture of where my blood has gone (see Photo A).

The dose of thallium given to a patient depends on his or her height and weight. For me, that meant enough radioactivity to measure 135×10^6 decays per second, or 135 MBq (megabecquerel). Because of the decay rate of thallium-201, I needed only 17×10^{-15} grams of radioactive thallium. The amount of mercury in a can of tuna is almost 4 billion times as large as this, and the amount of thallium that you are likely to eat in a day is 3.4 billion times as large.

The small amount of injected material needed to get a good image is a major advantage of nuclear imaging techniques over MRI or CT scans. These other imaging types typically require patients to be injected with milligrams of imaging agents, which delivers a high enough concentration that questions about toxicity and the time it takes to be removed from the body have to be addressed. In nuclear imaging, both the thallium-201 and its decay products are infinitesimal compared with naturally occurring sources. The other concern is that although we're talking about being injected with only femtograms of material, unlike the imaging agents used in MRI or CT scanning, the thallium I received *was* radioactive. The amount of radioactivity I was exposed to is approximately the same as the X-rays used in a routine CT scan, or the equivalent of about three years' worth of normal background radiation. No one knows exactly what effect these low-level doses of radiation have on humans. Most of our information on the effects of radiation comes from high-exposure cases. Because our cells have mechanisms for repairing minor damage to DNA, there is reason to believe that low-level

PHOTO A. Heart images from thallium-201 stress test.
Thallium-201 images taken from different angles, at rest and under exercise stress. The arrow indicates a lack of blood flow under stress conditions, indicating a blockage.
Source: Dartmouth-Hitchcock Medical Center, Department of Radiology, available from http://www.dhmc.org/webpage. cfm?site_id=2&org_id=72&morg_id=0&sec_id=0&gsec_id=1508&item_id=38906

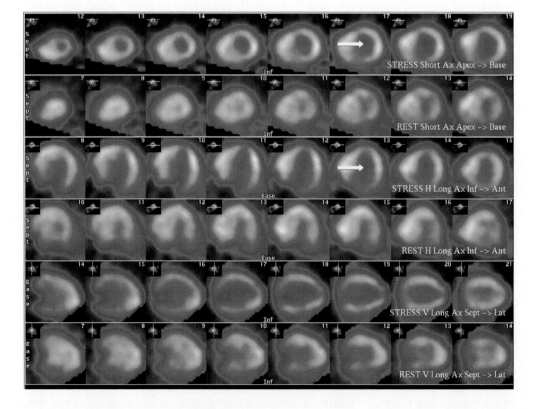

exposure to radiation has much less effect than would be predicted based on what we see from large, accidental exposure.

Thallium has about the same size and charge as potassium. It distributes well throughout the body and gives a good picture of blood flow. Also, its decay rate is neither too slow to make a bright image, nor too fast to conveniently work with. Radiologists sometimes have to work fast, since procedures or production steps that take too long can result in some quickly decaying isotopes disappearing. Thallium is not the only radioisotope useful for nuclear imaging. Each radioisotope has unique chemical properties and a unique decay rate. One thing they all have in common, however, is that they decay. So without a means of producing them anew, over time they disappear from the world.

Production of Radioisotopes and Canada's Role in Nuclear Imaging

The thallium used for my heart imaging came from the United States. At this time last year, it may have had to come from Belgium. Why ship something so far when half of the sample disappears every nine hours? Canada has traditionally been a supplier of radionuclides to hospitals and imaging centres all over the world. The Chalk River Labs (CRL), which opened in 1944 northwest of Ottawa, had until its temporary shutdown been producing a wide variety of isotopes for medical and other uses. One of the most common isotopes used in nuclear imaging is technetium-99m (Tc-99m or ^{99m}Tc). Technetium-99m is not produced in a reactor, but the closure of the Chalk River Labs has contributed to a worldwide shortage, because of the decreased production of an isotope of molybdenum. When molybdenum-99 (Mo-99) decays, it is converted to technetium-99m, which is used in 80 percent of nuclear imaging.

The National Research Universal (NRU) Reactor, the CRL reactor that has produced medical isotopes, was built in 1957. Aside from a pair of incidents in the 1950s, the CRL reactors had been running consistently and safely for decades. In November 2007, a shutdown of the NRU for routine maintenance was extended in order to make some needed upgrades; however, to prevent a shortage of isotopes, the Canadian government ordered that the NRU be restarted before the upgrades could be made. Heavy-water leaks in late 2008 and early 2009 have since led to the closure of the NRU for extensive repairs, and it is unclear at this time when, if ever, the reactor will be restarted.

Conclusions

Since the closure of the Chalk River reactor for repair in May 2009, Canada, along with the rest of the world, has had to import medical isotopes. At that time, South Africa, Belgium, France, and the Netherlands were the only countries with nuclear reactors set up for

PHOTO B. Chalk River Labs.
Source: Padraic Ryan/Wikipedia, available from http://en.wikipedia. org/wiki/Chalk_River_Laboratories

medical isotope production. They have each had to increase production to make up for the 40 percent of the Mo-99 produced worldwide that is no longer coming from Canada. With fewer reactors producing more of the isotopes, routine maintenance at one reactor puts added demands on the others. With Canada, for now, no longer a producer of medical isotopes, isotope shortages have been and will continue to be more common.

Luckily for me, I needed an image taken at a time when thallium-201 was readily available. When my results came back, the image showed good blood flow to all areas of my heart. Other patients haven't been as fortunate. Many patients' lives may depend on a timely diagnosis. Until the Chalk River reactor is back online, we have to hope those foreign reactors keep working.

Critical Thinking Questions

1. Thallium-201 decays by changing a proton in the nucleus into a neutron. Why does this happen, and what is the resulting atom?
2. Why is a too-short half-life a problem when dealing with isotopes for medical imaging?
3. What are the similarities and differences among MRI, CT, and nuclear imaging?

Further Research Question

The decay of different isotopes may release different types of radiation. Because of this, different imaging methods must be used, depending on the isotope. Technetium-94m can be imaged using positron emission tomography (PET), whereas Tc-99m is imaged with single photon emission computed tomography (SPECT). Why are these isotopes imaged differently, and what are the advantages of each method? Address such issues as sensitivity and resolution in your answer.

References

AECL [Internet]. Restarting safely: Reassuring Canadians [cited 2010 Apr 9]. Available from: http://www.nrucanada.ca/en/home/default.aspx

CBC News [Internet]. Global supply under pressure [modified 2009 Aug 21; cited 2010 Apr 9]. Available from: http://www.cbc.ca/health/story/2009/05/19/f-medical-isotopes.html

Erickson K. Unclear when Chalk River will produce isotopes again: officials. CBC News [Internet]; [modified 2009 Jun 11; cited 2010 Apr 9]. Available from: http://www.cbc.ca/canada/story/2009/06/11/chalk-river-isotope-0611.html

[IAEA] International Atomic Energy Agency. Manual for reactor produced isotopes [Internet]. Vienna (Austria): International Atomic Energy Agency; 2003 Jan [cited 2010 Apr 9]. Available from: http://www-pub.iaea.org/MTCD/publications/PDF/te_1340_web.pdf

Lide DR, editor. 2009. CRC handbook of chemistry and physics. 87th ed. Cleveland (OH): CRC Press.

Remote Sensing:
To Map or not to Map? Toward Characterizing the Distribution of Eastern Canada's Shallow Marine Vegetation from above the Sea Surface

Patrick Gagnon
*Memorial University of Newfoundland**

Introduction

Imagine you are asked to map the distribution (the way objects and organisms are spatially organized) of oak and elm trees in a 10 km^2 deciduous forest. You and a couple of friends are parachuted from an aircraft into a small opening in the middle of the forest. As you reach the ground, you realize (without surprise) that the forest contains not only oaks and elms, but also 10 additional species of trees. To add to your fortune, the only tools you have been given to do the work are a small field notebook, a pencil, and a global positional system (GPS) device. You designate one tree as your reference point and start recording the geographical position of each surrounding tree. Rapidly, as you are moving away from your reference tree, you realize the complexity of discarding the other trees while not missing any of the oaks and elms. You have been recording the position of elms and oaks for 10 consecutive hours when you realize that, when you look over your shoulder, you can still see the one tree that you initially measured! You think to yourself "there must be a quicker, more accurate way to do this." Here is where remote sensing is your best bet!

KEY CONCEPTS

- Ecology integrates all areas of biological research and informs environmental decision making.
- Dominant and keystone species exert strong control on community structure.
- Human activities threaten Earth's biodiversity.
- Determining the abundance of an aquatic organism is challenging.

Principles of Remote Sensing

Progress in remote sensing (the gathering and recording of information about Earth's surface by methods that do not involve contact with the surface) has led to important discoveries in many scientific disciplines, including geology, archeology, meteorology, and oceanography. Remote sensors are wireless, real-time recording sensing devices used to collect information on an object, phenomenon, or area. There are two classes of remote sensors: active and passive. **Active sensors** produce and emit energy (radiation) toward an object and measure the radiation that is reflected or backscattered by the object, along with the time delay between emission and return. For example, active sensors include radars used to track the trajectory of such meteorological phenomena as hurricanes and winter storms, as well as sonars used to locate fish and create bathymetric grids of seabed. **Passive sensors** capture the radiation that is naturally reflected (usually sunlight) or the radiation emitted by objects. Passive sensors range from analog and digital cameras (just like the ones we use to take pictures) to such sophisticated devices as radiometers that record radiation in specific regions of the electromagnetic spectrum

*The research described in this essay was funded by NSERC.

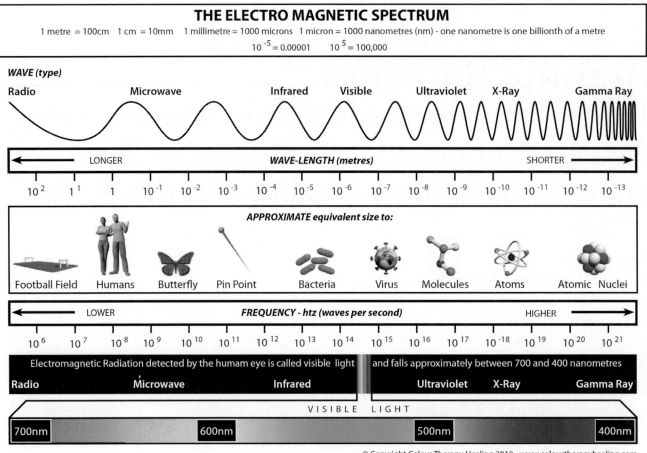

FIGURE 1. The electromagnetic spectrum.
Radiation at wavelengths between about 400 nm and 700 nm are visible to humans and used by plants in photosynthesis.
Source: © Copyright Colour Therapy Healing 2010. www.colourtherapyhealing.com

(see Figure 1). Active and passive sensors are mounted on a variety of ground, air, space, seaborne, or submersible platforms that move at speeds compatible with the sensor's acquisition time (the amount of time required to measure, process, and record each unit of information).

Many factors determine the quality and quantity of the remotely collected information. Each sensor has characteristic spatial, spectral, and radiometric resolutions, which together set the limits of detection. **Spatial resolution** refers to the size of the smallest (usually square) picture element, or pixel. Pixels typically range from one to several thousands of metres in side length. A group of contiguous pixels form an image just like the image on a plasma television. A high-resolution image has a small resolution size, whereas a low-resolution image has a large resolution size. **Spectral resolution** is defined by the width of the wavelengths (bandwidth) recorded in as many distinct frequency bands (channels) allowed by the device. Multispectral sensors, such as the Landsat Thematic Mapper (TM), usually possess five to 10 frequency bands of 0.07 to 2.1 μm each. They have reduced spectral capabilities compared with hyperspectral sensors, which typically possess around 200 contiguous frequency bands on the order of 0.01 μm each. The **radiometric resolution** corresponds with the number of different intensities of radiation that the sensor can measure, usually between 256 (8 bits) and 16 384 (14 bits) shades of grey and colour in each band. Those characteristics, along with the acquisition time, altitude, and speed of displacement of the sensor, as well as the size of the object being measured, largely determine the type of sensor used. Detecting a 4-m long elephant in the Serengeti region, for example, requires a sensor with a spatial resolution of 4 m or less. The elephant will appear increasingly blurred and become unnoticeable as the spatial resolution of the sensor increases.

The composition and concentration of photosynthetic pigments in plants (and seaweeds) tends to be more similar among individuals of a same species than between individuals of different species. Each class of pigments absorbs (and reflects) wavelengths differently, which causes variation in the amount of blue, green, and red wavelengths (wavelengths that make up the visible portion of the electromagnetic spectrum) reflected between leaves of different plant species. Also, the internal structure and water content of plant leaves affect the amount of near-infrared (wavelengths with lower energy than wavelengths in the visible spectrum; undetectable by the human eye) absorbed (and reflected) by plant tissues. By measuring reflectance (the ratio between the amount of energy that hits and is reflected by an object) throughout a continuum of visible and near-infrared wavelengths, one can obtain a **reflectance spectrum** (curve) that is unique to each species. Reflectance spectra are used with advanced image analysis software to transform (classify) the information acquired by a remote sensor into maps showing the spatial distribution of species or habitats. **Passive optical remote sensors** are specifically designed to measure ultraviolet, visible, near-, mid-, and thermal infrared wavelengths (0.3 to 14 μm). To name only a few examples, passive optical remote sensors are useful for quantifying large-scale phenomena on land, such as deforestations by pests or wildfires, and for maximizing agricultural yields

Using Remote Sensing to Study Ecosystems

Such global phenomena as changes in ocean circulation, temperature, acidification, increased coastal erosion, freshwater runoffs, and melting polar ice caps have an impact on marine (and terrestrial) ecosystems. Accidental introductions of non-native species to coastal ecosystems are a potential threat to biodiversity and the integrity of natural marine communities. Many marine species introduced to new environments have spread over considerable distances from their invasion epicenter. For example, Asian green alga *Codium* fragile ssp. *fragile* (formerly *C. fragile* ssp. *tomentosoides*; hereafter *C. fragile*) (see Photo A) was first sighted in Long Island Sound off the coast of New York in the mid-1950s, but its geographical range has since expanded considerably. Its current estimated distribution is from North Carolina to southern Quebec. In eastern Canada,

PHOTO A.
Along the Atlantic coast of Nova Scotia, *C. fragile* opportunistically exploits disturbance-generated gaps in kelp beds and, once established, forms dense meadows that inhibit subsequent recolonization by kelps and other native seaweeds.
Source: Photo courtesy of Robert Scheibling from Scheibling RE and Gagnon P. 2006. Competitive interactions between the invasive green alga Codium fragile ssp. tomentosoides and native canopy-forming seaweeds in Nova Scotia (Canada). Marine Ecology Progress Series 325:1–14.

C. fragile was first reported along the Atlantic coast of Nova Scotia in 1989. Within a decade, it competitively displaced native seaweeds, such as kelps, along large tracts of coastline. The replacement of luxuriant kelp beds by *C. fragile* meadows has had a significant impact on the structure of shallow vegetated habitats and their associated fauna. The rapid spread and persistence of *C. fragile* in this economically important marine ecosystem has stimulated a greater interest in the regional distribution of shallow vegetation in general.

Research Question

Can airborne passive optical remote sensing help to accurately determine the distribution of the shallow native and invasive marine seaweeds of eastern Canada?

As a marine benthic ecologist, I have developed a particular interest in the study of rocky subtidal ecosystems. I am interested in elucidating how shallow (0 to 40 m deep) marine invertebrates and seaweeds interact together and how the physical environment affects those interactions. An important aspect of my research lies in the study of how the distribution and structure of benthic populations and communities (those organisms that live in or on the seabed) change over time and what factors trigger such changes. To do this, my students and I make extensive use of scuba-diving and underwater videography techniques. Because such techniques are time-consuming and often require a great deal of planning, they are well suited to study patterns over relatively fine spatial (tens to hundreds of metres) and temporal (less than five years) scales; however, **synoptic tools and approaches** are also required to quantify the distribution of shallow benthic organisms at broader spatial and temporal scales and to determine the causes and consequences of such patterns. Recently, my collaborators and I used a state-of-the-art airborne passive optical remote sensor, the **Compact Airborne Spectrographic Imager (CASI)**, along with various sources of **bathymetry** (the measurement of water depth at various places in a body of water) to try to characterize the distribution of *C. fragile* and kelp in the shallow subtidal zone of Nova Scotia. Our results, outlined below, are encouraging.

Hypothesis

The accuracy of distributional maps of invasive (*C. fragile*) and native (kelp) seaweeds increases with increasing the spatial resolution of the bathymetric grids.

Because of the water column, the use of airborne passive optical remote sensing to detect such submerged vegetation as *C. fragile* and kelp is more challenging than it is to detect vegetation on land. As blue, green, and red wavelengths travel downward and upward in the water column, a fraction of the energy is absorbed and reflected by such things as dissolved and particulate organic matter, organisms in the water column, and the water itself. Consequently, the reflectance spectrum of an object on the seabed (e.g., a rock) varies with depth. This means that a *C. fragile* individual at a depth of 10 m may look much darker than the same individual at a depth of 2 m when viewed from above the sea surface, simply because there is less light reaching deeper seabed. This effect, called the **attenuation of light**, occurs as light passes through the water column and can be a major source of confusion during the classification of images into seabed habitats or vegetation types, especially when dealing with the relatively turbid seawater of eastern Canada. To further complicate the issue, *C. fragile* can grow individually or intersperse itself among kelp, therefore creating **mixels** on CASI images that contain mixed reflectance spectra of *C. fragile* and kelp. Also, near-infrared wavelengths are absorbed within the first few centimeters of water, and hence the reflectance spectra of vegetation on the seabed may lack details that could be used to differentiate species that are spectrally close to one another.

One way to overcome those problems and obtain more accurate classification maps is to acquire reflectance spectra of monospecific stands of *C. fragile* and mixed stands of *C. fragile* and kelp at different depths within the region the CASI is to fly over. If the geographical positions of many monospecific stands of *C. fragile* and mixed stands of *C. fragile* and kelp are measured (using a GPS device) during field surveys, then one can locate those stands on CASI images and use advanced image classification software to extract depth-specific reflectance spectra for each type of stand. If the depth of each pixel in the CASI image is known, then it is possible to assign one type of stand to each pixel; in our case, pure stands of *C. fragile*, mixed stands of *C. fragile* and kelp, and any other type of assemblage that does not correspond to either of the first two types of stands. An important corollary is that the accuracy of the classification maps of seabed should increase with increasing the **spatial resolution** (reduction in the distance between data points) of the **bathymetric** (depth) values assigned to each pixel. In practice, it can be costly and logistically challenging (not to say impossible) to measure the depth of each pixel in situ, especially when using high-resolution images, which increases the number of pixels to be analyzed per unit of surface area. A practical alternative is to **interpolate** (estimate using mathematical algorithms) depth values for pixels between two (or more) pixels with known depth values.

Methods and Results

The CASI system was flown with a small aircraft over a relatively small (~0.6 km^2) and shallow (0 to15 m deep) tract of seabed near Halifax, Nova Scotia (see Figure 2). Hyperspectral image data were collected at a spatial resolution of 1 m^2, in 17 spectral (frequency) bands ranging from 424 (blue) to 690 (red) nm. To test our hypothesis that the accuracy of distributional maps of *C. fragile* and kelp increases with increasing the spatial resolution of the bathymetric grids, we acquired three sets of bathymetry applicable to the area in question. The initial spatial resolution of the bathymetric sets differed, ranging from low (on average depth soundings were located 360 m away from one another), to intermediate (12-m distance), to high (1-m distance). To ensure that each pixel of 1 m^2 in the hyperspectral image was assigned a depth value (a necessity in order to transform the image into distributional maps of *C. fragile* and kelp), each raw bathymetric set was further transformed (using various interpolation techniques) into grids with identical spatial resolution of 1 m^2. This means that (1) the grid with the highest initial spatial accuracy (produced with a mathematical algorithm that relies solely on the hyperspectral imagery to compute a depth value for each image pixel) contained the highest number of estimated depth values (in fact all depth values were estimated), (2) the grid with the lowest initial spatial accuracy (produced with sonar soundings acquired by the Canadian Hydrographic Service [CHS]), contained an intermediate number of estimated depth values, and (3) the grid with the intermediate initial spatial accuracy (produced with sonar soundings we acquired ourselves with a recreational fish finder on board a small vessel) contained the lowest number of estimated depth values. Keep in mind that estimates can be misleading sometimes!

To provide **ground reference data** (training and test pixels) in support of hyperspectral image classification (this data is essential for extracting the reflectance spectra of pure and mixed stands of *C. fragile* and kelp from the CASI imagery), sections of the

FIGURE 2. Map of study site.
Top: Location of the study site (Flat Island, Mahone Bay, Nova Scotia) flown with a hyperspectral radiometer on board a small aircraft.
Bottom: Distributional map of the two algal classes (*C. fragile*; mixed *C. fragile* and kelp) in the study site created using a supervised classification scheme with low-resolution (CHS) bathymetry.
Source: Gagnon P, Scheibling RE, Jones W, and Tully D. 2008. The role of digital bathymetry in mapping shallow marine vegetation from hyperspectral image data. International Journal of Remote Sensing, *29(3): 879–904. © 2008 Taylor & Francis Group, http://www.informaworld.com*

(A)

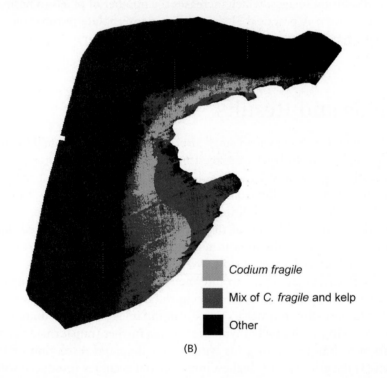

(B)

seabed within the site were monitored with a submersible digital video camera system that divers propelled 1.5 m above the seabed. Two categories of vegetation were used: (1) *C. fragile* as the dominant canopy species (>75 percent cover of *C. fragile*, no kelp), and (2) a mixture of *C. fragile* and kelp (>50 percent cover of a combination of *C. fragile* and kelp). The hyperspectral imagery was transformed into distributional maps of *C. fragile* and kelp using various combinations of presence and absence of training pixels and the three bathymetric grids.

We obtained noticeable differences among the three bathymetric grids interpolated from bathymetric soundings (CHS and fish finder) and computed directly from the hyperspectral imagery (mathematical algorithm). For example, the bathymetric grid interpolated using the lowest number of sonar soundings (from the CHS) showed a smooth, gradual transition in depth from shallow to deeper water, with most of the area shallower than 8 m (see Figure 3). The bathymetric grid interpolated using an intermediate

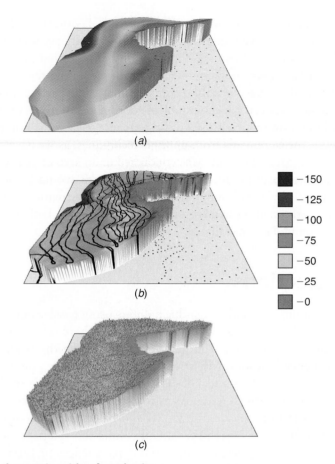

■	−150
■	−125
▨	−100
▨	−75
□	−50
▨	−25
■	−0

FIGURE 3. **Bathymetric grids of study site.**
This figure shows the three-dimensional colour-coded bathymetric grids of the shallow subtidal zone on the northwestern side of Flat Island as interpolated using soundings from (A) the Canadian Hydrographic Service, (B) a recreational fish finder, and (C) a hyperspectral scene of the site. The black dots overlaying the bathymetric grid in (A) and (B)—appearing as a continuous line in (B) because of the high volume of data—are point soundings used to interpolate depth in each 1-m^2 pixel. The black dots overlaying the flat, horizontal plane (which extends from beneath the bathymetric grid) are elevation points at the surface of the island (not shown). Note the greater topographic detail (ledges and troughs) in (B) versus (A), and the rough texture of the seabed in (C). Depths are expressed in decimetres (dm).
Source: Gagnon, P., Scheibling, R. E., Jones, W. and Tully, D. (2007) The role of digital bathymetry in mapping shallow marine vegetation from hyperspectral image data, International Journal of Remote Sensing, 29(3): 879–904.
© 2008 Taylor & Francis Group http://www.informaworld.com

number of soundings (from the fish finder) revealed comparatively more topographic features, with numerous outcrops and depressions in shallower water. As expected, supervised classification schemes (those schemes that used the information extracted from the video transects acquired by the divers) produced more accurate distributional maps of C. *fragile* and kelp than unsupervised schemes (the least accurate supervised classification scheme was 12 percent more accurate than the most accurate unsupervised classification scheme). But contrary to our expectation, the most accurate (76.2 percent) supervised classification scheme was with bathymetry from the CHS, which had the lowest (initial) spatial resolution of our three types of bathymetry (see Figure 3).

Conclusions

Many instruments, cartographic products, and software were used to acquire, convert, interpolate, and integrate various types of data. The highest consistency between the distribution of C. *fragile* and kelp that we observed in nature (using scuba diving and underwater videography) and that we obtained from the classification of the hyperspectral imagery occurred when we used the bathymetric grid with the lowest initial spatial resolution (CHS). This result does not support our hypothesis that the accuracy of distributional maps of *C. fragile* and kelp increases with increasing the spatial resolution of the bathymetric grids. Some inevitable errors are inherent in each of these techniques, including mismatches between the geographical coordinates of pixels in the hyperspectral imagery and the training pixels used during the image classification process; however, comparing the measurements from multiple techniques, as we have, helps identify and minimize those errors. Our study was conducted in an area of gently sloping, relatively homogeneous seabed; modifications to the methods would be needed in areas with different topography. Depth soundings acquired with recreational fish finders can provide reliable, operational bathymetry for those areas where bathymetry by hydrographic services is limited or unavailable.

Future Directions

Historically, the mapping of shallow benthic habitats using passive optical remote sensors has focused on clear, tropical water environments. There is less light attenuation in the water column of those environments compared with the cold, nutrient-rich waters found at higher latitudes. My research program includes the refinement and development of remote sensing and GIS-based approaches to the study of shallow benthic ecosystems in eastern Canada. As a first step, we used a state-of-the-art airborne hyperspectral remote sensor (the CASI) and basic image classification procedures to map native and invasive seaweeds. Our results showed promise, and we will continue to work on identifying the causes and consequences of variation in hyperspectral, bathymetric, and ground reference data on classification products. Part of our strategy will be to use more accurate devices to acquire ground data, to diversify the techniques used to classify the imagery, and to include additional information about habitats.

Critical Thinking Questions

1. Name and explain the three types of resolution that characterize remote sensors.
2. Name and explain the physical phenomenon that occurs as sunlight penetrates a water mass and how the visual aspect of objects and organisms on a seabed can be modified by this phenomenon.
3. Name and discuss the usefulness of the three types of complementary data that were used to map shallow native and invasive seaweeds of eastern Canada.

Further Research Question

Why is the presence of the green alga *Codium fragile* ssp. *fragile* in eastern Canada's shallow marine ecosystems causing concern?

References

Gagnon P, Scheibling RE, Jones W, Tully D. 2008. The role of digital bathymetry in mapping shallow marine vegetation from hyperspectral image data. *Int. J. Remote Sens.* 29:879–904.

Green EP, Mumby PJ, Edwards AJ, Clark CD. 2000. Remote sensing handbook for tropical coastal management. UNESCO, Paris.

Lillesand TM, Kiefer RW, Chipman JW. 2004. *Remote sensing and image interpretation.* New York: John Wiley & Sons.

Scheibling RE, Gagnon P. 2006. Competitive interactions between the invasive green alga *Codium fragile* ssp. *tomentosoides* and native canopy-forming seaweeds in Nova Scotia (Canada). Marine Ecology Progress Series 325:1–14.

Resistance to Antimalarial Drugs:
Adaptive Evolution and Genetic Interactions

Rick J. Scavetta
The Max Planck Institute for Evolutionary Biology

Introduction

When we talk about evolution, dinosaurs and fossils often come to mind, but evolution is an ongoing process happening all around us. Genetic analysis provides exciting new insights into the evolutionary dynamics shaping our world. The study of microevolution is concerned with populations and individuals, the smaller units of organization that define a species. In particular, microevolution often analyzes the genetic variation of individuals within different populations of a species, be it human, fish, or parasite. An exciting aspect of this approach to genetics is uncovering the special properties that make different populations unique, or rather, uncovering how different populations have adapted to their local environment. The environment includes everything with which the population comes into contact, including the complex climate, flora, and fauna, and also deadly chemicals and new food sources. When a population's genetic composition changes in response to external pressures, allowing it to thrive in the new environment, we refer to it as *adaptive evolution*, occurring through the process of natural selection. The population evolves an adaptation to a new living condition. This can happen in many ways; one example is the way is occurs with the malaria-causing parasite *Plasmodium falciparum* in Southeast Asia.

Malaria is caused by a parasite infection transmitted into the human blood stream from mosquitoes (see Photo A), leading to fever and flu-like symptoms that are treatable if detected early. Of the four parasites that can induce malaria, *P. falciparum* is the most

KEY CONCEPTS

- Populations undergo adaptive evolution in response to selective environmental pressures.
- Copy number variation can have functional consequences in gene expression.
- Gene expression can influence the efficacy of biochemical pathways.

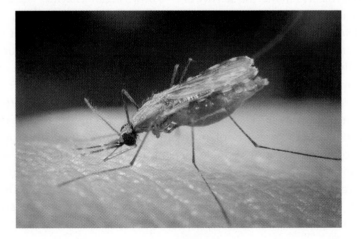

PHOTO A.
Mosquitoes, such as the pictured *Anopheles minimus* of Southeast Asia, transmit malarial parasites, such as *Plasmodium falciparum,* while feeding on our blood.
Source: James Gathany/Centers for Disease Control and Prevention.

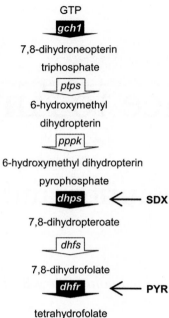

FIGURE 1. The *P. falciparum* folate biosynthesis pathway.
The production of folate is a multistep process catalyzed by several enzymes, proteins produced by genes in the parasite genome (in block arrows). A new compound is synthesized at each stage, beginning with GTP and progressing to tetrahydrofolate. Late-acting enzymes, such as dhps and dhfr (highlighted) are referred to as downstream in the pathway. These two enzymes are targets of antifolate drugs (arrows). The activity of upstream, early-acting enzymes, such as gch1 (highlighted), can have a profound effect on downstream catalysts by regulating the amount of starting material.
Source: Nair S, Miller B, Barends M, Jaidee A, Patel J, Mayxay M, Newton P, Nosten F, Ferdig MT, Anderson TJ. 2008. Adaptive copy number evolution in malaria parasites. PLoS Genet. Oct; 4(10):e1000243.

lethal, causing death if not treated properly. A devastating 1 million people die each year from malaria, placing greater strain on the already impoverished countries where the disease is most prevalent.

Several drugs are available that treat or protect against malaria. Parasites eventually developed resistance against the first drugs, which were first available in the 1940s. This resistance lead to the release of several different drug strategies, including inhibitors of the folate (vitamin B$_9$) biosynthesis pathway (see Figure 1). Folate is necessary for several metabolic activities, most notably DNA synthesis and repair. Like the parasite *P. falciparum*, humans need folate; however, the parasite can synthesize its own, while we must obtain it through our diet. Antifolate medicines have tried to exploit this parasite feature, because disrupting folate biosynthesis shouldn't have any adverse affects on people but should cause the parasite to perish. Antifolate drugs were initially successful in treating malaria infections. Fansidar (from Roche) inhibits the activity of two downstream enzymes (see Figure 1) in the biosynthesis pathway and was used as a first-line treatment in Thailand from 1970 to 1980.

Efficient folate biosynthesis inhibitors will kill the parasite, and so it is considered a strong selective pressure. That means any pre-existing genetic variation that allows parasites to live in the presence of the drug will be strongly favoured and any new mutations that confer resistance to the drugs will be selected for. To be *selected for* means a rapid increase in the frequency of a specific genetic variant in a population because it provides a fitness advantage. The fitness advantage in this instance is the ability to survive and reproduce in the presence of antifolate drugs. An example of drug resistance is the presence of point mutations (single nucleotide changes in the DNA sequence of a gene that changes the amino acid sequence of the corresponding protein product) in the enzymatic targets of Fansidar, which reduce the binding efficiency (and thus inhibitory ability) of the drug. The point mutations, however, also decrease the efficacy of the affected enzymes, which poses a new problem to the parasite.

Research Question

In the parasite *P. falciparum*, are changes in early-stage folate biosynthesis enzymes compensating for downstream loss in efficacy?

In Laos, older drugs that did not act on the folate biosynthesis pathway were still effective and remained in popular use. This fact means that the environment of the parasite in Thailand differed from the environment of the parasite in Laos. In Thailand, because of the historical choice of antimalarial drugs, the parasite is faced with strong antifolate selection, while Laos can be viewed as weak antifolate selection. Point mutations that confer resistance to Fansidar, used in Thailand, are much less frequent in Laos. The two environments present a situation in which scientists can look at how the parasite adapted to a new environment—namely, the presence of antifolate drugs.

Hypothesis

P. falciparum in Thailand have adapted to antifolate drug resistance mutations, which decrease efficacy of downstream folate biosynthesis enzymes, by increasing the efficacy of upstream folate biosynthesis enzymes.

Methods and Results

Researchers from the United States, Britain, Thailand, and Laos collaborated in collecting and analyzing *P. falciparum* DNA from infected individuals at public clinics. The copy number of a specific parasitic gene, *gch1*, was assessed. *gch1* is the necessary catalyst at the first stage of folate biosynthesis, and previous studies suggested it is found in a copy-number-variable region of the genome. These are genomic regions that are present in different numbers of copies (two, three, four, or more times) in different individuals within a population. An increase in copy number would potentially increase the efficacy of a gene by increasing its expression. To measure *gch1* copy number, the researchers used quantitative real-time polymerase chain reaction (qPCR). The standard PCR is a technique for amplifying small DNA fragments in cycles of in vitro reactions by using a mixture of enzymes, salts, and free nucleotides. Massive amounts of new DNA can be synthesized from even a tiny amount of starting material, but because of the variables involved in the reaction, the *quantity* of end product is often not proportional to the quantity of the initial target. qPCR attempts to address this by using fluorescent markers in the reaction, which allow the product to be quantified by scanning lasers at the end of every cycle. The pattern of amplification is a sigmodial curve, the middle phase being characterized as an exponential growth. Under these conditions, the cycle in which exponential growth is reached is directly related to the amount of starting material. Scientists use internal markers to measure the curves of an internal control (i.e., a gene of known copy number) and experimental loci. Observing the differences in exponential growth curves reveals the differences in initial starting amount of the target DNA and hence copy number differences.

In the Thai clinic, of 140 parasite samples, more than 72 percent carried more than 1 copy of *gch1*. In contrast, only 2/122 parasites in Laos (1.6 percent) had more than one copy (see Figure 2). This extreme geographic variation is not consistent with neutral evolution, which would dictate that the frequency profiles should be statistically equivalent, and suggests that copy number has increased throughout the Thai population in response to the selective pressure of the antifolate drugs.

qPCR was originally developed to measure gene expression. The amount of mRNA from any given gene is proportional to gene activity because it reflects the amount of

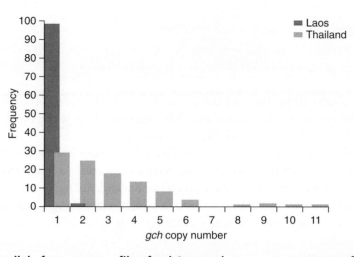

FIGURE 2. The allele frequency profile of *gch1* strongly suggests a pattern of recent strong selection.
The majority of parasites in Thailand were found to have more than one copy of *gch1*. However, in neighbouring Laos, only a small percentage had even two copies. The differences in frequency distribution of *gch1* copy number parallels the use of antifolate drugs, and mutations in other genes of the folate biosynthesis pathway, in the two countries.
Source: Reprinted from Anderson TJ, Patel J, Ferdig MT. 2009. Gene copy number and malaria biology. Trends Parasitol. *Jul; 25(7):336–43. © 2009, with permission from Elsevier.*

protein product that will be produced. To make qPCR more stable, mRNA is reverse transcribed back into DNA and is referred to as complimentary DNA (cDNA). cDNA can then be analyzed by qPCR as a readout of gene expression. Parasite strains with a greater *gch1* copy number have higher *gch1* expression levels throughout their life cycles, as shown in Figure 3.

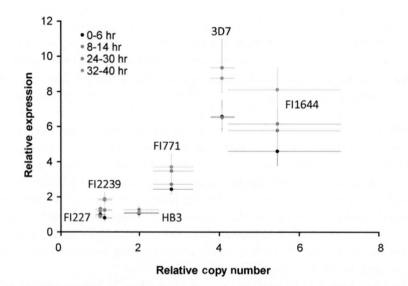

FIGURE 3. Correlation between *gch1* expression and copy number for six parasite lines at four different time points in its life cycle.
Gene expression was measured at four different time points in the asexual life cycle stages of six different parasite lines. The horizontal and vertical bars represent 95 percent confidence intervals on both gene expression and copy number measurements. Strong correlations between expression and copy number are present in all stages of the life cycle, providing evidence that the increase in *gch1* copy number provides a physiological difference.
Source: Nair S, Miller B, Barends M, Jaidee A, Patel J, Mayxay M, Newton P, Nosten F, Ferdig MT, Anderson TJ. 2008. Adaptive copy number evolution in malaria parasites. PLoS Genet. *Oct; 4(10).*

Conclusions

Point mutations in two downstream genes were already known to confer resistance against antifolate drugs. However, this study reveals that several loci are acting together in a multilocus model of antifolate resistance evolution. The increase in *gch1* copy number, and subsequently higher expression of this upstream enzyme in the folate biosynthesis pathway, likely compensates for the loss of downstream enzyme efficacy caused by the very point mutations that allow the parasite to survive in the presence of antifolate drugs.

Future Directions

From this study, it is still not clear what drives the increase in copy number of *gch1*. It is likely, given other experiments performed in the study, that there is a functional link between *gch1* and one of the downstream genes. That is, the increase in *gch1* copy number is driven by the decreased efficacy of downstream genes caused by mutations providing drug resistance. Which mutations in which gene is still unclear, and further experiments will help to determine how different alleles and copy numbers interact with one another to increase the parasite's fitness.

Critical Thinking Questions

1. Why is it necessary to use cDNA for qPCR when mRNA is already available?
2. Why was the folate biosynthesis pathway initially targeted by antimalarial drugs?
3. What is the relationship between *gch1* copy number and downstream genes in the folate biosynthesis pathway that already confer drug resistance to the parasite?

Further Research Question

How can scientists prepare for the possibility of evolved resistance when introducing a new drug?

References

Nair S, Miller B, Barends M, Jaidee A, Patel J, Mayxay M, Newton P, Nosten F, Ferdig MT, Anderson TJ. 2008. Adaptive copy number evolution in malaria parasites. *PLoS Genet.* 4(10):e1000243.

Seasonal Affective Disorder and Circadian Rhythms: Do You Get the Wintertime Blues?

Sarah Hewitt
Mount Royal University

Introduction

It's late November, coming up to exams, you have early morning classes, and you won't be finished until 7 p.m. It's still dark when you drag yourself out of bed in the morning, and the moon is high when you leave school that night. "Where did the day go?" you ask yourself when you get home, not having seen a sliver of sunlight that day; you know the next day will be the same (see photo A and B). How do you feel? If you're depressed, have no energy, want to sleep all the time, and are putting on weight because you just can't seem to stop eating, you may have a case of the wintertime blues. For some, the onset of winter brings on a period of depression called **seasonal affective disorder (SAD)**. Females of childbearing age appear to be the most susceptible population. The severity of the symptoms ranges from feeling a little down to major depression, and in most cases the symptoms disappear completely in the spring and summer months. What is it about the winter that triggers SAD? Other than temperature, the obvious difference between the summer and winter is the length of the day (at least, away from the equator). It is no surprise that SAD is most prevalent (affecting 2 to 5 percent of the population) in places where the change in day length from summer to winter is most pronounced. What is the relationship between the length of the day and physiological processes that can lead to feelings of depression?

KEY CONCEPTS
■ The change in day length in the winter can trigger changes in brain function.
■ Circadian rhythms are affected by day length.

Abnormalities of Circadian Rhythms Lead to the Development of SAD

Daily rhythms known as **circadian rhythms** play a prominent role in everything from sleep-wake cycles, body temperature, and hormone release, to cognition, attention, and mood. These rhythms cycle independently roughly every 24 hours. However, their cyclic activity is strongly influenced by a molecular clock that uses environmental cues, such as light, to determine the period of the cycle. The master biological molecular clock is a group of neurons in the hypothalamus in the **suprachiasmatic nucleus (SCN)**. Photoreceptors in the eyes convey information about the amount of light in the surroundings by sending neural signals to SCN neurons. Light information regulates the expression of various clock genes in SCN cells, causing protein transcription to be

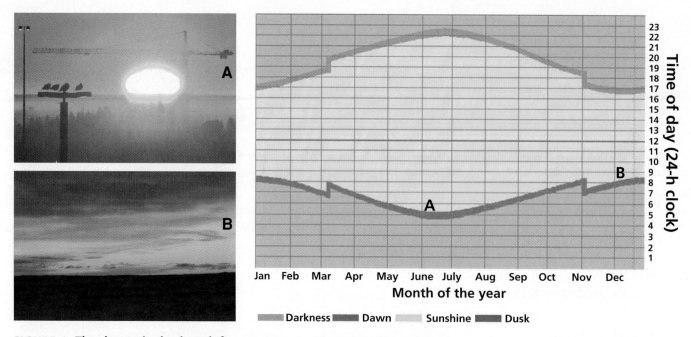

FIGURE 1. The change in day length from summer to winter in Calgary, Alberta.
The graph shows the approximate time of the sunrise and sunset in Calgary throughout the year. The photographs were taken in and near Calgary at (A) 6:30 a. m. at the beginning of June and (B) at 8:15 a. m. in early December. They clearly show the delayed onset of the dawn during the winter months.
Source: Photos by Dr. Evelyn Field. Graph based on http://www.gaisma.com/en/graph/calgary/png, accessed December 16, 2009.

turned on or off. This allows the SCN to function as the pacemaker for biological cycles, synchronizing the cycles to the length of the day.

Serotonin, dopamine, and norepinephrine are the major neurotransmitters that regulate mood. They all exhibit a circadian pattern in which their levels fluctuate according to the time of day. An abnormality in the circadian rhythm alters the normal levels of these neurotransmitters. In fact, the disruption of circadian cycles has been implicated in a number of mood disorders, including SAD, and these disorders all benefit from treatments that affect circadian cycles.

SAD arises from the failure of the circadian cycles to properly adapt to the change in the length of the day as the seasons progress. One hypothesis, called the circadian phase-shift hypothesis, proposes that the later onset of dawn during the winter causes the disruption of circadian rhythms (see Figure 1).

Treatments for SAD

Light Therapy

Light therapy is the most common treatment for SAD, and many people report a substantial improvement in mood and energy after only a few treatments. This treatment is more beneficial when used early in the morning than later in the day. If the delayed onset of the dawn is causing the phase delay in the circadian rhythm, the phase-shift hypothesis, then this result is exactly what you would expect. Therefore, mimicking dawn with bright light in the morning alleviates the symptoms by helping to shift circadian patterns.

To treat SAD effectively, it is important to use a light that that has some of the same properties as natural sunlight. Specific types of lights have been manufactured to satisfy the requirements, and other lights may not have the appropriate brightness or the correct ultraviolet filtration. The optimal regimen appears to be sitting in front of the light for half an hour a day before 8 a.m. Because of the seasonal nature of the symptoms, this treatment need be used only when the symptoms appear. It is not used as a preventative measure.

Intriguingly, even people who do not report any symptoms of SAD benefit from improved mood, energy, and alertness when they are given light treatments. Some companies in Finland, which has a particularly high rate of SAD, have applied this observation in the workplace. From November to February, these companies provide bright-light treatments for all their employees, regardless of whether they have SAD, and the businesses report improvements in mood and productivity in *all* their workers.

Although light therapy helps many people, its success varies. People who experience complete withdrawal of symptoms in the summer months are the most likely to benefit from light therapy. In contrast, people who have chronic forms of depression and do not experience summer remission may not see as much improvement. Most people tolerate light therapy very well, though headache, nausea, and agitation are the most common side effects.

Antidepressants

Treatments for SAD also include the use of antidepressants. Mood disorders, such as depression, bipolar disorder, and SAD, are characterized by irregular levels of neurotransmitters, an effect linked to altered circadian rhythms. Commonly used antidepressants, such as lithium and fluoxetine, have been shown to alter the circadian period. A Canadian study in 2006 found no difference in the effectiveness of light therapy or antidepressants over eight weeks of treatment for SAD (see Figure 2). However, light therapy may be preferable because it generally has fewer side effects than antidepressants.

Currently, light therapy and antidepressants are the most effective treatments for SAD. Other treatment methods have had mixed results. Exercise, for instance, shows mood-enhancing effects for people with SAD. People reported feeling happier, having more vitality, and being more productive following an exercise period in the middle of the workday. Doing exercise in bright light enhanced these benefits even further, but the question then is whether these effects were due to the exercise or exposure to light, or if a break from work in the afternoon makes everyone happy!

Conclusions

Advances in the treatment of mood disorders are certain to occur as new antidepressants arrive on the market. But with effective treatments as simple as light and exercise available, perhaps pharmaceuticals should not always be the first line of defence. The next time you are on your way to class on another dark winter day, keep in mind that a mid-morning stroll outside might do your brain more good than staying inside to study without a break.

Critical Thinking Questions

1. What makes SAD different from other types of depression? What are the similarities?
2. How does light therapy work in the treatment of SAD?
3. Why might mood disorders other than SAD be treatable with light therapy?

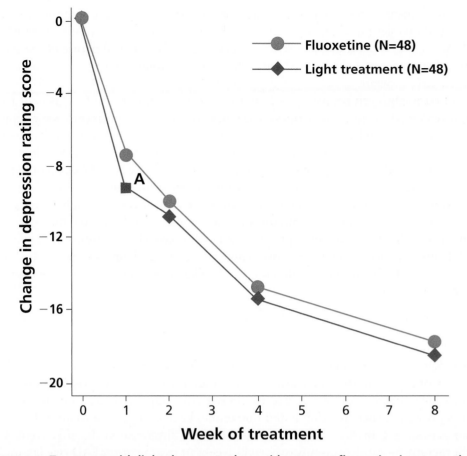

FIGURE 2. Treatment with light therapy or the antidepressant fluoxetine improves the depression rating scores in patients with SAD.
This graph shows that depression ratings start to improve soon after starting treatment with either fluoxetine or light therapy. At point A in the figure, light therapy provided significantly greater improvement than fluoxetine, but overall, there is no difference between the two therapies. Depression was measured by using the Hamilton Depression Scale, a questionnaire that measures the severity of depression symptoms and is commonly used in research to evaluate the effectiveness of depression treatments.
Source: Adapted from: Lam RW, Levitt AJ, Levitan RD, Enns MW, Morehouse R, Michalak EE, Tam EM. 2006. The Can-SAD study: a randomized controlled trial of the effectiveness of light therapy and fluoxetine in patients with winter seasonal affective disorder. American Journal of Psychiatry 163 (May): 805–812, Fig. 2, p. 809. Permission conveyed through Copyright Clearance Center, Inc.

Further Research Question

Other treatments for SAD include vitamin D and melatonin supplements. Why might these be considered viable targets? What is the current thinking about their effectiveness as treatments?

References

Eagles JM. 2003. Seasonal affective disorder. *Br. J. Psychiatry.* 182:174–176.

*Lam RW, Levitt AJ, Levitan RD, Enns MW, Morehouse R, Michalak EE, Tam EM. 2006. The Can-SAD study: a randomized controlled trial of the effectiveness of light therapy and fluoxetine in patients with winter seasonal affective disorder. *Am. J. Psychiatry.* 163:805–812.

Lewy AJ, Lefler BJ, Emens JS, Bauer VK. 2006. The circadian basis of winter depression. *PNAS*. 103:7414–7419.

*McClung CA. 2007. Circadian genes, rhythms and the biology of mood disorders. *Pharmacol. Ther.* 114:222–232.

Partonen T, Lonnqvist J. 2000. Bright light improves vitality and alleviates distress in healthy people. *J. Affective Disorders*. 57:55–61.

Singulair Success:
A Drug Discovery Classic

Alyson L. Kenward

Introduction

The last time you woke up with a fever and an aching body, what did you do? What would you do about a nagging cough, a skin rash, a hopeless case of allergies, or a battle with depression? If you're like most Canadians, you would probably visit a doctor to get a prescription for some medicine. And with that slip of paper covered in a doctor's illegible handwriting, you would go to a pharmacy to pick up a drug that made you feel better.

Most of us rely on prescription drugs at some point in our lives, but do we stop to think about how they work in our bodies? And where exactly do those drugs come from? Just a few hundred years ago, medicine consisted of tree barks, crushed leaves, and blood-sucking leeches. But the drug industry has come a long way since then. For most of the

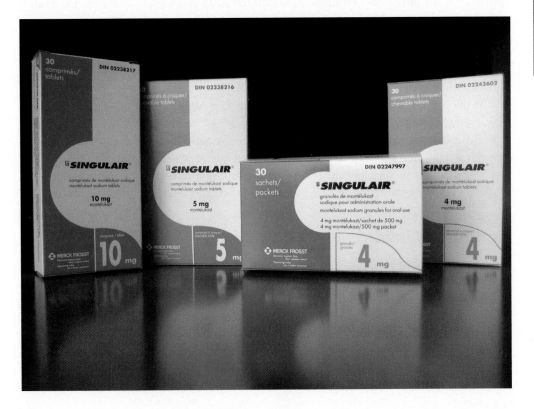

PHOTO A. **Singulair, the most successful drug developed in Canada.**
Source: Courtesy of Merck.

twentieth century, pharmaceutical companies designed drugs to cure specific ailments and, in most cases, made them from scratch instead of obtaining them from nature.

Perhaps the most famous example of a drug discovered by a Canadian pharmaceutical company is Singulair, from the Merck Frosst Centre for Therapeutic Research in Montreal. Singulair, also known as montelukast, is a popular asthma and allergy drug. As a modern classic of drug discovery, Singulair aptly illustrates not only the complex processes of **drug design** and **drug synthesis** but also the intimate relationship between chemistry and biology within our bodies.

Designing an Asthma Drug

Asthma is characterized by chronic inflammation of the airways. As the inflamed passages in the lungs narrow, or constrict, it becomes increasingly difficult to breathe. More than 5 percent of the Canadian adult population experience asthma symptoms.

A family of compounds called **leukotrienes**, which are produced naturally in the body, are responsible for causing the inflammation in asthma. The leukotrienes are made by white blood cells (leukocytes) from an essential fatty acid found in the body. They are released into tissues in an allergic response. When the leukotrienes are released into the lung tissue, they bind to **receptors** on cells lining the outside of the airways and initiate a cascade response that leads to an asthma attack. The muscles in the airways squeeze inward, and the tissue lining swells, reducing the space available for oxygen-rich air to enter the lungs.

In 1979, when leukotrienes were identified as critical mediators of asthma, drug developers (chemists) at Merck Frosst realized they could focus on leukotrienes in their search for a new asthma medication. When researchers understand how a disease manifests in the body, as was the case with asthma, they can choose from two general strategies when designing a new drug. One approach, the **inhibition strategy**, prevents the formation of the molecule that causes the problem (e.g., hormone, neurotransmitter). For asthma, an inhibitory drug would prevent the synthesis of leukotrienes. The other approach is the **antagonist strategy**, in which the drug is designed to mimic the body's natural signalling molecule. A good antagonist drug will bind preferentially to the receptor and prevent the natural molecule from docking, which blocks the natural molecule's effect. In the case of asthma, the drug would be a molecule with a similar shape to the leukotrienes. It would bind to the leukotrienes' receptor and prevent them from initiating their airway-reducing effect.

At the beginning of the drug discovery process, it is often unclear to the developers which strategy will yield the best drug. Both strategies might be effective, but they will typically also both have side effects. It is not uncommon to look for drugs by using both strategies. The Merck Frosst team that was hunting for a new asthma medication did investigate both strategies, but their success came from the antagonist approach. Singulair works by blocking the receptor to which the leukotrienes normally bind (see Figure 1).

Finding Singulair: 1 in 14 000

Whether the developers choose an inhibition or an antagonist approach, the process of discovering a drug takes many years. Chemists and biologists work together to find the right molecules and then test the efficiency and safety of the molecules.

As every new chemical is synthesized, its effectiveness is first tested in a very simple system (see Figure 2). For example, a small group of cells will be used to test whether the drug elicits any biological change within them. If a biological response similar to the desired outcome occurs, chemists will systematically tweak the chemical structure to maximize its positive biological activity. Next, biologists will test the drug

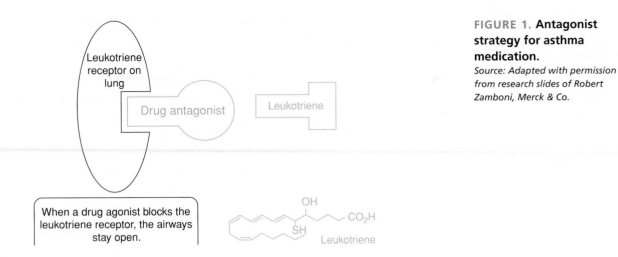

FIGURE 1. **Antagonist strategy for asthma medication.**
Source: Adapted with permission from research slides of Robert Zamboni, Merck & Co.

in an animal model, perhaps a mouse or rat, to see how safe the drug is. These early stages in the drug discovery process can take only a few years, or they can stretch on for a decade or more.

If no significant side effects are observed during the animal testing, then the drug will be used in human clinical trials, which usually occur in three phases. Early phases test the drug's safety at low levels in small groups of 20 to 50 people and monitor where exactly in the body the drug travels after it is taken. Drug developers want the drug to treat the disease well in small doses. In later phases, the groups have thousands of patients, and researchers assess how well the drug works across a large cross-section of the population. These large trials are very expensive and often take many years.

While working to discover Singulair, the Merck Frosst group investigated more than 14 000 chemicals as potential asthma drugs. In the early 1980s, researchers observed some biological activity from the compound called **L-603** (see Figure 3). L-603 doesn't *look* like a leukotriene, but it has a shape that allows it to bind effectively into the receptor that the researchers were hoping to block. Even though L-603 turned out not to be effective, the

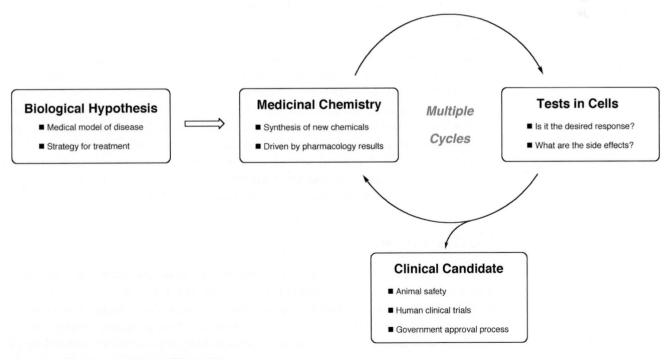

FIGURE 2. **The long process of drug discovery.**
Source: Adapted with permission from research slides of Robert Zamboni, Merck & Co.

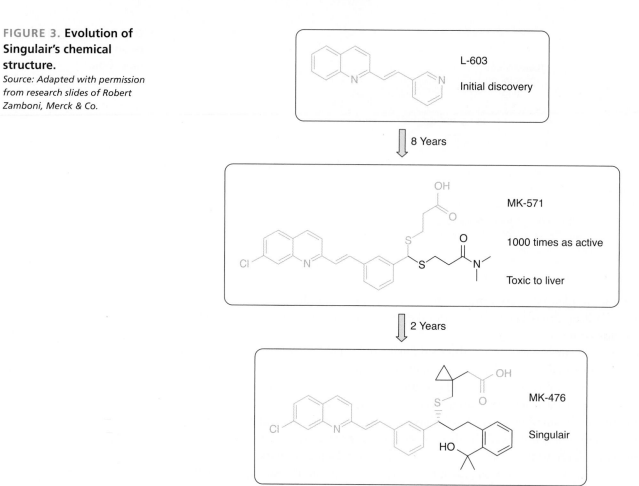

Merck Frosst chemists realized they could build from that chemical structure. By 1988, they had prepared **MK-571**, which was effective at relieving asthma symptoms in animals but unfortunately also caused toxins to build up in the liver—it wasn't safe for humans to use. Developers began tweaking the structure to get rid of the liver toxicity and, finally, in 1991, arrived at **MK-476**, soon to be called Singulair. In 1997, after extensive human clinical trials, the United States Food and Drug Administration (FDA) approved Singulair as an effective asthma medication. It was approved in Canada later that same year.

During the drug discovery process, chemists work to improve the process of preparing large quantities of the drug. Early in the discovery process, only small quantities (milligrams) are needed, so dangerous or expensive chemicals are tolerated. However, when it comes to animal testing and human clinical trials, much larger amounts (kilograms) are required. If a drug is approved, then pharmaceutical companies will have to manufacture it by the metric ton. Chemists need to choose inexpensive, non-toxic, and widely available starting materials, and they need to minimize the waste they generate.

Conclusions

After 18 years of hunting for a suitable asthma medication, Merck Frosst released the drug Singulair. Looking at its simple chemical structure, it's hard to imagine just how much work went into its discovery and production. The same effort goes into many of our pharmaceutical drugs. From identifying a target, through finding an effective and safe drug candidate, to preparing the drug on incredibly large scales, few steps along the way to drug discovery are easy. Perhaps the next time you pick up a prescription from the doctor or pharmacy, you'll think about where that drug came from.

Critical Thinking Questions

1. What are the general characteristics of a good drug?
2. What are two common approaches to drug design?
3. In the process of developing a new drug, why are there multiple phases to human clinical trials?

Further Research Question

What other types of drugs treat asthma, and how do they work?

References

*Corry DB. 2002. Emerging immune targets for the therapy of allergic asthma. *Nature Rev. Drug Discovery.* 1:55–64.

Dahlen SE, Hedqvist P, Hammarstrom S, Samuelsson B. 1980. Leukotrienes are potent constrictors of human bronchi. *Nature* 288:484–486.

*Leff JA, Busse WW, Pearlman D, Bronsky EA, Kemp J, Hendeles L, Dockhorn R, Kundu S, Zhang J, Seidenberg BC, Reiss TF. 1998. Montelukast, a leukotriene-receptor antagonist, for the treatment of mild asthma and exercise-induced bronchoconstriction. *NE J. Med.* 339:147–152.

---

*SINGULAIR is a registered trademark of Merck Sharp & Dohme Corp., a subsidiary of Merck & Co., Inc.

Speciation and the Threespine Stickleback:
The New Fishes of Paxton Lake

Joan Sharp
Simon Fraser University

Introduction

If you were asked to name an extinct species, you'd probably come up with several names. The dodo died out in the eighteenth century, passenger pigeons went extinct in the early twentieth century, and *Tyrannosaurus rex* was wiped out in a mass extinction that took place 65 million years ago. You can probably name threatened or endangered species, too: whooping cranes, spotted owls, and mountain gorillas. But here's a tougher challenge: Can you name a new species, one that has formed in the last few thousand years? In fact, very good examples of recent speciation exist, and one of the best examples are the **benthic** and **limnetic** threespine sticklebacks of British Columbia's Gulf Islands.

The Threespine Stickleback

Threespine sticklebacks are minnow-sized fish that live in streams, lakes, estuaries, and coastal marine environments throughout Europe, Asia, and North America. Although threespine sticklebacks lack scales, they are well armoured, with three dorsal spines and a row of bony lateral plates to protect them from predators.

Sticklebacks have long been studied for their interesting mating behaviours. In springtime, male sticklebacks build nests made of vegetation glued together by sticky secretions. A mating male develops bright colours (see Photo A) and becomes very aggressive, swimming out to defend his nest from all attackers. A researcher studying the sticklebacks described how the little males would swim up and try to nip at her as she waded into their territories.

When a female stickleback enters a male's territory, he recognizes her by her swollen belly, full of eggs. Instead of attacking, the male courts the female, performing a zigzag dance or nipping at her fins. If the female is receptive, she follows him to his nest. After

PHOTO A.
Male threespine stickleback (*Gasterosteus aculeatus*) in breeding colours.
Source: Piet Spaans/Wikipedia, http://commons/wikimedia.org/wiki/File:PICT0246-1.jpg.

she enters the nest, the male nudges her to encourage her to spawn. He then enters the nest himself and releases sperm to fertilize the eggs. The male guards the fertilized eggs until they hatch, oxygenating them by fanning the nest with his pectoral fins (see Photo B).

Benthic and Limnetic Stickleback Species Pairs

Twenty years ago, an angler friend approached Don McPhail at the University of British Columbia (UBC) to tell him about the odd sticklebacks of Paxton Lake on Texada Island. Texada Island is one of southwestern B.C.'s Gulf Islands, located in the Salish Sea between Vancouver Island and the British Columbia mainland (see Figure 1).

Two kinds of sticklebacks live in Paxton Lake. **Benthic sticklebacks** (see Figure 2, B) feed on worms, clams, and other invertebrates in the muddy shallows of the **benthic zone** (the lake bottom). These fish are stout bodied, with wide mouths to take in their large prey.

Like their marine relatives, **limnetic sticklebacks** (see Figure 2, A) feed on zooplankton in the **limnetic zone** (the open water in the centre of the lake). They are slim-bodied and feed by filtering small crustaceans out of a stream of water drawn into their small mouths and over their gills.

Benthic and limnetic sticklebacks differ in their protection against predators. Like marine sticklebacks, limnetics have three dorsal spines, as well as pelvic spines and

FIGURE 1. Texada Island lies in the Salish Sea between the B.C. mainland and Vancouver Island.
Source: Based on Wikipedia, Texada Island map http://commons.wikimedia.org/wiki/File:Locmap-Texada2.png

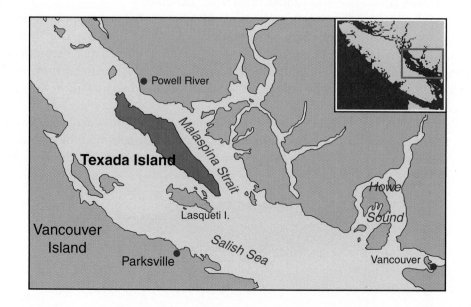

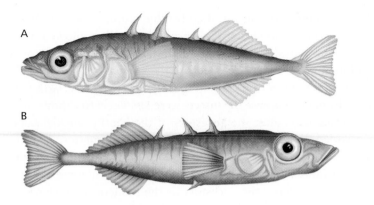

FIGURE 2. **Benthic stickleback (male). The top drawing shows a male limnetic stickleback and the bottom drawing shows a male benthic stickleback.**
Source: Artist: Elizabeth Carefoot.

bony lateral plates. This armour offers protection against predatory cutthroat trout (see Photo C), which feed on sticklebacks in the limnetic zone of the lake.

Benthics have lost one of their dorsal spines, and most have no pelvic spines or lateral plates. The main predators in the benthic zone are large insects, such as backswimmers and dragonfly larvae (see Photo D). These insects capture young sticklebacks by seizing their spines.

Benthics and limnetics live, feed, and face predation in different areas of the lake. However, males of both types build nests, court females, and care for their eggs side-by-side in the benthic zone of the lake.

The Origin of the Benthic and Limnetic Species Pairs

UBC's Dolph Schluter continues to study the benthic and limnetic stickleback pairs, now recognized as two of the youngest species on Earth. The first step to formation of these new species was the formation of the Gulf Islands, 13 000 years ago. Glaciers once covered British Columbia and the area that is now the Salish Sea. As the glaciers retreated, the land rebounded and islands rose from the sea. Seawater was trapped in depressions in the new islands, and over time, these newly formed lakes became brackish (less salty than seawater) and then became fresh water. Sticklebacks are very tolerant of salinity change, and the stickleback populations trapped in the lakes adapted well to their

PHOTO C.
Cutthroat trout prey on limnetic sticklebacks in the open waters of Paxton Lake.
Source: Jordan Allison/National Park Service, http://www.nps.gov/imr/ customcf/apps/pgallery/photo.cfm?pid=2603&aid=319&gid=319

PHOTO D.
Dragonfly larvae feed on young benthic sticklebacks after seizing them by their spines.
Source: Wikipedia, http://commons.wikimedia.org/wiki/File:Larve_ d%27Anax_empereur.JPG

increasingly freshwater environment. Rich benthic resources were available in the lakes, and natural selection favoured morphological changes that allowed the sticklebacks to feed on them. Stout-bodied fish with large mouths did well and left more offspring than slender, small-mouthed sticklebacks. Because the stouter fish fed in shallow-water benthic areas, they were subject to predation by large insects. Those with fewer spines were at a selective advantage, because the insects were less likely to capture and eat them.

Two thousand years after the ancestors of the benthic sticklebacks were isolated from their marine relatives, sea levels rose by nearly 50 metres. A second invasion of marine sticklebacks took place, as fish swam up short streams from the ocean to the lakes. The first invaders were already present in the lake, adapted to feed in the benthic zone. The second invaders—the ancestors of the limnetic sticklebacks—continued to live and feed in the limnetic zone, just as they had done in the ocean.

Dolph Schluter and his colleagues have been investigating the stickleback species pairs for more than a decade. They have found that the benthic and limnetic sticklebacks can mate in the lab to form viable and fertile hybrids. Despite this, the lake has few hybrids. Benthic and limnetic sticklebacks differ in morphology and courtship. Given a choice, a benthic or limnetic fish will always mate with its own kind. Approximately 1 to 2 percent of the fish in Paxton Lake are intermediate in morphology, likely produced by hybridization.

Why don't benthics and limnetics mate with each other? Hybrid sticklebacks do not do well in Paxton Lake. They feed less efficiently than benthics in the benthic zone and less efficiently than limnetics in the limnetic zone. They are more vulnerable to predation in both zones as they are too spiny to survive in the benthic zone and too weakly armoured to survive in the limnetic zone. If a hybrid survives and builds a nest, he has low courtship success compared with his competitors.

Benthics that mate with limnetics and limnetics that mate with benthics in Paxton Lake produce hybrid offspring with low relative fitness, while benthic and limnetic sticklebacks that mate with their own kind produce offspring that are well adapted to survive and reproduce in Paxton Lake. As a result, natural selection has favoured reproductive isolating mechanisms, such as courtship differences between the two populations. Although a small amount of gene flow (about 1 to 2 percent) occurs between the benthic and limnetic populations, the two types of sticklebacks are morphologically and genetically distinct. They have become different species.

Let's consider the mechanisms that have led to these new species. When the first sticklebacks were trapped in the newly formed lakes, they likely continued to filter-feed zooplankton while also feeding on the rich benthic foods available there. Natural selection favoured morphological changes that increased their ability to survive and feed in the benthic zone. With the second invasion, the first colonists now faced competition from newcomers in the open waters of the lake. The newcomers were unable to exploit benthic foods, because they were outcompeted by benthic sticklebacks. As a result, natural selection acting on the two populations favoured increased specialization and morphological divergence. The two populations mated side by side, and some sticklebacks would have mated with the other form. These fish produced hybrids that were less fit than the offspring of sticklebacks that mated with their own kind. The result was the evolution of prezygotic reproductive isolating mechanisms, such as courtship differences, reducing gene flow between the two populations and producing two species where there used to be one.

A Natural, Replicated Experiment in Speciation

The benthic and limnetic species pairs fascinate scientists because they are a natural, replicated experiment. The species pairs arose independently in six lakes in four separate drainage areas on Vancouver Island and the Gulf Islands in the Salish Sea. Benthics from one lake mate readily with benthics from other lakes, as do limnetics from different lakes. However, benthics and limnetics in the same lake mate only with their own kind. Natural selection has produced similar morphologically and ecologically distinct benthic and limnetic pairs of species in each lake.

SARA and the Sticklebacks

There's a problem, however. These young species are in trouble. They are classified by the B.C. Conservation Data Centre as "critically imperiled because of extreme rarity," and are protected under Canada's new Species at Risk Act (SARA), passed in 2002. Twenty-five years after the benthic and limnetic sticklebacks were discovered, the species pairs have gone extinct in Hadley Lake on Lasqueti Island. The species pairs have collapsed into a hybrid population in Enos Lake on Vancouver Island, and they are endangered in the other four lakes.

What threats endanger the species pairs? An alien catfish, the brown bullhead, was illegally released in Hadley Lake. Brown bullheads are nest predators, and the sticklebacks went extinct because of bullhead predation on stickleback eggs. Another alien species, the signal crayfish, was released in Enos Lake. These crayfish churn up the sediment in the benthic zone and destroy the benthic vegetation that harbours the invertebrates on which benthic sticklebacks feed. The crayfish also compete with benthic sticklebacks for food. The increased turbidity of the water in the benthic zone makes it difficult for benthics and limnetics to use visual cues, such as colour, body shape, and courtship activities to select suitable mates. Now, 24 percent of the sticklebacks in Enos Lake are hybrids.

Under SARA, the federal government is evaluating the status and developing recovery plans for the survival of the remaining benthic and limnetic species pairs. In this process, habitat features necessary for the survival and recovery of the sticklebacks are being identified and an action plan is being developed to protect these features. The most important steps necessary to protect the benthic and limnetic sticklebacks are protection of water clarity and benthic vegetation in the lakes and prevention of the introduction of alien species. The sticklebacks have evolved with cutthroat trout, but other predators may pose a serious threat to the little fish. Yellow perch and largemouth bass have been introduced by anglers to other lakes on the Gulf Islands, but such introductions are prohibited in the lakes with the benthic and limnetic species pairs. Land development around the lakes may also be restricted, as increasing runoff from disturbed land increases sedimentation and prevents sticklebacks from making accurate mate choices.

Conclusions

With their small populations and limited distribution, the benthic and limnetic species pairs are likely to remain at risk of extinction. It is hoped that the actions taken under the protection of the Species at Risk Act will protect these young and fascinating species from the fate that befell the Hadley Lake species pair.

Critical Thinking Questions

1. Why are hybrids at a selective disadvantage in Paxton Lake?
2. Did benthic and limnetic sticklebacks arise by allopatric or sympatric speciation? Explain your answer, including a definition for the mode of speciation that you have identified.
3. The benthic and limnetic species pairs of threespine stickleback are among the youngest species on Earth. They are also listed as a species at risk under SARA, Canada's Species at Risk Act. Describe the threats that the benthic and limnetic stickleback species pairs face.

Further Research Question

What genetic differences have been identified between benthic and limnetic sticklebacks? What microevolutionary processes likely led to the genetic differences between the two species? See Peichel et al.

References

Behm JE, Ives AR, Boughman JW. 2010. Breakdown in postmating isolation and the collapse of a species pair through hybridization. *Am. Natural.* 175(1):11–26.

Hatfield T, Schluter D. 1996. A test for sexual selection on hybrids of two sympatric sticklebacks. *Evol.* 50:2429–2434.

McKinnon JS, Mori S, Blackman BK, David L, Kingsley DM, Jamieson L, Chou J, Schluter D. 2004. Evidence for ecology's role in speciation. *Nature.* 429:294–298.

McPhail JD. 1992. Ecology and evolution of sympatric sticklebacks *(Gasterosteus):* Evidence for a species pair in Paxton Lake, Texada Island, British Columbia. *Can. J. Zool.* 70:361–369.

McPhail JD. 1993a. Ecology and evolution of sympatric sticklebacks *(Gasterosteus):* origin of the species pairs. *Can. J. Zool.* 71:515–523.

McPhail JD. 1993b. *Evolution in action.* Burnaby (BC): Open Learning Agency.

*Peichel CL, Nereng KS, Ohgi KA, Cole BLE, Colosimo PF, Buerkle CA, Schluter D, Kingsley DM. 2001. The genetic architecture of divergence between threespine stickleback species. *Nature.* 414:901–905.

Schluter D. 1993. Adaptive radiation in sticklebacks: Size, shape and habitat use efficiency. *Ecol.* 74:699–709.

Schluter D. 1995. Adaptive radiation in sticklebacks: Tradeoffs in feeding performance and growth. *Ecol.* 76:82–90.

Schluter D. 1996. Ecological speciation in postglacial fish. *Philos. Trans. R. Soc. London, Ser. B.* 351:807–814.

Vamosi SM, Hatfield T, Schluter D. 2000. A test *of* ecological selection against young-of-the-year hybrids of sympatric sticklebacks. *J. Fish Biol.* 57:109–121.

Vamosi SM, Schluter D. 1999. Sexual selection against hybrids between sympatric stickleback species: evidence from a field experiment. *Evol.* 53:874–879.

Vamosi SM, Schluter D. 2002. Impacts of trout predation on fitness of sympatric sticklebacks and their hybrids. *Philos. Trans. R. Soc. London, Ser. B.* 269:923–930.

Sustainable Agriculture:
How Can We Eat without Wrecking the Place?

Brenda Frick
University of Saskatchewan

Introduction

We all need to eat. Our relationship with food is the most intimate relationship we have with nature. Agriculture is spread over virtually all the productive land on Earth; 40 percent of Earth's surface is agricultural land. Agriculture also uses significant amounts of water and energy. The way we manage our food system defines our culture and determines much of our environmental impact. We make food choices every day that determine what those impacts will be. Will we use up Earth's resources, leaving a toxic trail behind us? Or will we learn to feed ourselves in a sustainable fashion, one that will leave the planet capable of feeding us well into the foreseeable future?

> **KEY CONCEPTS**
> - Soil is a living, finite resource.
> - Agriculture is necessary to maintain modern society.
> - Developing a sustainable agriculture model is a complex issue.

Agriculture Faces Many Risks

Agricultural production depends on the weather. Drought, flooding, early frost, late frost, heat waves, and cold spells all take their toll. Weather is probably the most obvious risk to agriculture, but it is not the only one.

Loss of Agricultural Biodiversity

The loss of **agricultural biodiversity** (the variability of animals, plants, and microorganisms used directly or indirectly for food and agriculture) may also be a problem. In the past, approximately a quarter of a million species of plants have provided our food. Today, as much as half of our food comes from rice, corn, and wheat alone (IDRC, 2003). Within species, the variability has declined even more dramatically. This narrowing of genetic diversity makes us vulnerable to disaster. Our crops have less chances of having the "right stuff" to thrive as climate changes and pests evolve. Similarly, our livestock options have been severely depleted, with few varieties of few species providing all our meat.

Loss of Agricultural Land

Prime agricultural land is a precious resource. Most of the land with good agricultural potential is already under cultivation. There is no "brave new world" to conquer so we had better use what we have as effectively as possible.

PHOTO A.
Prime agricultural land is a precious resource.
Source: Filtv/Dreamstime.com/ Getstock.com

Redistribution of agricultural land to non-agricultural use has been happening for years. Throughout history, as agriculture has been successful, increased availability of food has allowed villages and then towns and cities to spring up in its midst. The result has been that the best lands are paved over, and as cities sprawl, more and more agricultural land is lost.

Many demands compete for the use of agricultural lands: food for people, food for livestock, fibre, and fuel. When we consider the ability of the land to meet our food needs, we must consider the competition between these conflicting land uses. Corn is the main feed grain for cattle in the United States and in eastern Canada. On the one hand, if land dedicated to feed corn were used to grow food for people, more people would be fed. On the other hand, raising livestock can be an environmentally sound use of land. Native pasture and perennial forage are good cover for land that is not suitable for cultivation. Livestock also eat weeds and grain unfit for food while providing nutrient rich manure as fertilizer.

Increasingly, **biofuel crops** (grown directly for fuel as wood or for conversion into fuels as oilseeds) compete for land with food crops. Some people argue that diverting land that could grow food to fuel production is immoral in a world where people go hungry. Others argue that renewable energy sources are more environmentally sound than fossil fuels. This debate will likely rage on for many years to come.

Finally, agricultural land can be lost because of erosion and diminishing soil quality. When organisms above and below the soil surface are healthy, they help hold the soil together. Synthetic fertilizers, pesticides, drought, flooding, compaction, and tillage can kill soil organisms. Soil can also be exposed to erosion when the covering of plants is removed by deforestation, overgrazing, digging, and even excessive traffic.

Every year, a vast amount of our limited topsoil blows away in the wind or washes away with the rainfall and snowmelt. Much of it ends up clogging rivers and washing

PHOTO B.
Agricultural land can be lost because of erosion and diminishing soil quality.
Source: © FLPA/David Burton/Age Fotostock/Maxx Images.

or blowing out to sea. As much as 10 million hectares of cropland may be lost every year to erosion (Lang, 2006). As topsoil is lost, land becomes less fertile and less able to hold water and nutrients even when they are available.

Loss of Water Sources

In many areas, irrigation is used to increase crop production. Animal production is also a significant user of water. Extensive use of underground aquifers has made agriculture possible in such areas as California. These water systems are being drained faster than they are being replenished. In Canada, most irrigation is from surface water. In the Canadian prairies, much of that water is also at risk, as glaciers disappear. No water means no crops.

Loss of Expertise

The number of farmers in Canada is less than half of what it was in the 1950s. The high cost of farm inputs (what the farmer pays for supplies like fertilizers and herbicides) and the low prices for farm **commodities** (for example wheat or corn) have put farmers in a financial squeeze. Many get out of farming. This situation is repeated around the world. As farmers move toward retirement, they are not being replaced. With few farm apprentices, farmer wisdom is being lost. Farmers manage complex biological systems and are the main stewards of the land.

Agriculture Has a Large Environmental Footprint

Agriculture is the largest human land use. The technology used to increase food production has had side effects. Reducing agriculture's footprint without compromising our ability to produce adequate amounts of quality food is a necessary challenge.

Loss of Habitat in Agricultural Landscapes

Vast areas are now seeded to **monocultures** (a single species grown over a vast area), and the land is kept weed-free with herbicides, which further reduces the diversity within farmland. Moreover, farmers no longer vary their crops by rotating them over time. Whereas a diverse rotation (many different crops in sequence) is healthy for diversity, farmers' single-crop fields have become virtual deserts to wildlife. Farmers are often encouraged to drain wetlands, cut woodlots, and remove edge habitat to increase their cultivated land and to allow for easier use of huge equipment.

Greenhouse Gases

Plants take up carbon dioxide through photosynthesis; however, industrial agriculture also contributes to greenhouse gas emissions, from 14 to 35 percent of global amounts (IPCC, 2007). Intensive confined livestock operations generate large amounts of methane, a greenhouse gas 25 times stronger than carbon dioxide. The manufacture and use of nitrogen fertilizers generate nitrous oxide, a greenhouse gas 300 times stronger than carbon dioxide.

Energy Consumption

Agriculture uses energy in three main ways. First, manufacturing agricultural inputs, particularly nitrogen fertilizers, is energy intensive. Secondly, farming operations, especially heavy **tillage** (preparation of the land or removal of weeds by equipment that turns, lifts, or mixes the soil), consume energy. Thirdly, our food travels an average of 3000 kilometres to get to us, adding shipping costs to the energy costs of global agricultural.

Nutrient Loss

Farmers apply fertilizers to improve the yields of their crops. Some of these nutrients are lost because of over-application, misapplication, and erosion of nutrient rich soils. The result is pollution, particularly of waterways. A particularly vivid example of this is the dead zone in the Gulf of Mexico, an area of thousands of square kilometres that is no longer able to sustain life because of the wash of fertilizers out of the American Corn Belt (Nicholson, 2009).

Farmers use a range of poisons to kill weeds, insects, and diseases. Although great efforts are made to assure that the poisons are directed at the proper target, some misuse and "off-target losses" are inevitable. These can be harmful to plants, beneficial insects, birds, and especially aquatic animals. They can also be harmful to farmers, their families, food handlers, and consumers.

Options to Improve the Sustainability of Agriculture

A truly sustainable agriculture system would provide adequate amounts of quality food for the world without compromising its ability to do so in the future. To create such a system, we need to reduce our environmental footprint. Sustainable systems need to be environmentally, socially, and economically viable.

The Green Revolution

The first "green revolution" took place in the sixties and seventies as researchers developed grain varieties able to produce greater amounts of grain. These higher yields were possible only when the plants were given large amounts of fertilizer and protected from pests and weeds by fungicides, insecticides, and herbicides. These crops are credited with saving millions of people in developing countries from starvation. Unfortunately, not all the effects of the green revolution were positive. The new crops require fertilizers and pesticides to meet their potential, and, unfortunately, they were often too expensive for small-scale farmers to afford. Converting to high-input crops disrupted local food systems. Where once farmers had been able to sell rice and also harvest the vitamin-rich "weeds" and grow protein-rich fish in the flooded paddies, now the herbicides and insecticides kill the weeds and fish. Power changed hands from small-scale growers to corporate farms and **agribusiness** (people developing, promoting, and selling the seeds, chemicals, and equipment). The green revolution was highly successful at increasing food production. It was far less successful at reducing poverty, which today is the root cause of hunger. The environmental, economic, and social costs have been substantial.

The New Green Revolution

The introduction of genetically engineered (GE) crops is promoted as a second "green revolution." Like the first, it offers new varieties dependent on technology that lies in the hands of the seller (not the farmer). There has been a strong backlash among farmers and consumers opposed to GE crops.

Weed control that was once accomplished with tillage now often depends on herbicides. In the past, tillage was used to prepare land for planting, to work plant residues into the soil for easier decomposition and to remove weeds. Heavy tillage uses a great deal of energy. Tillage disrupts soil organisms, loosens soils, and breaks soil into finer particles that are more easily picked up by wind and water and thus lost to erosion. Recognizing these potential problems, farmers everywhere have reduced the frequency and intensity of their tillage operations.

Crop varieties have been developed (often through genetic engineering methods) that are resistant to herbicides that will eliminate most weeds. This makes herbicidal weed control easier but has several risks. Increased use of the herbicide speeds the selection of herbicide-resistant weeds. GE plants themselves leave seeds that grow into plants that can become weeds for the next crops because they are now resistant to the herbicide when it is used in the future. As well, the use of GE technology increases the farmer's dependence on the company, which sells both seed and chemical, and sets the price for the final crop.

Organic

Organic agriculture is a holistic system that uses ecological processes rather than synthetic chemicals. Organic farms tend to be smaller than conventional farms, and to have smaller fields, a broader range of crops, and a greater amount of non-crop land, such as undisturbed natural areas, shelterbelts, and grassed waterways. This improves their suitability for wildlife.

Organic producers use green manures, composts of animal manure, and plant residues for fertility. This reduces the amount of nutrient runoff. Organic agriculture also avoids pollution from off-target pesticide losses. By avoiding synthetic fertilizers, organic agriculture reduces its greenhouse gas emissions and its energy use. According to one source, if organic methods were used on all cultivated acres in the United States, the greenhouse gas savings would be 25 percent (Baker, 2009). Energy savings of organic agriculture are usually in the range of 50 percent (Hoeppner et al., 2006).

Organic methods have been criticized on two main fronts: they depend on tillage, and they yield less than high-input methods. Yields tend to be 10 to 20 percent less for organic agriculture globally but may be as high as 50 percent on the Canadian prairies (MacRae et al., 2007). Research is active on both fronts: to reduce tillage while still maintaining adequate weed control and to improve yields.

Buy Local

An increasing number of farmers are selling directly to consumers, either at their farm gates or at local farmers markets. Some are selling through small-scale local groceries. This business model drastically reduces the distance food travels from where it is produced to your kitchen table. It also allows consumers and farmers to chat, improving

PHOTO 3.
Locally grown organic apples.
Source: Laura Berman Green/Fuse Images.com

the understanding that the public has about farming and allowing consumers to make more informed food choices.

Conclusions

Agriculture has an enormous environmental impact. All sustainable systems involve compromises and trade-offs. For instance, producers may choose between herbicides and tillage for weed control. Both have negative impacts. Daily, we support the agricultural systems that bring us food. What would sustainable agriculture look like to you? How would you support it in your daily food choices? Do you buy local? Do you buy organic?

Critical Thinking Questions

1. How does agriculture contribute to greenhouse gases? How might that contribution be reduced?
2. How can we improve biodiversity in agricultural landscapes?
3. How does reducing tillage help reduce erosion?

Further Research Question

Every agricultural system involves some compromises. How would you design a food system that works for you and the environment? Which sustainable measures would be most important, and where would you be willing to compromise?

References

Baker D (international director at the Centre for Food Safety). Quoted in: McGiffin E. 2009 Nov/Dec. Industrial agriculture linked to greenhouse gas. *Small Farm Can.*

Feenstra G, Ingels C, Campbell D. What is sustainable agriculture? [Internet]. Davis (CA): UC Sustainable Agriculture Research and Education Program; c1997 [cited 2010 Apr 11]. Available from: http://www.sarep.ucdavis.edu/Concept.htm

Hoeppner JW, Emtz MH, McConkey BG, Zentner RP, Nagy CN. 2006. Energy use efficiency in two Canadian organic and conventional crop production systems. *Renewable Agric. Food Syst.* 21:60–67.

[IDRC] International Development Research Centre [Internet]. Ottawa (ON): IRDC. Facts and figures on food and biodiversity; 9 Jun 2003 [modified 2003 June 18; cited 2010 Apr 11]. Available from: http://www.idrc.ca/en/ev-31631-201-1-DO_TOPIC.html

[IPCC] Intergovernmental Panel on Climate Change [Internet]. Geneva (Switzerland): IPCC; c2010 [cited 2010 Apr 11]. Available from: http://www.ipcc.ch

[ISIS] Institute of Science in Society [Internet]. London: ISIS; c1999–2010. Why sustainable agriculture. 4 Oct 2006 [cited 2010 Apr 11]. Available from: http://www.i-sis.org.uk/FTWUCC.php

Lang, SS. 'Slow, insidious' soil erosion threatens human health and welfare as well as the environment, Cornell study asserts. Chronicle Online [Internet]. 2006, Mar 20 [cited 2010 Apr 11]. Available from: http://www.news.cornell.edu/stories/march06/soil.erosion.threat.ssl.html

MacRae RJ, Frick B, Martin RC. 2007. Economic and social impacts of organic production systems. *Can. J. Plant. Sci.* 87:1037–1044.

Nicholson C. Gulf of Mexico Dead Zone Shrinks. Scientific American [Internet]. 2009 Jul 27 [cited 2010 Apr 11]. Available from: http://www.scientificamerican.com/podcast/episode.cfm?id=gulf-of-mexico-dead-zone-shrinks-09-07-27.

Index